INTERNATIONAL SERIES OF MONOGRAPHS ON

ELECTRONICS AND INSTRUMENTATION

GENERAL EDITORS: D. W. FRY AND W. A. HIGINBOTHAM

VOLUME 10

LAPLACE TRANSFORMS
FOR
ELECTRONIC ENGINEERS

OTHER TITLES IN THE SERIES

LAPLACE TRANSFORMS
FOR
ELECTRONIC ENGINEERS

by

JAMES G. HOLBROOK

Research Engineer
Missile and Space Division, Lockheed Aircraft Corporation

PERGAMON PRESS
NEW YORK · LONDON · PARIS · LOS ANGELES
1959

PERGAMON PRESS INC.
122 East 55th Street, New York 22, N.Y.
P.O. Box 47715, Los Angeles, California
PERGAMON PRESS LTD.
4 & 5 Fitzroy Square, London W.1
PERGAMON PRESS S.A.R.L.
24 Rue des Écoles, Paris V^e

Library of Congress Card Number 59–12607

Made and Printed in Great Britain by the Pitman Press, Bath

THIS BOOK IS DEDICATED
TO MY WIFE, LOIS

CONTENTS

PREFACE

THIS book is written primarily for the practicing electronics engineer. It will be of most interest and benefit to those who devote a portion of their leisure time to self-study and improvement. The material covers a rather wide area of modern ideas, concepts, methods, and logic, but is arranged and presented in a manner which will allow the conscientious electronics engineer to advance gradually and consistently to a thorough and practical knowledge of Laplace transform theory.

Laplace transform theory is difficult to express in a brief, clear, concise definition. Its purposes are many and varied. Perhaps a good starting definition for the electronics engineer is to observe that:

> Laplace transform theory is a philosophy of logic and analytical reasoning which allows one to analyze and synthesize electronic circuitry, networks, filters, oscillators, servo-systems, etc., with much less effort and far more accuracy and depth of understanding than most engineers can develop when using older methods.

It will be assumed at the outset that the electronic engineers who study this text will have completed the usual college level courses in differential and integral calculus, as well as the usual B.S. courses in circuit analysis.

There is today a growing tendency in many colleges and universities to present a course in Laplace transform theory in the undergraduate program, and the relative merits are being argued for and against such an undergraduate course. It is true that a good background in Laplace transform theory gives one far more insight into the useful and interesting phases of advanced circuitry and networks than the usual introductory work with the j-operator alone; however, it must also be admitted that the usual college courses in classical steady-state circuit analysis are presented while the student is still in the process of finishing his studies of the calculus, and certainly long before he has had the advantages of any graduate courses in subjects such as vector analysis or complex variable theory. It would seem that to inject a Laplace transform course at such a period would deprive the student of the more firm development that he could attain were he to receive the classical circuit analysis courses (adequate for his undergraduate level work) and then to study the more advanced Laplace transform theory after having had a chance to digest his calculus, and gain some measure of practical experience with it. The writer will not attempt to take sides, except to observe that time will eventually tell at what scholastic level the Laplace transform theory should be introduced for maximum effectiveness.

Laplace transform theory allows one to perform a complete analysis of electronic network problems, in contrast with the "steady-state" solution arrived at by classical network analysis using the j-operator. When the reader recalls that the terms "inductive reactance," and "capacitive reactance" are only valid when speaking strictly of sine wave excitation, and become meaningless when applied to any of the many waveshapes we use today, he should see the vital necessity of devoting a moderate amount of time to the study of more general methods and ways of thinking. The Laplace transform is a general method, and permits the introduction of any waveshape into the network being analyzed.

To begin the text directly with a derivation of the Laplace integral would be to assume a good working knowledge of functions of a complex variable. This would make the book unreadable to a large number of highly skilled engineers who entered the electronic industry after receiving their first degree, but who have not had occasion to acquire a complex variable course as background. I have therefore chosen to begin the book with a review of complex variable theory as applicable to the Laplace transform. By the time he is finished with Chapter I, the reader will be speaking casually of poles, zeros, residues of functions and integration in the complex plane. The actual Laplace transform theory begins in Chapter II and occupies the remainder of the book.

The emphasis throughout has been on a clear, free style of writing. It is rigorous and thorough, but devoid of the heavily abstract terminology of pure mathematics which so often defeats self-study. Symbolism and definitions are explained in simple terms as they are introduced, and some proofs of theorems, unless germane to the discussion, are omitted. The real purpose of the text is to allow the practicing electronics engineer to develop and expand his knowledge of circuitry and networks by a careful program of study of the modern method of Laplace transform theory and applications.

I am most indebted to numerous friends and associates who have contributed to the text in one way or another. My special interest began while attending a semester of lectures given by Dr. Charles R. Hausenbauer, of the University of Arizona. His superb presentation of Laplace transform theory was truly outstanding, and notes taken from his lectures served as a basis for much of Chapter II.

Many of the concepts presented throughout the text have evolved gradually during the past century, and it is doubtful if the origin of most of them is properly known. The writer, therefore, must express general thanks to one and all whose original work has been sampled, and must, of course, assume full responsibility for such errors in presentation as may occur.

Thanks are due also to Dorothy Deuel, who typed much of the manuscript, and to numerous engineers who assisted in editing and checking equations at various times. The writer will feel amply rewarded if the book provides someone with a few pleasant weeks of suggestive thought. Best wishes to you as you begin your trip into the new world of the s-domain.

JAMES G. HOLBROOK

Santa Maria, California
September, 1958.

CHAPTER I

FUNCTIONS OF A COMPLEX VARIABLE

1.1. Introduction

AN introductory course on the functions of complex variables usually lasts for one semester and takes one through the major part of a sizeable text devoted exclusively to that subject. We must therefore limit our objective in this first chapter to presenting only those elements of complex variable theory which are actually necessary for the logical development of the Laplace transform material which will occupy the remainder of the book.

From Chapter II on, we will do most of our traveling in the complex world of the s-domain, carrying out the major part of the work in this new and interesting territory, and returning home to our real world of the familiar time, or t-domain, only to convert the results into suitable form for practical use. Fortunately, as the reader spends more and more time in the new world of the s-plane, he begins first to gradually take up the speech, and later to actually think in the new language of the s-world. Of course, when one actually thinks in a new language it is no longer necessary to translate back into the original. This is the real goal of the text, to enable the reader to visualize his circuitry and networks in the s-domain.

It is strongly recommended that the reader does not hurry in studying the material to follow. A good rule for self-study would be to set a definite, self-enforced limit of one numbered article per day. Self-study at a faster rate will most likely cause the reader to start neglecting fine points and missing new concepts as they are presented. With this mild word of caution, we now proceed to work.

1.2. Complex numbers

Algebra, of course, has been studied for centuries, and the early mathematicians who encountered the square roots of negative numbers merely labeled such quantities as imaginary, because no one in those days had assigned any meaning to such numbers. It was not until 1797 that the Norwegian surveyor, Casper Wessel, in a paper read before the Royal Academy of Denmark, brought out the fact that since

$$\sqrt{-1}^2 = -1 \tag{1.1}$$

and since the -1 could be looked upon as a unit vector which had been rotated through 180° from the standard position shown in

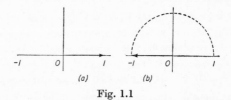

Fig. 1.1

Fig. 1.1(a), then the $\sqrt{-1}$ could be considered as a unit vector which had been rotated only half-way around from the standard position, and stopped as shown in Fig. 1.2.

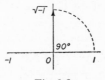

Fig. 1.2

Now the idea of negative numbers had already been long accepted, as they were relatively easy to picture along a one-dimensional line as a magnitude to the right or left of some arbitrary zero reference, as in Fig. 1.3. Using the new concept of Wessel, one could then

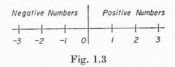

Fig. 1.3

suppose that any positive number in Fig. 1.3 might be considered as a simple vector from 0 to the number, and that this vector could be rotated half-way around by multiplying it by $\sqrt{-1}^2$, or one-quarter way around by multiplying only by $\sqrt{-1}$. Thus the positive number 3, Fig. 1.4(a), can be rotated 90° by multiplying it by

$\sqrt{-1}$, and shown in Fig. 1.4(b). This special rotating property leads us to call the $\sqrt{-1}$ an operator, and we assign the symbol j to represent it.

The symbol j allows us to mark off a vertical line at right angles to the horizontal line of Fig. 1.3, thereby creating a two-dimensional

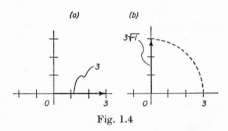

Fig. 1.4

surface, rather than a single line. This surface will be called the complex plane. We note in passing that

$$\left.\begin{array}{l} j^2 = -1 \\ j^3 = -j \\ j^4 = 1 \\ j^5 = j, \text{ etc.} \end{array}\right\} \qquad (1.2)$$

The complex plane may be thought of as a map whereon it is possible to locate any number (point) by specifying its distances x and y, measured from zero in the horizontal and vertical directions.

The complex number p, $4 + j3$, is shown in the complex plane as the sum of two components 4 and $j3$ (Fig. 1.5(a)), and as a single

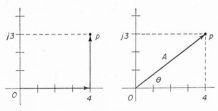

Fig. 1.5

vector $(4 + j3)$ in Fig. 1.5(b). The complex number p is of course the same quantity, or point, either way.

There are two basic ways of describing the location of a complex number such as p in the complex plane. The first, called the rectangular, or algebraic form, locates the complex number by giving its xy components as

$$p = 4 + j3$$

or in general

$$p = x + jy \qquad (1.3)$$

The second way of describing the location of a complex number is to give its magnitude A as well as its direction, or angle θ. It is noted that in Fig. 1.5(b)

$$A = \sqrt{(4^2 + 3^2)} = 5$$

$$\theta = \tan^{-1} \tfrac{3}{4} = 36.9°$$

so that

$$p = 5\underline{/36.9°}$$

or in general

$$p = A\underline{/\theta} \qquad (1.4)$$

which is read "p equals the magnitude A at an angle of θ degrees". This is called the polar form.

The rectangular form and the polar form are equally useful, although there are advantages to using one form or the other in a given case. It is easy to convert from one form to the other, because we see from Fig. 1.5(b) and equation (1.3) that

$$x = A \cos \theta \qquad (1.5)$$

and

$$y = A \sin \theta \qquad (1.6)$$

thus equation (1.3) may be re-written as

$$p = A(\cos \theta + j \sin \theta) \qquad (1.7)$$

Now the factor $(\cos \theta + j \sin \theta)$ may be simplified by the use of Euler's theorem, which says

$$\cos \theta + j \sin \theta = \varepsilon^{j\theta} \qquad (1.8)$$

This identity is shown to be true by adding the infinite series for $\cos \theta$ to the infinite series for $\sin \theta$ multiplied by j, and noting that the sum is the same as the infinite series for $\varepsilon^{j\theta}$. Using Euler's theorem, we may re-write equation (1.7) as

$$p = A\varepsilon^{j\theta} \qquad (1.9)$$

Equation (1.9) is called the exponential form, and is most useful for raising a complex number to a power or extracting a root, as we may apply the usual rules of exponents and logarithms. In summary then, we may express any complex number in four ways:

$$p = x + jy \tag{1.10}$$

$$p = A\underline{/\theta} \tag{1.11}$$

$$p = A(\cos\theta + j\sin\theta) \tag{1.12}$$

$$p = A\varepsilon^{j\theta} \tag{1.13}$$

The form (1.11) has little use except in description, while form (1.12) is used chiefly to convert from form (1.10) algebraic to form (1.13) exponential. Almost all of our work will be carried out using either the algebraic or the exponential form.

1.3. Complex planes

In art. 1.2 the complex number $4 + j3$ was pictured as a point located four units to the right and three units up from the zero point. Thus any complex number whose component real and imaginary parts are given can be located as a point in the xy-plane. It has become a tradition in mathematics to call the variables x and y, and to call z the resulting complex number. That is, by definition

$$z = x + jy \tag{1.14}$$

therefore, any specific complex number z consists of a real part x and imaginary part y, and occupies a definite point in the complex plane. The particular plane used to plot z-values will therefore be called the z-plane. The z-plane is adequate for plotting a wide variety of relations between the variables x and y. The y-dimension is used to plot any function of x and is therefore called a function of x. Thus to say that

$$y = x^2 - 2$$

or

$$y = \sin x$$

is the same as saying

$$f(x) = x^2 - 2$$

or

$$f(x) = \sin x$$

which is read "the function f of x equals sin x", etc. Such functions are readily graphed in the z-plane, as shown in Fig. 1.6.

Note that any line in the z-plane is actually a chain of connected points, each point having a particular value of x and y. Thus if the function $f(x)$ is known, the graph of the function can be presented in the z-plane.

Now each of us is familiar with the Mercator projection used for making maps, wherein the graticule is composed of vertical lines, representing x-values of longitude, and horizontal lines, showing y-values of latitude. This graticule of lines is very similar to our

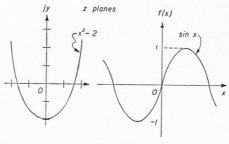

Fig. 1.6

z-plane, and curves in the z-plane could possibly be coast lines on the Mercator map.

Ordinarily the Mercator map might serve our needs, but perhaps the need arises for some accurate information about the northern coast of Greenland. In this case a polar projection map would probably be better.

We note at once that coast lines are not at all familiar in the two projections, in fact, at some points the familiar areas are so different and striking that it is hard to think of them as being the same. Of course we learned early that it was not really a difference in land shape, but only a difference in the nature of the plane.

Seeing the desirability of more than one type of geographical plane, let us grant for the time being that there is need for other mathematical planes in addition to the z-plane. We will call such an additional plane the s-plane.

This new s-plane will be drawn with vertical and horizontal lines the same as the z-plane, but here the co-ordinates of the point locations will be given as σ (sigma) units to the right and ω (omega) units up from the zero reference.

At this point the pure mathematician may object, saying that it is customary and traditional to introduce this second plane as the w mapping, with the real and imaginary components u and v. To this my reply is that ordinarily it is good to keep to tradition, but two facts lead me to prefer the term "s-plane" here.

First, the reader who is highly versed in complex variable theory will find little of value in this chapter and will have begun directly with Chapter II.

Second, to the reader not acquainted with the details of complex variable theory, one name is as good as another, and I prefer to

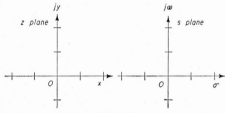

Fig. 1.7

start with the term "s-plane" because this is the nomenclature used throughout in the literature on the Laplace transformation, and it would seem especially confusing to become familiar with certain symbols in this chapter and then to change abruptly at the start of Chapter II.

Let us not for the moment give any special significance to the component variables σ and ω. Think of them simply as co-ordinates of the various complex numbers s which may be plotted in the s-plane. That is, by definition

$$s = \sigma + j\omega \qquad (1.15)$$

In summary, we now have two planes available, the z-plane and the s-plane. Functions of x, such as

$$f(x) = x^3 - 2x + 3$$

will be graphed in the z-plane as in Fig. 1.6, while functions of s will be plotted only in the s-plane.

As in the case of the two map projections, it will not be likely that a function plotted in the z-plane will resemble the corresponding function graphed in the s-plane.

1.4. Relations between the z- and s-planes

Suppose we make the statement that s is a function of z, that is to say

$$s = f(z) \tag{1.16}$$

This is a general statement and tells little except that there will be some complex point in the s-plane corresponding to some complex point in the z-plane. To say more than this we need to choose a specific $f(z)$ and say, perhaps, that

$$s = z^2 \tag{1.17}$$

By the definitions (1.14) and (1.15) therefore

$$\sigma + j\omega = (x + jy)^2 \tag{1.18}$$

or

$$\sigma + j\omega = x^2 + 2jxy - y^2 \tag{1.19}$$

and if we group real and imaginary terms,

$$\sigma + j\omega = x^2 - y^2 + j2xy \tag{1.20}$$

then, equating reals to reals, and imaginaries to imaginaries, we have

$$\sigma = x^2 - y^2 \tag{1.21}$$

and

$$\omega = 2xy \tag{1.22}$$

Now this is specific information relating the function of s to the function of z. As an example of its use, let us take as a "coast line"

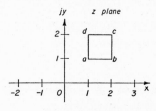

Fig. 1.8

the square in Fig. 1.8, bordered by the lines $x = 1$, $x = 2$, $y = 1$, $y = 2$; and transform this square into the s-plane.

The transformation may be carried out one point at a time, choosing first the corner points a, b, c and d.

The four corners of the area in the s-plane may now be located at a', b', c' and d', as in Fig. 1.10, and if we transform intermediate points between a and b, etc., we note that there is actually a slight curve to the sides in the s-plane, as shown. If we now pick one general point inside the z-plane square, we see that it transforms into a point inside the border of the s-plane figure. Hence we may say that all points inside the square, and thus the interior region of the square, transforms into the entire region inside the new figure in the

point	z		$\sigma = x^2 - y^2$	$\omega = 2xy$	s
	x	y			$\sigma + j\omega$
a	1	1	0	2	$0 + j2$
b	2	1	3	4	$3 + j4$
c	2	2	0	8	$0 + j8$
d	1	2	-3	4	$-3 + j4$

Fig. 1.9

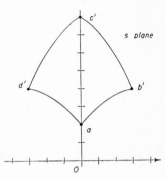

Fig. 1.10

s-plane. As was the case with the map projections, there is little resemblance between the two figures.

Let us examine several more transformations in art. 1.5, and then we shall work a practical problem to demonstrate the value of such transformations.

1.5. Additional transformations between the z- and s-planes

The reason for future transformation between planes will be to effect extreme simplification in solving problems. Fortunately, transformations of the type we will be using from Chapter II on, follow a very straightforward and standardized procedure. However, to develop a feeling for operation in the complex plane, it will be desirable at this time to examine a few of the more common transformations.

(a) Let us look at a very interesting and useful transformation between the z-plane and the s-plane. This transform is

$$z = \varepsilon^s \tag{1.23}$$

This transform tells us that every point in the s-plane can be mapped into the z-plane by the use of (1.23). As a matter of fact, note carefully that since any line is merely a collection of points, any line in the s-plane can also be redrawn in the z-plane by using (1.23).

To draw anything in the z-plane, it is of course necessary to solve for the values of x and y, which are the components of the complex number z. We replace the s and z in (1.23) by their component parts as a first step:

$$x + jy = \varepsilon^{(\sigma + j\omega)} \tag{1.24}$$

Now observe that the $\sigma + j\omega$ follows the usual rule of exponents and the expression can thus be rewritten as

$$x + jy = \varepsilon^\sigma \varepsilon^{j\omega} \tag{1.25}$$

On the left, the x and y values are seen to be the usual co-ordinates of points in the z-plane. On the right, the ε^σ is a magnitude and the $\varepsilon^{j\omega}$ is an angle. Looking back at (1.11), (1.12) and (1.13) it is seen that the $\varepsilon^{j\omega}$ term can be rewritten as

$$x + jy = \varepsilon^\sigma \underline{/\omega} \tag{1.26}$$

or

$$x + jy = \varepsilon^\sigma (\cos \omega + j \sin \omega) \tag{1.27}$$

where ε^σ is the magnitude of a vector reaching from zero to the point in the s-plane, and ω is the angle of the vector. Since real terms must equal real terms on each side, we have from (1.27)

$$x = \varepsilon^\sigma \cos \omega \tag{1.28}$$

and

$$y = \varepsilon^\sigma \sin \omega \tag{1.29}$$

Therefore, if we are given any point, or set of points in the s-plane, we can place the σ and ω values of the point into (1.28) and (1.29) and learn the values of x and y for the location of the point in the z-plane.

PROBLEM. We are given a straight line, $\sigma = 0$ in the s-plane, reaching from $\omega = 0$ to $\omega = 2\pi$. Plot the path of this line in the z-plane.

HINT. Use (1.28) and (1.29) and choose values of ω such as $\omega = 0°$, $\omega = 30°$, $\omega = 60°$, etc., which are easily looked up in tables or found by observation, and plot the xy points carefully. Draw a smooth curve through the points.

ANS. The s-plane line becomes a circle of radius 1 in the z-plane. The results of this problem will be used in art. 1.6 to work a practical electronics problem. For the moment, however, let us examine one more transformation.

(b) Suppose one is given the function

$$z = \ln s \qquad (1.30)$$

then for every point in the z-plane there will be a value corresponding to the natural logarithm of the complex variable s. As usual, it is necessary to solve for the individual values of x and y in order to plot a given point or curve.

$$x + jy = \ln (\sigma + j\omega) \qquad (1.31)$$

By the definition of a logarithm, namely the power to which ε must be raised to equal the number

$$\varepsilon^{x+jy} = \sigma + j\omega \qquad (1.32)$$

or

$$\varepsilon^x \varepsilon^{jy} = \sigma + j\omega \qquad (1.33)$$

or

$$\varepsilon^x \underline{/y} = \sqrt{(\sigma^2 + \omega^2)} \Big/ \tan^{-1} \frac{\omega}{\sigma} \qquad (1.34)$$

and we see that the magnitude on the left must equal the magnitude on the right, thus

$$\varepsilon^x = \sqrt{(\sigma^2 + \omega^2)} \qquad (1.35)$$

from which

$$x = \ln \sqrt{(\sigma^2 + \omega^2)} \qquad (1.36)$$

It is noted that the phase angle on both sides must also be equal, hence

$$y = \tan^{-1} \frac{\omega}{\sigma} \qquad (1.37)$$

Therefore, with the last two equations we can transform any equation or curve in the s-plane into its corresponding curve in the z-plane.

PROBLEM. Show that the circle of radius 2.718 in the s-plane transforms into the straight line of 6.28 units length, at $x = 1$, as shown in Fig. 1.11.

(c) Transformation of a region. Thus far we have talked about transforming points, and have noted that lines were merely chains of points placed side by side. The thought now occurs that the

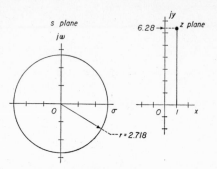

Fig. 1.11

region inside a closed curve in a plane is also only a collection of more points, and thus we may say that it is possible to transform regions in one plane to corresponding regions in the other plane. More will be said later of regions, but for the moment, merely

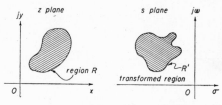

Fig. 1.12

observe that Fig. 1.12 represents a transformation of a region, similar to our practice here in transforming lines and points.

1.6. Simplification of problems by transforming into the complex s-plane

In this article we shall see the advantages of transforming a problem from the original plane into a new plane for solution. The procedure can best be illustrated by means of a sample problem.

PROBLEM. Calculate the capacity of a 1 m length section of coaxial cable, whose inner conductor is a m in radius, and whose outer thin conductor is b m in radius; b is greater than a.

First, the cross-section of the cable is shown in the z-plane, Fig. 1.13. The values of points making up the inner circle may be easily expressed by writing z in polar form,

$$z_a = a\varepsilon^{j\theta} \tag{1.38}$$

and it is seen that as θ goes from 0 to 2π, the z-points will trace out the inner circle. It is also noted that for the outer circle

$$z_b = b\varepsilon^{j\theta} \tag{1.39}$$

where again θ varies from 0 to 2π rad.

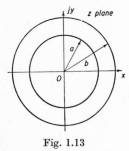

Fig. 1.13   Fig. 1.14

Now let us transform these two circles into the s-plane by use of the transformation

$$z = \varepsilon^s \qquad \tag{1.40}$$

For the inner circle only,

$$a\varepsilon^{j\theta} = \varepsilon^\sigma \varepsilon^{j\omega} \tag{1.41}$$

from which it is seen that

$$\varepsilon^\sigma = a \tag{1.42}$$

or

$$\sigma_1 = \ln a \tag{1.43}$$

and also

$$\omega = \theta \tag{1.44}$$

Plotting the inner circle first, it is found from (1.43) that we have a straight vertical line $\sigma_1 = \ln a$, and that (1.44) shows this line to extend from $\omega = 0$ to $\omega = 2\pi$. Thus the inner z-plane circle has been transformed into a straight line segment in Fig. 1.14.

Next, let us repeat this process, and transform the outer circle into the s-plane. For the z-points making up the outer circle,

$$b\varepsilon^{j\theta} = \varepsilon^\sigma \varepsilon^{j\omega} \tag{1.45}$$

and we see that

$$b = \varepsilon^{\sigma} \tag{1.46}$$

or

$$\sigma_2 = \ln b \tag{1.47}$$

and again

$$\omega = \theta \tag{1.48}$$

Therefore, the outer circle transforms into the s-plane as a line segment, $\sigma_2 = \ln b$, going from $\omega = 0$ to $\omega = 2\pi$.

The length dimension was not transformed, so we now have our coaxial cable in the shape of two identical, flat strips, 1 m long, of width 2π m, and separation $\ln b - \ln a$ m.

If we cared to plot the radial flux lines between conductors a and b in the z-plane, we would find that the corresponding flux in the s-plane was exactly uniform between the flat sheets, and that there is no fringing at the edges. We may therefore use the simple formula for the capacity of parallel plate condensers, which is:

$$C = \frac{\varepsilon A}{d} \tag{1.49}$$

where C = capacity (F)

ε = permittivity (F/m)

A = area of plates (m²)

d = distance apart (m)

Thus, our two plates in the s-plane have a capacity

$$C = \frac{\varepsilon 6.28}{\ln b - \ln a} \tag{1.50}$$

which is simplified to

$$C = \frac{2\pi\varepsilon}{\ln\left(\dfrac{b}{a}\right)} \tag{1.51}$$

Now (1.51) is the general formula for capacity per unit length of a coaxial transmission line of radii a and b. It is an exact solution. Those of you who have calculated the formula by other methods will agree, I am sure, that this simple transformation into the s-plane is a very simple means of solution.

We note in passing that there is no reason to think of transforming anything back into the z-plane, as the problem is identical in either plane. In future work, it may or may not be necessary to transform a solution back into the original plane for use.

1.7. Functions in the complex plane

It has been previously stated that if the equation of a z-plane curve is given, then y is a function of x and is usually written $f(x)$. The x is a real variable, and thus the y, or $f(x)$ is called a function of a real variable. In a particular work, different functions of x may be called $f(x)$, $g(x)$, $h(x)$, etc. The graphs of functions of x can be plotted in two dimensions.

Now instead of having a function of only one real variable x, it is possible to define a function of the complex variables z or s, for example, one may have given the function* of s

$$F(s) = \frac{1}{s} \tag{1.52}$$

It is seen here that instead of being merely a curve above the real axis, as was the case for $f(x)$, this function $F(s)$ has a value for every point in the s plane.

Thus the magnitude of $F(s)$ may be thought of as a surface. For much of our work with the Laplace transform, the surface will be adequate, and if necessary to consider phase angle, the situation will be analyzed at that time.

Suppose we wish to draw a picture of the $F(s)$ in (1.52). The first steps would be to get it into the form of an absolute magnitude.

$$F(s) = \frac{1}{\sigma + j\omega} \tag{1.53}$$

or

$$|F(s)| = \frac{1}{\sqrt{(\sigma^2 + \omega^2)}} \tag{1.54}$$

To plot the $F(s)$, it is best to select a line $\sigma_1 = $ constant, and then find the values of $F(s)$ along this line as ω varies. The procedure can be repeated along another line $\sigma_2 = $ constant, etc., so that eventually the entire surface is created. For the $F(s)$ of (1.52) it is noted that the value becomes infinite at one point only, at $s = 0$.

* From now on, functions of s will use capital F, or other capital letters, while functions of z, functions of time, etc., will use lower case letters.

A portion of the surface may be sketched in three dimensions as suggested in Fig. 1.15, where it is seen that the surface is an infinitely high peak at $s = 0$ and falls off rapidly in both the σ and ω directions.

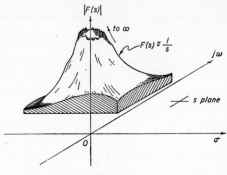

Fig. 1.15

1.8. Poles of complex functions

In the last article a simple function

$$F(s) = \frac{1}{s} \tag{1.55}$$

was shown in Fig. 1.15 to resemble a steep mountain peak reaching up to infinity. This peak is of such major importance in future work that a special name has been assigned to it. It is called a "pole". We speak of the function $F(s)$ as having poles at certain values of s, wherever the magnitude $F(s)$ goes to infinity.

EXAMPLE 1. Poles of the function

$$F(s) = \frac{1}{s(s + 2)} \tag{1.56}$$

occur at

$$s = 0 \tag{1.57}$$

$$s = -2 \tag{1.58}$$

since at either of these two points the surface rises up to infinity.

EXAMPLE 2. The function

$$F(s) = \frac{1}{s(s + 2)(s - 2j + 2)} \tag{1.59}$$

has poles at

$$s = 0$$
$$s = -2$$
$$s = -2 + 2j$$

because at each of these three points the $F(s)$ becomes infinite.

It is customary to indicate the location of poles in the s-plane with small crosses. The poles of (1.59) are thus illustrated as in Fig. 1.16.

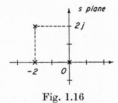

Fig. 1.16

We will merely hint at interesting things to come by saying that later on we will express entire complicated electronic networks as groups of poles in the s-plane, analyze them in the s-domain, and then transform the results back into the time plane for use.

PROBLEMS.   Find the poles of the following functions of s, and indicate by crosses in the s-plane.

(a) $$F(s) = \frac{1}{s(s - 1)(s - 4)}$$

(b) $$F(s) = \frac{1}{s(s^2 - 1)}$$

(c) $$F(s) = \frac{1}{(s - 1)(s^2 + 1)}$$

ANS.   (a) $s = 0$, $s = 1$, $s = 4$;   (b) $s = 0$, $s = 1$, $s = -1$;

(c) $s = 1$, $s = j$, $s = -j$.

Poles are found one at a time by taking each individual factor in the denominator, setting it equal to zero, and solving for s. A pole is associated with a particular factor creating it. Thus in problem (a) the pole at 0 is caused by the factor s, the pole at $s = 1$ is created by the factor $(s - 1)$, etc.

We will digress for a few moments on the subject of zeros, and then return to discuss the general subject of poles and zeros at greater length.

1.9. Zeros of complex functions

A zero of a complex function is defined as a value of s which makes the entire function equal zero, thus

$$F(s) = \frac{(s-2)(s+1)}{(s-4)} \tag{1.60}$$

has zeros at $s = 2$ and $s = -1$, because if $s = 2$ the first factor in the numerator becomes zero, making the entire $F(s)$ zero, and if $s = -1$ the second factor is zero and makes the entire $F(s)$ zero.

The zeros of a function are found then, by setting each factor in the numerator to zero, and solving for s. The zeros are located in the s plane by using small circles as markers. Equation (1.60) therefore has its zeros shown in the s-plane as in Fig. 1.17.

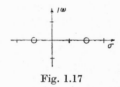

Fig. 1.17

PROBLEMS. Find the zeros of the following functions, and plot in the s-plane. Use small circles as in Fig. 1.17

(a) $F(s) = \dfrac{s}{s+1}$

(b) $F(s) = \dfrac{s-13}{s}$

(c) $F(s) = \dfrac{(s-1)(s+j)}{s^2+2}$

(d) $F(s) = s + \dfrac{1}{s}$

(e) $F(s) = \dfrac{(s^2+1)s}{(s^2-1)}$

(f) $F(s) = \dfrac{(s-3-j4)}{(s+j)^2}$

ANS. (a) $s = 0$; (b) $s = 13$; (c) $s = 1, s = -j$; (d) $s = j, s = -j$;
(e) $s = 0, s = j, s = -j$; (f) $s = 3 + j4$.

Functions will often appear as the ratio of two polynomials, as in the following example:

$$F(s) = \frac{s^3 + as^2 + bs + c}{s^2 + ds + e} \tag{1.61}$$

In such a case it is necessary to set the numerator equal to zero and solve the resulting higher order equation. In this case the roots of the cubic equation would then be used to form the same $F(s)$ rewritten as a product of factors. Thus, if the roots are a_1, a_2, and a_3, the function can be expressed as

$$F(s) = \frac{(s - a_1)(s - a_2)(s - a_3)}{s^2 + ds + e} \qquad (1.62)$$

1.10. The pole–zero diagram

A given function of s can always be drawn as a pole–zero diagram. This is merely a picture of the small crosses and circles in the s plane which locate the poles and zeros. The function

$$F(s) = \frac{(s + 3)}{(s^2 + 4)} \qquad (1.63)$$

has a zero at $s = -3$, and poles at $j2$ and $-j2$. Thus the pole–zero diagram appears as in Fig. 1.18.

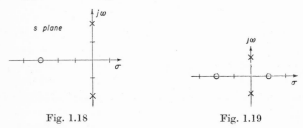

Fig. 1.18   Fig. 1.19

Conversely, if one is given the pole–zero diagram, it is easy to write the corresponding function of s. As an example, suppose we are given Fig. 1.19. Taking the zeros first, the zero at $s = 1$ creates a factor $(s - 1)$ to be placed in the numerator. The zero at $s = -2$ creates a factor $(s + 2)$ to be placed as a second factor in the numerator, while the pole at $s = j$ gives a factor $(s - j)$, and the pole at $s = -j$ gives the factor $(s + j)$, both of which go into the denominator. Collecting the factors gives:

$$F(s) = \frac{(s - 1)(s + 2)}{(s - j)(s + j)} \qquad (1.64)$$

which can also be expressed as

$$F(s) = \frac{s^2 + s - 2}{s^2 + 1} \qquad (1.65)$$

Pole–zero diagrams are of special importance in the analysis of R–L–C networks, and we shall be using them throughout the remainder of the book.

PROBLEM. Write the function $F(s)$ corresponding to the pole–zero diagram in Fig. 1.20.

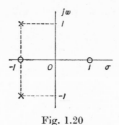

Fig. 1.20

ANS.

$$F(s) = \frac{s^2 - 1}{s^2 + 2s + 2}$$

1.11. Integration along a curve in the s-plane

The objective in this and other articles in Chapter I is to present only the parts of complex variable theory necessary to prepare the reader for the study of Laplace transforms. It would be highly desirable to have everyone complete a formal course in complex variables before beginning the study of Laplace transformations, but actually this is neither possible nor necessary. If the reader will master one or two more definitions and concepts, he will have ample background to begin Chapter II with confidence. One such concept is the subject of integration of a function $F(s)$ in the complex s-plane.

The reader will recall that in his earlier days of studying the calculus, integration was always carried out along the real or x-axis only, usually between specific upper and lower limits. It is not difficult to generalize this procedure.

First of all, let us examine, or review the procedure used in setting up a real integral for the area under a curve (see Fig. 1.21). It is recalled that the elementary, or differential area is length times width

$$\Delta A = y \Delta x \tag{1.66}$$

and a specific elementary area is

$$\Delta A_n = y_n \Delta x_n \tag{1.67}$$

The subscript may be dropped from the Δx since all Δx's are identical, and y is known at any specific point y_2, y_3, etc., because y is a $f(x)$ and this function is known. Now if the individual small areas are summed up, the total area is

$$A = y_1 \Delta x + y_2 \Delta x + y_3 \Delta x + \ldots y_n \Delta x \qquad (1.68)$$

or since $y = f(x)$

$$A = f(x_1)\Delta x + f(x_2)\Delta x + f(x_3)\Delta x + \ldots f(x_n)\Delta x$$

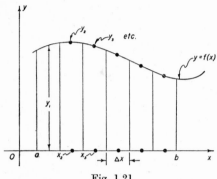

Fig. 1.21

Fortunately, this series simplifies to the basic integral

$$A = \int_a^b f(x)\,dx \qquad (1.69)$$

which represents exactly the sum of the elementary areas from $x = a$ to $x = b$, as Δx approaches zero.

Note that in the above discussion, we merely divided the x-axis segment from a to b into n equal parts of Δx width each. We then took the value of $f(x)$ at the particular segment center times Δx to get the product $f(x)\Delta x$. It was not particularly important that the product was an area, and many useful products such as force times distance, voltage times current, etc., are not usually thought of as areas when integrating. Let us therefore look at Fig. 1.22. This is a plan view of the s-plane, and the path over which we wish to integrate is shown as the line from $s = a$ to $s = b$; a and b are of course both complex numbers, or limits. Note that this path follows a devious course through the s-plane, and that all points s on the path are complex. Thus the path itself requires a plane (two dimensions) rather than merely the x-axis.

Of course we must be given a formula for $F(s)$, so that we know $F(s_1)$, $F(s_2)$, etc., at the center of each of the small segments Δs. The integral, then, is of exactly the same form as (1.68) and (1.69), or

$$\int_a^b F(s)\,ds = F(s_1)\Delta s + F(s_2)\Delta s + F(s_3)\Delta s + \ldots F(s_n)\Delta s \quad (1.70)$$

if Δs approaches zero and n approaches infinity.

Note very carefully the major difference between Figs. 1.21 and 1.22. In Fig. 1.22 a third dimension is required (up and out of the

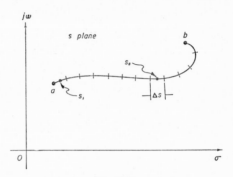

Fig. 1.22

page) to show the value $F(s)$, because both the σ and ω directions are used to show the path of integration in the plane, whereas in Fig. 1.21 only two dimensions are required, one to show the path of integration and one to show the value $f(x)$.

Note further that $F(s)$ is actually a surface, weaving above, in, and under the s-plane. If the s-plane is thought of as terrestrial sea level, then $F(s)$ will appear somewhat like the surface of the earth, i.e. some parts of the surface are above, and some are below sea level.

The magnitude of $F(s)$ can usually be drawn as a surface as shown in Fig. 1.15 in three dimensions, but for most of our work this will not be necessary.

We will be particularly interested in cases where the integral is around a complete closed loop, from one point, around an area, and back to the same point. Thus we will not take space to discuss integration from one point a to another point b as in Fig. 1.22, but will use this merely to visualize the setting up of the integral. We mention in passing that the value of the integral is a function only of the end points a and b, the same as for real integrals.

This last statement requires one qualification to be correct, and this is that the function in question must be analytic. We will avoid discussing the difference between analytic and non-analytic functions by saying that all of the functions we will normally deal with in our electronics work will be analytic, and we will leave the discussion of function analyticity to a formal text on complex variables. If the student is particularly curious, he may read up on the subject of analytic or non-analytic functions, and learn how to apply the Cauchy–Riemann criteria to determine whether or not the given function meets the requirements for analyticity. This subject is discussed in all complex variable texts.

1.12. Integration around a pole

In this article we will examine a procedure for integrating around a pole in the complex plane. This topic is of fundamental importance. Suppose we are interested in the function

$$F(s) = \frac{1}{s - a}$$

This factor, taken n times, and with different complex constants for a, can be used to represent the denominator of any $F(s)$. That

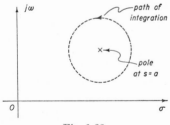

Fig. 1.23

is, the poles of any $F(s)$ are created by just such factors as this. It is vital then, to be able to integrate $F(s)$ around a path enclosing the pole at $s = a$. A typical path of integration is shown in Fig. 1.23, and a may be anywhere in the plane.

Now if we select a general point s on the circular path of integration shown in Fig. 1.23, we may draw vectors from the origin to this general point s, and also to the pole at a. These are the vectors s and a. It is seen then, that the radius vector reaching from the pole to the point s is $s - a$, shown together with s and a in Fig. 1.24. Our specific problem then is to integrate the function $F(s)$ around the dotted, circular path.

$$\oint F(s)\,ds = \oint \frac{ds}{s - a} \tag{1.71}$$

where the small circle on the integral sign indicates that the integration begins at one point on a closed path, and goes around once,

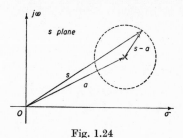

Fig. 1.24

ending at the same point. Let the $s - a$ vector shown in Fig. 1.24 be replaced by a magnitude A at an angle θ:

$$s - a = A\varepsilon^{j\theta} \tag{1.72}$$

then, differentiating,

$$ds = jA\varepsilon^{j\theta}d\theta \tag{1.73}$$

and if we replace s and ds in (1.71) by these substitutions

$$\oint \frac{ds}{s - a} = \int \frac{jA\varepsilon^{j\theta}d\theta}{A\varepsilon^{j\theta}} \tag{1.74}$$

which after simplification becomes

$$\oint \frac{ds}{s - a} = j\int_0^{2\pi} d\theta \tag{1.75}$$

and where we have added the limits, noting that the $s - a$, or A vector travels once around during the integration. Continuing,

$$\oint \frac{ds}{s - a} = j[\theta]_0^{2\pi} \tag{1.76}$$

and inserting limits gives

$$\oint \frac{ds}{s - a} = 2\pi j \tag{1.77}$$

Now the radius vector A could have been any assumed value to accommodate any circular path around the pole. Thus the actual size of the circle of integration is not important, and we can say that (1.77) is a general result valid for any circle, large or small.

Observe one point very carefully. It appears trivial, but we remark that if the original $F(s)$ had had a constant multiplier K, then the constant could have been carried as such through the entire process and the answer would have been K times the $2\pi j$. This point will be expanded upon later, when we discuss integration around multiple poles of functions of s.

1.13. Integration around a path not containing a pole

We saw in the previous article that different paths of integration around a pole gave the same value of the integral. It is stated now without proof that the path of integration is of no importance, and that integration around any path (uniform, or irregular) which encloses the pole will have the same value, $2\pi j$. The question now arises as to what the value of the integral would be if there is no pole enclosed within the integration path.

Suppose we redraw Fig. 1.24, but keep the pole outside the path of

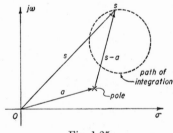

Fig. 1.25

integration (see Fig. 1.25). Using the same $F(s)$, we again set up the integral

$$\oint F(s)\, ds = \oint \frac{ds}{s - a} \tag{1.78}$$

and if we keep a circular path of integration, the magnitude of the $s - a$ vector will vary, and we may merely write it as a function of θ. Thus

$$s - a = f(\theta)\varepsilon^{j\theta} \tag{1.79}$$

and differentiating,

$$ds = jf(\theta)\varepsilon^{j\theta}d\theta + \varepsilon^{j\theta}df(\theta) \tag{1.80}$$

then (1.78) becomes

$$\oint \frac{ds}{s-a} = \int \frac{jf(\theta)\varepsilon^{j\theta}d\theta}{f(\theta)\varepsilon^{j\theta}} + \int \frac{\varepsilon^{j\theta}df(\theta)}{f(\theta)\varepsilon^{j\theta}} \tag{1.81}$$

We note that the angle θ merely starts at some value, oscillates once as the point s goes around the path, and ends at the same angle as at the start. Thus the upper and lower limits can be the same general angle. Using ψ for this angle, and simplifying, (1.81) becomes

$$\oint \frac{ds}{s-a} = j\int_{\psi}^{\psi}d\theta + \int_{\psi}^{\psi}\frac{df(\theta)}{f(\theta)} = [\ln f(\theta)]_{\psi}^{\psi} \tag{1.82}$$

or

$$\oint \frac{ds}{s-a} = \ln\left[\frac{f(\psi)}{f(\psi)}\right] = \ln(1) \tag{1.83}$$

and finally

$$\oint \frac{ds}{s-a} = 0 \tag{1.84}$$

Equation (1.84) is a general result, and tells us that the value of any integral of $F(s)$ taken around a closed path not enclosing poles is zero.

As in the last article, if there is a constant multiplier for $F(s)$, it is brought out and carried through the entire procedure, until it can be dropped, upon being multiplied by the zero value of the integral. Suppose for example that one is given the function

$$F(s) = \frac{6}{s-a} \tag{1.85}$$

to be integrated around a path such as in art. 1.12, around a pole, or around a particular path not including a pole, as we have done in this article. One might be tempted to divide by 6, as

$$F(s) = \frac{1}{s/6 - a/6} \tag{1.86}$$

Note, however, that it is not possible to write this denominator as a vector from a to s, as shown in Figs. 1.24 and 1.25, and thus the substitutions as we have made them would not be valid. One must therefore remove the constant multiplier before performing the substitutions, and keep the factor which creates the pole in exactly the same form as in the worked out procedure.

1.14. Residues

The present article on the subject of residues of functions will serve to bring together several seemingly unrelated topics which have been discussed in previous articles. The residues of functions of s are extremely important to our later study of the Laplace transform, and therefore it is well at this time to attain a clear, physical picture of what residues are and how they are used.

We have noted previously that an $F(s)$ could be visualized as a surface, with the s-plane itself corresponding to sea level, and the height from the s-plane (sea level) to the surface being the magnitude of $F(s)$. For the particular function

$$F(s) = \frac{1}{s-a} \tag{1.87}$$

it is seen that there will be a pole at $s = a$, which can be visualized as a high mountain peak where the surface rises to infinity at a point directly over the pole location.

For purposes of developing the concept of residues, let us at the moment confine our pole locations to the σ-axis in the s-plane. This

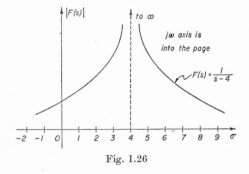

Fig. 1.26

will allow us to use a two-dimensional graph to show the σ-axis cross-section of the s-plane and the magnitude of $F(s)$ as well. It will not be difficult afterwards to enlarge the concept to three dimensions, so that the pole may be anywhere in the s-plane. If (1.87) is drawn for $a = 4$ we have Fig. 1.26.

Note again that Fig. 1.26 represents magnitude only, and thus all of the surface will be above the σ-axis. We will take actual numerical values from the equations, and therefore it will not be necessary to calibrate the vertical scale.

Let us now look at a slightly more elaborate function of s, composed of the two factors,

$$F(s) = \frac{1}{(s-4)(s-7)} \tag{1.88}$$

where we have used specific, real pole locations. It will be apparent that this function can be thought of as the product of two surfaces, or rewritten slightly as

$$F(s) = \frac{1}{(s-4)} \times \frac{1}{(s-7)} \tag{1.89}$$

where the first factor creates the same surface as in Fig. 1.26, while the second factor creates a second identical surface, except that the second surface rises to infinity above the pole located at $s = 7$, rather than 4. Both surface cross-sections are shown in Fig. 1.27.

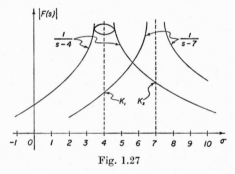

Fig. 1.27

Of course the over-all function $F(s)$ is the product of these two surfaces for each point in the s-plane, as in Fig. 1.28, but there are advantages to be had by considering the over-all $F(s)$ as the product of the two surfaces shown in Fig. 1.27 rather than as a single surface, as we shall now see.

Let us climb up rather high on the side of the $1/(s-4)$ mountain which rises over the pole at $\sigma = 4$. If we climb up a moderate distance, we will be able to reach around the peak and draw a small circle, as shown in Fig. 1.27 also. Now observe carefully that if we keep the radius of the circle very small, the value of the second surface will be almost constant within the interior of the same circular region in the s plane. As a matter of fact, if we let the radius approach zero, the value of the other surface $1/(s-7)$ becomes the constant value K_1. Within the small circle in Fig. 1.27, then, we may consider the over-all surface $F(s)$ to consist of the product of the two surfaces, or factors

$$F(s) = K_1 \times \frac{1}{(s-4)} \tag{1.90}$$

Now we have seen previously that an integral around a pole is independent of the path of integration, as long as the path of

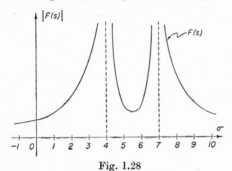

Fig. 1.28

integration encloses the pole. Thus to integrate around the pole at $s = 4$, it is perfectly valid to make the radius of the path of integration very small, so that (1.90) holds. Then

$$\oint F(s)\,ds = \oint \frac{ds}{(s-4)(s-7)} = \oint \frac{K_1\,ds}{(s-4)} \tag{1.91}$$

but the K_1, being a constant, can be brought outside the integral, i.e.

$$\oint F(s)\,ds = K_1 \oint \frac{ds}{s-4} \tag{1.92}$$

and it was found in art. 1.12 that the integral around such a pole was equal to $2\pi j$. Therefore

$$\oint F(s)\,ds = K_1 2\pi j \tag{1.93}$$

K_1 of course can be found by inspecting Fig. 1.27 and evaluating the surface $1/(s-7)$ at the pole $s = 4$. So that

$$K_1 = \frac{1}{s-7}\bigg|_{s=4} = -\frac{1}{3} \tag{1.94}$$

Therefore

$$\oint F(s)\, ds = -\frac{2\pi j}{3} \tag{1.95}$$

If it is desired to integrate around the pole at $s = 7$, the procedure is exactly the same, except that within a small circle around the second mountain peak, we replace the surface $1/(s - 4)$ by the constant K_2. Thus the value of the integral around the pole at $s = 7$ is

$$\oint F(s)\, ds = K_2 \cdot 2\pi j \tag{1.96}$$

We see then, that it is possible to simplify the $F(s)$ within a small circle surrounding each pole. Since the $F(s)$ may always be written as a product of factors, and since only one of the factors can contribute a particular pole, we may say that within a very small area surrounding any pole of any $F(s)$, the given $F(s)$ may be simplified as

$$F(s) = K \times \frac{1}{(s - a)} \tag{1.97}$$

where K is the product $K_1 K_2 K_3 \ldots$ of all the values of the surfaces created by all the terms of $F(s)$ except the surface $1/(s - a)$, which creates the actual pole at a.

DEFINITION. The constant that, when multiplied by the one factor that creates a pole, causes the product to be a valid simple substitution for the more elaborate $F(s)$ within an infinitely small diameter circle around the pole at $s = a$, is called the residue of the function at the pole $s = a$. By this definition, it is seen that the constant K_1 in Fig. 1.27 is the residue of $F(s)$ at the pole $s = 4$. Similarly, for this same function (1.88) K_2 is the residue at the pole $s = 7$.

Using the concept of the residue then, a complicated function of s can be replaced within a very small circle of integration around a pole by the residue at the pole times the one factor which creates the pole. This makes it possible to integrate very complex functions of s around poles. Using a previous example, where

$$F(s) = \frac{6}{s - a} \tag{1.98}$$

one notes that by the above definition, 6 is a residue of $F(s)$ at the pole $s = a$. The 6 can be considered as a constant surface 6 units above the s-plane "sea level".

In the brief art. 1.15 to follow, it will be found that the value of an integral taken around two or more poles is the same as the sum of the integrals taken around each pole separately. After this statement is proved, a summary of all the ideas and concepts up to this point should enable us to integrate any $F(s)$ around any number of poles in the s-plane. For the moment, however, let us take the statement on faith, and as a last topic in this article, show how to find the residue at a given pole. If the given function is:

$$F(s) = \frac{1}{(s - a)(s - b)(s - c)} \qquad (1.99)$$

then each of the three factors will create a pole. In particular, if we are interested first in the pole at $s = a$.

$$F(s) = \frac{1}{(s - b)(s - c)} \times \frac{1}{(s - a)} \qquad (1.100)$$

we may consider the $1/(s - a)$ in the usual way, as a surface rising to infinity at $s = a$, and the remainder of the function surfaces to be constant within the very small circle of integration. We may thus substitute the value $s = a$ into the first of the above factors on the right-hand side to give

$$F(s) = \frac{1}{(a - b)(a - c)} \times \frac{1}{(s - a)} \qquad (1.101)$$

or

$$F(s) = K_a \times \frac{1}{(s - a)} \qquad (1.102)$$

where K_a is the residue of $F(s)$ at the pole $s = a$. For the residue at the pole $s = b$, one would write

$$F(s) = \frac{1}{(s - a)(s - c)} \times \frac{1}{(s - b)} \qquad (1.103)$$

and evaluate

$$\frac{1}{(s - a)(s - c)} \bigg|_{s=b} \qquad (1.104)$$

to find the residue

$$\frac{1}{(b - a)(b - c)} = K_b \qquad (1.105)$$

Stated in another way, one finds the residue of a function at a pole by removing the factor creating the pole, and evaluating the remainder of s at the pole. As an example, let

$$F(s) = \frac{3}{(s-1)(s+2)} \qquad (1.106)$$

To evaluate the residue at the pole $s = -2$, remove this factor, and evaluate the remainder for $s = -2$.

$$K_{-2} = \frac{3}{s-1}\bigg|_{s=-2} = \frac{3}{-2-1} = -1 \qquad (1.107)$$

We also speak of this as "removing a pole".

PROBLEMS

(1) Show that the sum of the residues at the poles of (1.88) is zero.

(2) (a) Find the residue of the function

$$F(s) = \frac{s^2}{(s-3)(s+6)}$$

at the pole $s = -6$.

ANS. $K_{-6} = -4$.

(b) Show that the sum of the two residues is not zero for this function.

(3) Show that the sum of all residues of the function

$$F(s) = \frac{s}{s^2+1}$$

is unity.

(4) Show that the sum of all residues of

$$F(s) = \frac{s^2}{s^2+1}$$

is zero.

1.15. Integration around two or more poles in the s-plane

Let us look again at the equation

$$F(s) = \frac{1}{(s-4)(s-7)} \qquad (1.108)$$

which we examined earlier in art. 1.14 and Fig. 1.27. The poles are at $s = 4$ and $s = 7$ and are shown in the usual pole–zero diagram as in Fig. 1.29. Suppose that for our path of integration about the pole at $s = 4$ we choose the circular path beginning at point a. In actual practice we would choose a much smaller radius, but we merely illustrate the procedure here. It will be recalled that the integral around this particular type of path is the sum of the incremental products of $F(s)\Delta s$ (see Fig. 1.22).

Now if we sum up these small quantities from point a all the way around the pole to point b, where b is close to, but not quite touching

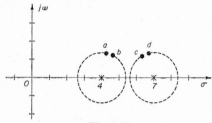

Fig. 1.29

point a, then the value of the integral from a to b is essentially the same as the circular integral completely around the pole. Our only inaccuracy is to leave off the last small term $F(s)\Delta s$ where the Δs reaches from b to a. As Δs approaches zero in the limit anyway, we say that in this case, around the pole $s = 4$

$$\oint F(s)\,ds = \int_a^b F(s)\,ds \qquad (1.109)$$

By the same line of reasoning, around the pole $s = 7$

$$\oint F(s)\,ds = \int_c^d F(s)\,ds \qquad (1.110)$$

It may not be obvious, and thus we point out that if a and b are close enough together, for practical purposes the value of $F(s)$ is the same at both points.

Now let us add the two paths from d to a, and from b to c, as in Fig. 1.30. We keep the paths very close together, but not actually touching. Thus, as we divide the total path up into the elementary sections Δs as shown, the value $F(s)$ at the center point e of such an element is essentially the same on both lines, or, for these two segments

$$F(s)_e \Delta s \text{ from } d \text{ to } a = F(s)_e \Delta s \text{ from } c \text{ to } b \qquad (1.111)$$

As the same situation will be valid for each increment, we may sum along the entire path from d to a and from c to b

$$\sum_d^a F(s)\Delta s = \sum_c^b F(s)\Delta s \tag{1.112}$$

or in the limit, as $s \to 0$

$$\int_d^a F(s)\,ds = \int_c^b F(s)\,ds \tag{1.113}$$

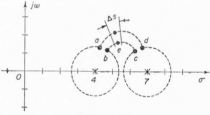

Fig. 1.30

Note carefully now that if we reverse the limits on the right-hand integral, we must also reverse the sign, i.e.

$$\int_d^a F(s)\,ds = -\int_b^c F(s)\,ds \tag{1.114}$$

We are now in a position to integrate around a complete path enclosing both poles. The complete integral may be written as the sum of the four sections starting at point a and returning to the same point. Thus

$$\oint F(s)\,ds = \int_a^b F(s)\,ds + \int_b^c F(s)\,ds + \int_c^d F(s)\,ds + \int_d^a F(s)\,ds \tag{1.115}$$

The last term on the right may be replaced by its equivalent from (1.114) as

$$\oint F(s)\,ds = \int_a^b F(s)\,ds + \int_b^c F(s)\,ds + \int_c^d F(s)\,ds - \int_b^c F(s)\,ds \tag{1.116}$$

The second and last terms on the right side cancel, leaving

$$\oint F(s)\,ds = \int_a^b F(s)\,ds + \int_c^d F(s)\,ds \tag{1.117}$$

Let us now close the small gap between b and a, and between d and c, Fig. 1.30, so that (1.117) becomes

$$\underbrace{\oint F(s)\,ds}_{\substack{\text{integral around} \\ \text{both poles}}} \quad = \quad \underbrace{\oint F(s)\,ds}_{\substack{\text{integral around} \\ \text{one pole}}} \quad + \quad \underbrace{\oint F(s)\,ds}_{\substack{\text{integral around} \\ \text{other pole}}} \qquad (1.118)$$

Thus we say that the integral of a function of s taken around all poles equals the sum of the separate integrals around each pole. If the residue at each pole is K_n, the integral around all poles then is the sum of all residues times $2\pi j$.

$$\oint F(s)ds = 2\pi j[K_1 + K_2 + \cdots] \qquad (1.119)$$

We shall make good use of this result in the evaluation of inverse Laplace transforms later in the book.

PROBLEMS. Integrate the functions shown around all poles:

(a) $\displaystyle\oint \frac{s^2\,ds}{(s-3)(s+6)}$ (c) $\displaystyle\oint \frac{s^2\,ds}{s^2+1}$

(b) $\displaystyle\oint \frac{s\,ds}{s^2+1}$ (d) $\displaystyle\oint \frac{(4js-2)ds}{s^2+1}$

ANS. (a) $-j6\pi$; (b) $j2\pi$; (c) 0; (d) -25.13.

1.16. Summary of Chapter I

As the reader is without doubt anxious to move on to more interesting and practical things, let us take just a few moments to summarize the more important points in this chapter.

(a) Complex numbers were introduced and illustrated in several forms useful for analytical work. The j-operator was defined, and it was pointed out that there are advantages to be had by thinking of complex numbers as vectors.

(b) Complex planes were introduced and it was shown that a function plotted in one plane could be transformed or transferred on to another plane by the use of transformations as (1.17) and (1.23). In complex variable theory this is called conformal mapping, and is most useful for simplifying functions or more properly, for making intricate functions more symmetrical.

(c) Functions in the complex plane were introduced and it was suggested that the magnitude of $F(s)$ be thought of as a surface, much like the irregular surface of the earth, over the s-plane itself, which was compared to sea level.

(d) Poles of complex functions were treated and their location in the s-plane pictured. Poles are especially important and the reader should develop the habit of making a rough sketch of the s-plane and poles of functions with which he is working. This concept will be used throughout the material on the Laplace transform and should eventually become second nature. After finishing this text, one should be able to deduce the behavior of rather complicated electrical networks merely by looking at their pole–zero diagrams. Zeros, although of importance, do not concern us much when they are in the numerator of functions of s. Zeros of the denominator, of course, are poles of the over-all function.

(e) Art. 1.11 discussed ways of forming line integrals, or integrals along a curve in the s-plane. It was shown that one extra dimension was necessary to illustrate this procedure, but that the path of integration could be shown in a plan view of the complex plane if $F(s)$ is thought of as coming out of the page toward the reader.

It was mentioned that the value of a line integral was a function of the end points only and thus the path of integration from one end to the other was not ordinarily of importance.

(f) The line integral was extended to reach completely around a pole, and with $F(s)$ as a simple factor it was shown that the integral around the pole was $2\pi j$. It was also brought out that the particular size of the path around the pole was not important. Art. 1.13 brought out the fact that integration along the closed path not containing a pole was zero.

(g) The previous ideas were extended in art. 1.14 to include the subject of residues. It was shown that rather complex functions of s could be represented as a product of surfaces, and that the entire function could be written inside a very small circle around the pole as simply the product of the residue and the one factor that created the pole.

(h) It was finally shown in art. 1.15 that the integral of $F(s)$ around all poles in the plane was the same as the sum of the integrals around each pole separately. This gave us a simple way to evaluate all such circular integrals, namely that the integral of $F(s)$ around all poles is equal to $2\pi j$ times the sum of the residues at all poles.

CHAPTER II

THE FOURIER SERIES AND INTEGRAL

2.1. The Fourier Series

THE electronics engineer will have already studied some material on the subject of Fourier Series. Actually, almost everyone who works with electricity and radio has a fair idea of the qualitative relations between fundamental frequencies and the harmonics which make up complicated waveshapes. However, since our work in the present

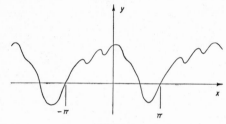

Fig. 2.1

chapter and those to follow grows increasingly complex, it is well to begin with the basic steps to make sure that we will all be using the same symbols and terminology.

Suppose we are given a function $p(x)$ which repeats itself exactly at regular intervals of x. Such a function is said to be periodic, where the period is defined as the interval shown in Fig. 2.1 between $-\pi$ and π.

The complex waveform in Fig. 2.1 can be shown to consist of the sum of a fundamental component and various harmonics, where the fundamental occupies the period from $-\pi$ to π. Therefore,

$$p(x) = a_0 + a_1 \cos x + a_2 \cos 2x + a_3 \cos 3x + \cdots$$
$$+ b_1 \sin x + b_2 \sin 2x + b_3 \sin 3x + \cdots \quad (2.1)$$

The a_0 term is the only constant quantity and is immediately found to be the average of $p(x)$ over the interval, thus

$$a_0 = \frac{1}{2\pi} \int_{-\pi}^{\pi} p(x)\, dx \qquad \blacktriangleleft \qquad (2.2)$$

For ease in writing, we may restate (2.1) in the following form:

$$p(x) = \sum_{n=0}^{\infty} (a_n \cos nx + b_n \sin nx) \qquad (2.3)$$

which will be found to contain the a_0 term when $n = 0$, since $\sin (0) = 0$, and $\cos (0) = 1$. Let us now multiply (2.3) by the term $\cos n'x$.

$$p(x) \cos n'x = \cos n'x \sum_{n=0}^{\infty} a_n \cos nx + \cos n'x \sum_{n=0}^{\infty} b_n \sin nx \qquad (2.4)$$

We now integrate this expression from $-\pi$ to π

$$\int_{-\pi}^{\pi} p(x) \cos n'x\, dx = \int_{-\pi}^{\pi} \cos n'x \sum_{n=0}^{\infty} a_n \cos nx\, dx +$$

$$+ \int_{-\pi}^{\pi} \cos n'x \sum_{n=0}^{\infty} b_n \sin nx\, dx \qquad (2.5)$$

This looks rather formidable. However, it really is not too difficult to handle, as we now show. Suppose we examine the first integral on the right. This is observed to consist of a summation of an infinite number of integrals of the form

$$a_n \int_{-\pi}^{\pi} \cos n'x \cos nx\, dx \qquad (2.6)$$

Fortunately, this integral is found to be zero for all cases where n' does not equal n. For the one term where n' does equal n, the value is π. Thus,

$$a_n \int_{-\pi}^{\pi} \cos n'x \ \cos nx\, dx = \begin{cases} \pi a_n \text{ if } n = n' \\ 0 \text{ if } n \neq n' \end{cases} \qquad (2.7)$$

The second term on the right of (2.5) also creates an infinite number of integrals of the form

$$b_n \int_{-\pi}^{\pi} \cos n'x \sin nx\, dx \qquad (2.8)$$

By using the trigonometric identity

$$\cos n'x \sin nx = \tfrac{1}{2}[\sin (nx + n'x) + \sin (nx - n'x)] \qquad (2.9)$$

it can easily be shown by integrating and substituting limits that (2.8) equals zero for all cases, whether $n' = n$ or not.

If we now let n' be the general nth term, we may rewrite (2.5), substituting for the intricate right-hand expressions the simple quantity πa_n from (2.7). That is

$$\int_{-\pi}^{\pi} p(x) \cos nx \, dx = \pi a_n \qquad (2.10)$$

from which a_n may at last be found as

$$a_n = \frac{1}{\pi} \int_{-\pi}^{\pi} p(x) \cos nx \, dx \qquad \blacktriangleleft \qquad (2.11)$$

The coefficients b_n may be found in exactly the same manner, by multiplying (2.3) by $\sin n'x$ and integrating from $-\pi$ to π. The final result is

$$b_n = \frac{1}{\pi} \int_{-\pi}^{\pi} p(x) \sin nx \, dx \qquad \blacktriangleleft \qquad (2.12)$$

The formulas (2.2), (2.11) and (2.12) are marked with small triangles as an aid to future location.

If $p(x)$ is known, any of the coefficients, or "magnitudes" of the harmonic terms can be found simply by placing $p(x)$ into one of the desired formulas.

In our work with electronics, the independent variable is often time. We therefore define a fundamental frequency ω_1 as

$$\omega_1 = 2\pi f = \frac{2\pi}{T} \qquad (2.13)$$

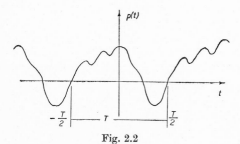

Fig. 2.2

where T is the period in seconds from $-\pi$ to π, as illustrated in Fig. 2.2. Any harmonic frequency ω will therefore be

$$\omega = n\omega_1 = \frac{n2\pi}{T} \qquad (2.14)$$

We may now rewrite the Fourier series (2.3) in terms of frequency and time rather than the angle x. Thus

$$p(t) = \sum_{n=0}^{\infty} (a_n \cos n\omega_1 t + b_n \sin n\omega_1 t) \qquad (2.15)$$

The corresponding formulas in x and t are collected in Table 2.1 for easy reference.

TABLE 2.1

Variable x	Variable t
$p(x) = \sum_{n=0}^{\infty} (a_n \cos nx + b_n \sin nx)$ where $a_0 = \dfrac{1}{2\pi} \int_{-\pi}^{\pi} p(x)\, dx$ $a_n = \dfrac{1}{\pi} \int_{-\pi}^{\pi} p(x) \cos nx\, dx$ $b_n = \dfrac{1}{\pi} \int_{-\pi}^{\pi} p(x) \sin nx\, dx$	$p(t) = \sum_{n=0}^{\infty} (a_n \cos n\omega_1 t + b_n \sin n\omega_1 t)$ where $a_0 = \dfrac{1}{T} \int_{-\frac{T}{2}}^{\frac{T}{2}} p(t)\, dt$ $a_n = \dfrac{2}{T} \int_{-\frac{T}{2}}^{\frac{T}{2}} p(t) \cos n\omega_1 t\, dt$ $b_n = \dfrac{2}{T} \int_{-\frac{T}{2}}^{\frac{T}{2}} p(t) \sin n\omega_1 t\, dt$

2.2. Exponential form of the Fourier series

It will be the purpose of this article to convert the Fourier series as written in (2.15) into exponential form. This is one of the numerous stages in the gradual development of the Laplace transform, and has considerable application in its own right, as we shall see in some later examples.

Let us begin by writing (2.15) with the following notation, as

$$p(t) = \sum_{n=0}^{\infty} z_n \qquad (2.16)$$

where

$$z_n = a_n \cos n\omega_1 t + b_n \sin n\omega_1 t \qquad (2.17)$$

Now by the use of Euler's theorem (see art. 1.2) we have the exponential form for a sine and cosine, namely:

$$\cos \theta = \frac{\varepsilon^{j\theta} + \varepsilon^{-j\theta}}{2} ; \qquad \sin \theta = \frac{\varepsilon^{j\theta} - \varepsilon^{-j\theta}}{2j} \qquad (2.18)$$

Using these, the cosine and sine terms in (2.17) may be rewritten as

$$z_n = a_n \left(\frac{\varepsilon^{jn\omega_1 t}}{2} + \frac{\varepsilon^{-jn\omega_1 t}}{2} \right) + b_n \left(-j \frac{\varepsilon^{jn\omega_1 t}}{2} + j \frac{\varepsilon^{-jn\omega_1 t}}{2} \right) \quad (2.19)$$

which can be factored into the following form:

$$z_n = \tfrac{1}{2}[(a_n - jb_n)\varepsilon^{jn\omega_1 t} + (a_n + jb_n)\varepsilon^{-jn\omega_1 t}] \quad (2.20)$$

Note that the coefficients are complex conjugates. We take their actual values from Table 2.1. Therefore,

$$a_n + jb_n = \frac{2}{T} \int_{-\frac{T}{2}}^{\frac{T}{2}} p(t) \cos n\omega_1 t \, dt + j \frac{2}{T} \int_{-\frac{T}{2}}^{\frac{T}{2}} p(t) \sin n\omega_1 t \, dt \quad (2.21)$$

This is simplified to

$$a_n + jb_n = \frac{2}{T} \int_{-\frac{T}{2}}^{\frac{T}{2}} p(t)[\cos n\omega_1 t + j \sin n\omega_1 t] \, dt \quad (2.22)$$

Euler's theorem (1.8) is again used to simplify the bracketed term still further, to give

$$a_n + jb_n = \frac{2}{T} \int_{-\frac{T}{2}}^{\frac{T}{2}} p(t)\varepsilon^{jn\omega_1 t} \, dt \quad (2.23)$$

or, if we use both the plus and minus signs, we have both complex conjugates.

$$a_n \pm jb_n = \frac{2}{T} \int_{-\frac{T}{2}}^{\frac{T}{2}} p(t)\varepsilon^{\pm jn\omega_1 t} \, dt \quad (2.24)$$

We are now in a position to solve (2.20) for z_n, by using both values of (2.24), thus

$$z_n = \frac{1}{T} \left[\int_{-\frac{T}{2}}^{\frac{T}{2}} p(t)\varepsilon^{-jn\omega_1 t} \, dt \; \varepsilon^{jn\omega_1 t} + \int_{-\frac{T}{2}}^{\frac{T}{2}} p(t)\varepsilon^{jn\omega_1 t} \, dt \; \varepsilon^{-jn\omega_1 t} \right] \quad (2.25)$$

Note carefully that the exponential term immediately following each dt is not part of the integral.

Equation (2.25) is now placed back into the original equation in this article, (2.16), which expresses the series. This gives

$$p(t) = \frac{1}{T} \sum_{n=0}^{\infty} \begin{bmatrix} \text{sum of the integral} \\ \text{terms in (2.25)} \end{bmatrix} \quad (2.26)$$

Now note carefully that if we let n in (2.25) assume both plus and minus values, then we can omit the right-hand integral, as the values $\pm n$ placed in the left-hand integral will create both terms as shown. We can include all minus values of n by summing (2.26) from $-\infty$, rather than 0. Using this new limit of $-\infty$, (2.26) now becomes

$$p(t) = \frac{1}{T} \sum_{n=-\infty}^{\infty} \int_{-\frac{T}{2}}^{\frac{T}{2}} p(t)\varepsilon^{-jn\omega_1 t}\, dt\ \varepsilon^{jn\omega_1 t} \qquad (2.27)$$

Note again that the exponential term following the dt is not part of the integral. Let us now define a new expression $P(\omega)$ as

$$P(\omega) = \int_{-\frac{T}{2}}^{\frac{T}{2}} p(t)\varepsilon^{-jn\omega_1 t}\, dt \qquad (2.28)$$

(This is a definition, not a derivation) and it merely is defined to simplify the mathematics. If it proves useful as such then the definition is justified. Equation (2.27) therefore becomes

$$p(t) = \frac{1}{T} \sum_{n=-\infty}^{\infty} P(\omega)\varepsilon^{jn\omega_1 t} \qquad (2.29)$$

As one last item in this article, we note again that ω_1 is the fundamental angular frequency, and that any harmonic may be simply expressed as

$$\omega = n\omega_1 \qquad (2.30)$$

or

$$\omega = \frac{n2\pi}{T} \qquad (2.31)$$

from which

$$\frac{T}{2} = \frac{n\pi}{\omega} \qquad (2.32)$$

and

$$n = \frac{\omega T}{2\pi} \qquad (2.33)$$

(2.29) is now recopied with these new quantities as

$$p(t) = \frac{1}{2\pi} \sum_{\omega=-\infty}^{\infty} P(\omega)\varepsilon^{j\omega t} \frac{\omega}{n} \qquad \blacktriangleleft \qquad (2.34)$$

and (2.28) is rewritten as

$$P(\omega) = \int_{-\frac{T}{2}}^{\frac{T}{2}} p(t)\varepsilon^{-j\omega t}\, dt \qquad \blacktriangleleft \qquad (2.35)$$

Equation (2.35) is called the direct Fourier transform of a function of time $p(t)$, and (2.34) is known as the inverse transform.

We have been using the term $p(t)$ and $P(\omega)$ to signify work with periodic functions. Therefore this work can later be distinguished from material dealing with non-periodic functions. For those functions we will use the expressions $f(t)$ and $F(\omega)$.

The results to be retained from this article are equations (2.34) and (2.35). Before finishing the article, however, it is desirable to present an example of their use in the form of a worked out typical problem.

PROBLEM 1 (art. 2.2). Given the periodic square wave shown in Fig. 2.3, find: (a) the frequency spectrum $P(\omega)$. (b) find $p(t)$.

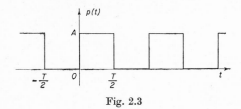

Fig. 2.3

(a) The frequency spectrum, may be found by direct application of (2.35). Thus

$$P(\omega) = \int_{-\frac{T}{2}}^{\frac{T}{2}} p(t)\varepsilon^{-j\omega t}\, dt = \int_{-\frac{T}{2}}^{0} (0)\varepsilon^{-j\omega t}\, dt + A \int_{0}^{\frac{T}{2}} \varepsilon^{-j\omega t}\, dt \quad (2.36)$$

$$P(\omega) = \left[\frac{-A\varepsilon^{-j\omega t}}{j\omega} \right]_{0}^{\frac{T}{2}} = \frac{jA}{\omega}\left(\varepsilon^{-\frac{j\omega T}{2}} - 1 \right) \qquad (2.37)$$

Using the trivial relations (2.30) to (2.33), we may rewrite this as

$$P(\omega) = \frac{jAT}{2\pi n}\left(\varepsilon^{-jn\pi} - 1 \right) \qquad (2.38)$$

We now begin the seemingly endless task of evaluating this result for all values of n from $-\infty$ to ∞. First, for $n = 0$, let us expand the exponential term as a series, and retain the first two terms, i.e.

$$P(\omega) = \frac{jAT}{2\pi n} \left(1 - jn\pi + \cdots - 1\right) \tag{2.39}$$

Canceling the one's and the n's, we have

$$P(\omega)\big|_{\omega=0} = \frac{AT}{2} \tag{2.40}$$

This same result could also have been obtained by evaluating (2.38) by the use of l'Hospital's rule. Now for other values of n from $-\infty$ to ∞, we may save several years time if we note that

$$\left(-\frac{1}{2}\right)(\varepsilon^{-jn\pi} - 1) = \begin{cases} 0 \text{ for } n \text{ even} \\ 1 \text{ for } n \text{ odd} \end{cases} \tag{2.41}$$

(see art. 1.2 for notation).

Retaining only odd values of n, we prepare a chart such as Table 2.2, using only odd values of n in (2.38).

TABLE 2.2

n	$P(\omega)$
0	$\dfrac{AT}{2}$
± 1	$\mp \dfrac{jAT}{\pi}$
± 3	$\mp \dfrac{jAT}{3\pi}$
± 5	$\mp \dfrac{jAT}{5\pi}$

The spectrum $P(\omega)$ is now plotted, using the values in Table 2.2, and is shown in Fig. 2.4. Fig. 2.4 is called the frequency spectrum, $P(\omega)$.

It is observed that the spectrum is discontinuous, having values only at certain discrete points 0, ω_1, $3\omega_1$, etc. Later on we will find that certain other functions of time produce continuous spectra.

(b) The time function $p(t)$ may now be found by placing the coefficients of the frequency spectrum back into (2.29). That is

$$p(t) = F^{-1}(\omega) = \frac{1}{T} \sum_{n=-\infty}^{\infty} P(\omega) \varepsilon^{jn\omega_1 t} \qquad (2.42)$$

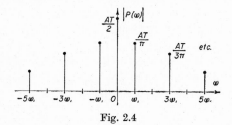

Fig. 2.4

We now insert the $P(\omega)$ values (both plus and minus) from Table 2.2, thus (2.42) becomes

$$p(t) = \frac{1}{T} \left[\underbrace{\frac{AT}{2}}_{n=0} - \underbrace{\frac{jAT\varepsilon^{j\omega_1 t}}{\pi}}_{n=1} + \underbrace{\frac{jAT\varepsilon^{-j\omega_1 t}}{\pi}}_{n=-1} - \right.$$

$$\left. - \underbrace{\frac{jAT\varepsilon^{j3\omega_1 t}}{3\pi}}_{n=3} + \underbrace{\frac{jAT\varepsilon^{-j3\omega_1 t}}{3\pi}}_{n=-3,\ \text{etc.}} + \cdots \right] \qquad (2.43)$$

The T's are all canceled, and each term except the first is multiplied by $2/2$. The result is factored as follows:

$$P(t) = \frac{A}{2} + \frac{2A}{\pi} \left(\frac{\varepsilon^{j\omega_1 t} - \varepsilon^{-j\omega_1 t}}{2j} \right) + \frac{2A}{3\pi} \left(\frac{\varepsilon^{j3\omega_1 t} - \varepsilon^{-j3\omega_1 t}}{2j} \right) + \cdots$$

$$\qquad (2.44)$$

and by Euler's theorem,

$$p(t) = \frac{A}{2} + \frac{2A}{\pi} \sin \omega_1 t + \frac{2A}{3\pi} \sin 3\omega_1 t + \cdots \qquad (2.45)$$

and the problem is solved.

The original square wave, Fig. 2.3, is thus seen to consist of a d.c. term, a fundamental, a third harmonic, and all odd harmonics following, with the magnitude of the harmonics given by the coefficients in (2.45).

Note that the above problem had only sine terms in the output. It is often advantageous to draw the original function so that it is perfectly symmetrical about $t = 0$. This will insure that only cosine terms are present.

Of course we should mention at this point that if one is merely interested in finding the magnitudes of the various harmonics which make up a given waveform, he may solve directly for the values a_n and b_n from the appropriate formulas. The definition of $P(\omega)$, and the concept of the frequency spectrum will be of great assistance to our future work, however, and it is for this reason that they are introduced in this way. Try to follow the same steps we have just illustrated when working the following exercise.

PROBLEM 2 (a).   Find the frequency spectrum of $p(x)$ in Fig. 2.5. (b) Find $p(x)$ from the frequency spectrum $P(\omega)$ in (a).

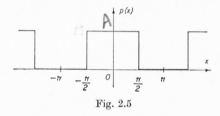

Fig. 2.5

2.3. The Fourier integral

All of the previous material has considered only periodic waveforms. It will now be interesting to see if we can generalize the foregoing ideas to include non-periodic waves as well.

We know that periodic non-sinusoidal waves give rise to a real, discrete, frequency spectrum. That is, the period of the waveform provides a knowledge of the fundamental frequency. The harmonics occupy discrete positions which are n times the fundamental frequency, where n is always integral.

Let us now examine Fig. 2.6, where ω_1 is the first division. Since the spacing between adjacent harmonics will be equal to ω_1 we may also define ω_1 as $\Delta\omega$. It is observed that if ω_1 is quite small, $\Delta\omega$ is very small and hence any frequency may be defined as

$$\omega = n\Delta\omega \tag{2.46}$$

Since ω_1 is inversely proportional to T, we see that it should be possible to let T approach infinity and accomplish this result. Thus we might say that a non-periodic waveform could be considered to have an infinitely long period. Or looking at it another way, we see that

$$T = \frac{1}{f} = \frac{2\pi}{\omega_1} = \frac{2\pi}{\Delta\omega} \tag{2.47}$$

or

$$\frac{T}{2} = \frac{\pi}{\Delta\omega} \tag{2.48}$$

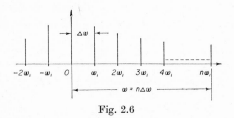

Fig. 2.6

If we now recopy (2.35) from the last article, but use the above value of $T/2$ for the limits, we have

$$F(\omega) = \int_{-\frac{\pi}{\Delta\omega}}^{\frac{\pi}{\Delta\omega}} f(t)\varepsilon^{-j\omega t}\,dt \tag{2.49}$$

(note that when dealing with non-periodic waveforms we will use the letters F and f, rather than P and p). Also, we found earlier (2.34) that

$$f(t) = \frac{1}{2\pi} \sum_{\omega=-\infty}^{\infty} F(\omega)\varepsilon^{j\omega t}\,\frac{\omega}{n} \tag{2.50}$$

Substituting (2.49) into (2.50) gives

$$f(t) = \frac{1}{2\pi} \sum_{\omega=-\infty}^{\infty} \left[\int_{-\frac{\pi}{\Delta\omega}}^{\frac{\pi}{\Delta\omega}} f(t)\varepsilon^{-j\omega t}\,dt\right] \varepsilon^{j\omega t}\Delta\omega \tag{2.51}$$

Note also from (2.48) that as $\Delta\omega \to 0$, $T \to \infty$, thus

$$\lim_{\Delta\omega \to 0} f(t) = \frac{1}{2\pi} \int_{-\infty}^{\infty} \left[\int_{-\infty}^{\infty} f(t)\varepsilon^{-j\omega t}\,dt\right] \varepsilon^{j\omega t}\,d\omega \tag{2.52}$$

The quantity inside the bracket is defined as

$$F(\omega) = \int_{-\infty}^{\infty} f(t)\varepsilon^{-j\omega t}\, dt \qquad \blacktriangleleft \qquad (2.53)$$

and thus (2.52) reduces to

$$f(t) = \frac{1}{2\pi} \int_{-\infty}^{\infty} F(\omega)\varepsilon^{jt\omega}\, d\omega \qquad \blacktriangleleft \qquad (2.54)$$

Equation (2.53) will be called the direct Fourier integral, and (2.54) will be defined as the inverse Fourier integral. Equation (2.53) will be very useful in much future work, and is therefore illustrated here by a sample problem.

EXAMPLE. Fourier integral analysis of a simple rectangular pulse. Let us examine a symmetrical pulse as shown in Fig. 2.7, of T sec

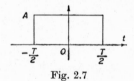

Fig. 2.7

duration and magnitude A. To find the frequency spectrum of this pulse, we use (2.53), and the integral will be broken down into three sections, as

$$F(\omega) = \int_{-\infty}^{-\frac{T}{2}} 0 \cdot \varepsilon^{-j\omega t}\, dt + A\int_{-\frac{T}{2}}^{\frac{T}{2}} \varepsilon^{-j\omega t}\, dt + \int_{\frac{T}{2}}^{\infty} 0 \cdot \varepsilon^{-j\omega t}\, dt \quad (2.55)$$

The first and last terms on the right are zero, therefore

$$F(\omega) = \frac{-A}{j\omega} \left[\varepsilon^{-j\omega t} \right]_{-\frac{T}{2}}^{\frac{T}{2}} \qquad (2.56)$$

or

$$F(\omega) = \frac{-A}{j\omega} \left[\varepsilon^{-\frac{j\omega T}{2}} - \varepsilon^{\frac{j\omega T}{2}} \right] \qquad (2.57)$$

Rearranging slightly

$$F(\omega) = \frac{2A}{\omega} \left(\frac{\varepsilon^{\frac{j\omega T}{2}} - \varepsilon^{-\frac{j\omega T}{2}}}{2j} \right) \qquad (2.58)$$

which becomes finally

$$F(\omega) = \frac{2A}{\omega} \sin \frac{\omega T}{2} \qquad (2.59)$$

To get the over-all curve, it is best to graph the numerator and denominator separately, and then divide the two curves at appropriate points (Fig. 2.8). The dotted curve shows the resulting

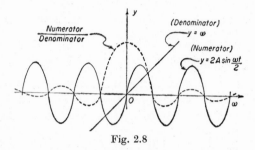

Fig. 2.8

function, which is redrawn in Fig. 2.9 for positive frequencies, and for magnitudes only. Compare Fig. 2.9 with Fig. 2.4, which was an analysis of the same rectangular pulse repeating itself at regular intervals.

We note that for the periodic case there were only certain harmonically related frequencies present, at discrete points in the

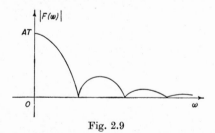

Fig. 2.9

spectrum. If we had tuned a receiver to frequencies other than those discrete points we would have received nothing.

In the case of the isolated, non-periodic pulse, however, note that the opposite is true. All frequencies are present except at discrete points, and unless our exploring receiver were accidentally tuned to one of the frequencies in Fig. 2.9 where a null occurs, there would be output when the pulse occurs. Such output would be created at the time of occurrence of the leading edge of the pulse, and would decay gradually depending upon the Q of the receiver tuned circuits. When the trailing edge of the pulse occurred, energy would be delivered to or absorbed from the receiver tuned circuit, depending on its phase at the instant when the trailing edge occurred. This topic will be discussed later in the book when we talk about application of the Laplace transformation to shock spectrum analysis.

PROBLEM. Show that the spectrum in Fig. 2.9 has the magnitude AT at $\omega = 0$, i.e. evaluate (2.59) at $\omega = 0$.

2.4. The unit step function

One of the most useful functions in applied electronics is also the simplest. This function is called the *unit step*, and is shown in Fig. 2.10. Thus, the unit step function is seen to be a curve which

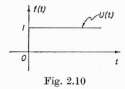

Fig. 2.10

has the value 0 at all points to the left of the origin, and is unity at all points to the right of the origin. The unit step function will be called $U(t)$.

One useful property of the unit step function $U(t)$ is that any other function multiplied by it will be zero for all values to the

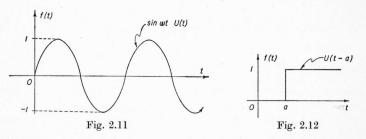

Fig. 2.11   Fig. 2.12

left of the origin. This is illustrated in Fig. 2.11 for the product of a sine wave and a unit step.

The displaced unit step function is also used extensively, and is illustrated in Fig. 2.12. The discontinuity occurs at $t = a$ rather than

$t = 0$. The displaced unit step function will be called $U(t - a)$, where the time a is to the right of the origin.

As a typical introduction to the use of step functions, we see that a rectangular pulse of A volts magnitude, and a sec duration, such as shown in Fig. 2.13, can be completely described as

$$f(t) = A \cdot U(t) - A \cdot U(t - a) \qquad (2.60)$$

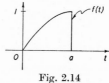

Fig. 2.13   Fig. 2.14

As another example, suppose that one cycle of a sine wave has a period $4a$ sec. A unit rectangular pulse of length a sec can be used to sample the first $90°$ of the sine wave, resulting in Fig. 2.14, and the result is

$$f(t) = \sin\left(\frac{\pi t}{2a}\right) \cdot [U(t) - U(t - a)] \qquad (2.61)$$

Further discussion could bring out the fact that any function could be broken down into a combination of step functions, in the same way that a complex periodic wave can be dissected into sine wave components. We shall return later to this topic, but the next step in our approach to our subject is to try to take the Fourier integral transform of the unit step function $U(t)$.

2.5. The Fourier transform of the unit step function

One of the conditions which a function must normally satisfy to be Fourier transformable is that the following integral must exist.

$$\int_{-\infty}^{\infty} |f(t)| \, dt \leqslant \infty \qquad (2.62)$$

This automatically excludes all periodic functions such as sines, square waves, etc. Therefore if we try to transform the function $U(t)$ we must first see if it will pass the test given by (2.62).

$$\int_{-\infty}^{\infty} U(t) \cdot dt = \int_{-\infty}^{0} 0 \cdot dt + \int_{0}^{\infty} 1 \cdot dt = [t]_{0}^{\infty} = \infty \qquad (2.63)$$

So that ordinarily we could not take the Fourier transform of the unit step function. However, suppose we multiply $U(t)$ by a decay factor to get the curve shown in Fig. 2.15, where c is any positive

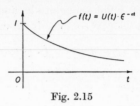

Fig. 2.15

constant. We then may write the Fourier transform of this new function as

$$F(\omega) = \int_{-\infty}^{\infty} f(t)\varepsilon^{-j\omega t}\, dt \qquad (2.64)$$

or

$$F(\omega) = \int_{-\infty}^{0} 0 \cdot \varepsilon^{-j\omega t}\, dt + \int_{0}^{\infty} \varepsilon^{-ct}\varepsilon^{-j\omega t}\, dt \qquad (2.65)$$

$$F(\omega) = \int_{0}^{\infty} \varepsilon^{-(c+j\omega)t}\, dt = -\frac{1}{c+j\omega}\left[\varepsilon^{-(c+j\omega)t}\right]_{0}^{\infty} \qquad (2.66)$$

Therefore

$$F(\omega) = \frac{1}{c+j\omega}$$

or

$$|F(\omega)| = \frac{1}{\sqrt{(c^2 + \omega^2)}} \qquad (2.67)$$

Now if we look back at Fig. 2.15, we see that if $c \to 0$, then $f(t)$ becomes our unit step function $U(t)$. The Fourier transform of $U(t)$ is therefore

$$|F(\omega)| = \frac{1}{\omega} \qquad (2.68)$$

2.6. Convergence factors

We saw in art. 2.5 that it was possible to evaluate the Fourier transform of a step function by the artifice of making it appear to converge. Suppose that we are interested in functions which have values only after $t = 0$. If such a function $f_1(t)$ does not meet the requirement that

$$\int_{0}^{\infty} f_1(t)\, dt < \infty \qquad (2.69)$$

it is often possible to multiply it by a convergence factor to form a new function $f(t)$

$$f(t) = f_1(t)\varepsilon^{-ct} \tag{2.70}$$

which does satisfy (2.69). The value of c which just makes the entire function convergent is called σ_a, or in other words $\sigma_a = $ abscissa of absolute convergence.

EXAMPLE. Suppose we are given a diverging function

$$\left.\begin{aligned} f_1(t) &= 2\varepsilon^{3t} \ \ \text{for} \ \ t > 0 \\ f_1(t) &= 0 \qquad\quad t < 0 \end{aligned}\right\} \tag{2.71}$$

as shown in Fig. 2.16. To make this function converge, it is necessary to multiply $f_1(t)$ by a suitable convergence factor

$$f(t) = f_1(t)\varepsilon^{-ct} \tag{2.72}$$

$$= 2\varepsilon^{3t} \cdot \varepsilon^{-ct} \tag{2.73}$$

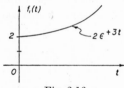

Fig. 2.16

We see by inspection that any value of c greater than 3 will make the over-all function convergent. In particular, (2.73) is convergent for

$$c > \sigma_a; \ \sigma_a = 3 \tag{2.74}$$

Now for functions such as (2.72), which have values only to the right of $t = 0$, we may write the Fourier integral transform as

$$F_1(\omega, c) = \int_0^\infty [f_1(t)\varepsilon^{-ct}]\varepsilon^{-j\omega t} \, dt \tag{2.75}$$

Suppose that we now move the convergence factor outside of the bracket, and remove the subscripts. Then the result becomes a function both of ω and c. That is

$$F(\omega, c) = \int_0^\infty f(t)\varepsilon^{-ct}\varepsilon^{-j\omega t} \, dt \tag{2.76}$$

In cases of most interest for our future work, the functions will always be made 0 to the left of the origin by multiplying all functions by $U(t)$. Removal of the integral to the left of the origin gives rise to the term *unilateral Fourier integral transform* for the above.

2.7. The complex Fourier integral transform

At this point the reader may begin to grow impatient and ask where we are going. Fortunately we are just on the verge of coming to the final form—the Laplace transform. This chapter will complete the actual formulation of the Laplace transform, and the remainder of the book will be devoted to practical theorems and engineering applications.

To continue, suppose we combine the exponents in (2.76) as follows, we thus have a specific function of $(c + j\omega)$,

$$F(c + j\omega) = \int_0^\infty f(t)\varepsilon^{-(c+j\omega)t}\, dt \qquad \blacktriangleleft \qquad (2.77)$$

The only condition here is that $c > \sigma_a$. Equation (2.77) is called the direct unilateral Fourier integral transform. We write (2.77) as follows

$$F(c + j\omega) = \int_0^\infty [f(t)\varepsilon^{-ct}]\varepsilon^{-j\omega t}\, dt \qquad (2.78)$$

And going back to (2.54), we can write the inverse by inspection as

$$[f(t)\varepsilon^{-ct}] = \frac{1}{2\pi} \int_{\omega=-\infty}^\infty F(c + j\omega)\varepsilon^{jt\omega}\, d\omega \qquad (2.79)$$

Now let us multiply both sides by ε^{ct}

$$f(t) = \frac{1}{2\pi} \int_{\omega=-\infty}^\infty F(c + j\omega)\varepsilon^{(c+j\omega)t}\, d\omega \qquad (2.80)$$

The ε^{ct} on the right has been brought through the integral sign and combined with the other exponent. This is permissible as the integration is with respect to ω.

Let us now change our variable of integration from

$$\omega \text{ to } (c + j\omega) \qquad (2.81)$$

which requires only that

$$d(c + j\omega) = j\, d\omega \qquad (2.82)$$

We now re-write (2.80) in the new variable as

$$f(t) = \frac{1}{2\pi j} \int_{c-j\omega}^{c+j\omega} F(c + j\omega)\varepsilon^{(c+j\omega)t} \, d(c + j\omega) \qquad (2.83)$$

Again, the only restrictions are that $c > \sigma_a$, and $t > 0$.

Note that the integration in (2.83) is performed in the complex plane as in Fig. 2.17. Note also that c is a real number, located on the real axis.

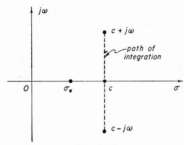

Fig. 2.17

2.8. The Laplace transform

Up to now we have treated c as a constant. We recognized, however, that it was necessary to use different values of c to make the over-all function convergent, and thus c might actually be called a parametric variable, i.e. compare this concept with the inductance L in a resonant L–C circuit. The inductance is usually considered a constant, as when one listens to a favorite radio program. When he wishes to change programs, however, the inductance becomes a variable while he is tuning in a new station, whereupon it resumes its constant characteristic. Such a quantity is called a parametric variable.

Letting c become a real variable σ, we can now define a complex variable s as

$$s = \sigma + j\omega \qquad (2.84)$$

and with this new variable, (2.77) can be re-written as

$$F(s) = \int_0^\infty f(t)\varepsilon^{-st} \, dt \qquad \blacktriangleleft \qquad (2.85)$$

This will be called the direct Laplace transform. Here the restriction on c has passed on to σ. Using the new complex variable s, (2.83) is also re-written as

$$f(t) = \frac{1}{2\pi j} \int_{c-j\omega}^{c+j\omega} F(s)\varepsilon^{ts}\, ds \tag{2.86}$$

We can leave the limits as shown for the time being, since they represent definite points in the s plane. The physical interpretation is this: one multiplies the quantity $F(s)\varepsilon^{ts}$ at a point on the path of integration by ds, and sums these quantities along the path from $\omega = -\infty$ to $\omega = \infty$. The only restriction on the path (the line $\sigma = c$) is that it be to the right of all poles of $F(s)\varepsilon^{ts}$.

It is shown in more advanced texts, and merely stated here without proof, that such an integration is equivalent to integrating around any closed path which includes all of the poles. We shall therefore write the definition of the inverse Laplace transform as

$$f(t) = \frac{1}{2\pi j} \oint F(s)\varepsilon^{ts}\, ds \qquad \blacktriangleleft \tag{2.87}$$

where the small circle on the integral represents a line integral around all poles, as was discussed in detail in Chapter I. We shall issue a command, proclaiming $F(s)$ to be defined throughout the entire s-plane. Such a decree is enough justification at the moment to satisfy our electronic engineering readers.

CHAPTER III

THE LAPLACE TRANSFORMATION

3.1. Introduction

In Chapter II the Fourier transforms were developed and progressively generalized into the Laplace integral. This development was necessary to understand and appreciate the origin of the Laplace transform. A number of texts omit the detailed material which we have just covered and begin directly with the definition of the Laplace integral. However, the student cannot help but have a much greater feeling and appreciation for the subject if he has followed carefully the material in the previous chapter.

In this chapter we will begin at last to work directly with Laplace transforms. Our first task will be to prepare a table of elementary Laplace transform pairs. This will be done by selecting various common functions of time, and transforming them into functions of s in accordance with the Laplace integral. The direct and inverse Laplace integrals are repeated here at the beginning of this chapter for future reference. The direct Laplace transform is:

$$F(s) = \int_0^\infty f(t)\varepsilon^{-st}\,dt \qquad (3.1)$$

and the inverse transform is:

$$f(t) = \frac{1}{2\pi j} \oint F(s)\varepsilon^{ts}\,ds \qquad (3.2)$$

The reader will recall from his early work in mathematics that it was possible to simplify the process of multiplication by the use of logarithms. Each number was transformed into a corresponding logarithm and the multiplication was replaced by the simpler process of adding the logarithms. To use the method it was necessary to have a table of logarithms, but this was usually available.

Tables of integrals, trigonometric tables, and others are also common, as well as tables of Laplace transforms. However, it will be remembered that when studying the calculus, it was necessary to do considerable work with the elementary forms before one could use the tables with any efficiency. In like manner it will be necessary here to develop a sufficient number of elementary Laplace transform pairs to have a feel for the subject. In much the same way that logarithms simplify the process of multiplication, so Laplace transforms will be found to simplify many types of operations.

As an example, it will be possible through the use of Laplace transforms to simplify the processes of differentiation and integration into simple algebraic operations. As another illustration, the solutions of complicated differential equations are often obtained with startling simplicity.

At this point we shall make use of the basic Laplace integral (3.1) to derive several important transform pairs. As they are derived, each pair will be numbered and listed in Table 3.1, which will serve as an elementary table of transforms for future work.

3.2. Transforms of constants

Perhaps the simplest function of time is a constant. For example, the voltage of a battery may be considered a constant for its useful life. In all of our work here, we will be concerned only with the value of the function after the time $t = 0$, as the defining Laplace integral has 0 as a lower limit.

Now any function of time which has a constant value from the time $t = 0$ can be written as A times the unit step function $U(t)$. See art. 2.4 for a review of $U(t)$. Suppose we begin by finding the Laplace transform of

$$f(t) = A \cdot U(t) \tag{3.3}$$

We can find $F(s)$, the transform, by using this value for $f(t)$ in (3.1), that is

$$F(s) = \int_0^\infty A \cdot U(t)\varepsilon^{-st}\, dt \tag{3.4}$$

The A, being a constant, can be brought through the integral sign as usual, and the $U(t)$ has the value unity between the limits of integration (see Fig. 2.10). Therefore (3.4) becomes

$$F(s) = A \int_0^\infty \varepsilon^{-st}\, dt \tag{3.5}$$

$$F(s) = \frac{A}{-s} [\varepsilon^{-st}]_0^\infty \tag{3.6}$$

and substituting the limits

$$F(s) = \frac{A}{s} \tag{3.7}$$

which is the Laplace transform of the constant A. If A should be unity, then (3.7) would give us the transform of unity, or the unit step function $U(t)$.

The operation of taking the Laplace transform is indicated by the symbol $\mathscr{L}$. This symbol placed in front of a quantity means that its Laplace transform is indicated. It is an operator, in the same manner that differential and integral symbols are operators. As an example:

$$\mathscr{L}[f(t)] = F(s) = \int_0^\infty f(t)\varepsilon^{-st}\,dt \tag{3.8}$$

From the results of this article therefore, we can also write

$$\mathscr{L}[A] = \frac{A}{s} \tag{3.9}$$

or

$$\mathscr{L}[U(t)] = \frac{1}{s} \tag{3.10}$$

This symbolism is read "the Laplace transform of U of t is one over s." These forms are listed as #1 and #2 in Table 3.1 of "transform pairs".

3.3. The Laplace transform of exponentials

Probably the next form in order of complexity is the function

$$f(t) = \varepsilon^{-at} \tag{3.11}$$

which is a decaying exponential. It may be placed into the Laplace integral and transformed into a function of s as follows:

$$F(s) = \int_0^\infty \varepsilon^{-at}\varepsilon^{-st}\,dt \tag{3.12}$$

Performing the indicated integration, one first combines the exponents

$$F(s) = \int_0^\infty \varepsilon^{-(s+a)t}\,dt \tag{3.13}$$

$$F(s) = -\frac{1}{(s+a)}\left[\varepsilon^{-(s+a)t}\right]_0^\infty \tag{3.14}$$

and when the limits are inserted

$$F(s) = \frac{1}{s + a} \qquad (3.15)$$

We could also say symbolically that

$$\mathscr{L}[\varepsilon^{-at}] = \frac{1}{s + a} \qquad (3.16)$$

This form is listed as #3 in Table 3.1.

It is easy to see that we can replace the a in (3.11) by $-a$, and merely change the sign of the resulting a in (3.15). We therefore have another form

$$\mathscr{L}[\varepsilon^{at}] = \frac{1}{s - a} \qquad (3.17)$$

which is listed as form #4 in Table 3.1.

3.4. The Laplace transform of imaginary exponents

To continue with the development of our table of Laplace transforms, suppose we have the function

$$f(t) = \varepsilon^{j\omega t} \qquad (3.18)$$

It would be easy enough to insert this function directly into the Laplace integral, and solve directly for $F(s)$. However, we should take advantage of the work already done. We note that we can let the $j\omega$ in (3.18) be represented by the constant a in form #4 which we have developed before. Using form #4 therefore, we can write the transform of (3.18) by inspection as

$$\mathscr{L}[\varepsilon^{j\omega t}] = \frac{1}{s - j\omega} \qquad (3.19)$$

By exchanging signs of the constants, we can also write by inspection

$$\mathscr{L}[\varepsilon^{-j\omega t}] = \frac{1}{s + j\omega} \qquad (3.20)$$

These two new forms are listed as pairs #5 and #6 in Table 3.1.

3.5. The Laplace transform of trigonometric terms

In future work with electronic networks and circuits it will often be necessary to take the Laplace transform of sine and cosine waveforms. We will begin by assuming a function

$$f(t) = \cos \omega t \tag{3.21}$$

We may write this function as the sum of two conjugates as

$$\cos \omega t = \tfrac{1}{2}\varepsilon^{j\omega t} + \tfrac{1}{2}\varepsilon^{-j\omega t} \tag{3.22}$$

The coefficient $\tfrac{1}{2}$, being a constant, is not affected by the transformation, and we have already derived the transforms for both exponential terms (pairs #5 and #6). We therefore write the function of s by inspection as

$$\mathscr{L}[\cos \omega t] = \frac{1}{2} \cdot \frac{1}{(s-j\omega)} + \frac{1}{2} \cdot \frac{1}{(s+j\omega)} \tag{3.23}$$

We now find a least common denominator

$$F(s) = \frac{(s+j\omega) + (s-j\omega)}{2(s-j\omega)(s+j\omega)} \tag{3.24}$$

which simplifies nicely to

$$F(s) = \frac{s}{s^2 + \omega^2} \tag{3.25}$$

which is listed as pair #7 in Table 3.1.

If we are required to find the transform of $\sin \omega t$, the same procedure can be employed.

$$\sin \omega t = \frac{j\varepsilon^{-j\omega t}}{2} - \frac{j\varepsilon^{j\omega t}}{2} \tag{3.26}$$

The constant $j/2$ is not affected by the transformation, and pairs #5 and #6 can be used to write the transform of (3.26) by inspection.

$$\mathscr{L}[\sin \omega t] = \frac{j}{2} \cdot \frac{1}{(s+j\omega)} - \frac{j}{2} \cdot \frac{1}{(s-j\omega)} \tag{3.27}$$

We find the least common denominator to be

$$F(s) = \frac{j(s-j\omega) - j(s+j\omega)}{2(s+j\omega)(s-j\omega)} \tag{3.28}$$

and the resulting expression simplifies to

$$F(s) = \frac{\omega}{s^2 + \omega^2} \tag{3.29}$$

which is listed as transform pair #8 in Table 3.1.

It might be well at this time to mention the fact that the transform of a sum of terms is equal to the sum of the transforms of the individual terms. That is

$$\mathscr{L}[f_1(t) + f_2(t)] = \mathscr{L}[f_1(t)] + \mathscr{L}[f_2(t)] \tag{3.30}$$

This statement will be apparent upon recalling the integral definition of the Laplace transformation, and noting that the integral of a sum of terms is equal to the sum of the integrals of the individual terms.

3.6. The Laplace transform of hyperbolic functions

In developing a table of elementary transform pairs, it will be well to include the hyperbolic sine and hyperbolic cosine, as these functions play an important part in many branches of electronics. The hyperbolic cosine may be written

$$\cosh \omega t = \frac{\varepsilon^{\omega t}}{2} + \frac{\varepsilon^{-\omega t}}{2} \tag{3.31}$$

and by the use of transform pairs #3 and #4 we may write

$$\mathscr{L}[\cosh \omega t] = \frac{1}{2} \cdot \frac{1}{(s-\omega)} + \frac{1}{2} \cdot \frac{1}{(s+\omega)} \tag{3.32}$$

This expression is further simplified to give

$$\mathscr{L}[\cosh \omega t] = \frac{s}{s^2 - \omega^2} \tag{3.33}$$

The hyperbolic sine can be expressed as

$$\sinh \omega t = \frac{\varepsilon^{\omega t}}{2} - \frac{\varepsilon^{-\omega t}}{2} \tag{3.34}$$

and the same pairs may be used to write

$$\mathscr{L}[\sinh \omega t] = \frac{1}{2} \cdot \frac{1}{(s-\omega)} - \frac{1}{2} \cdot \frac{1}{(s+\omega)} \tag{3.35}$$

which simplifies into

$$\mathscr{L}[\sinh \omega t] = \frac{\omega}{s^2 - \omega^2} \tag{3.36}$$

These forms are listed as #9 and #10 in Table 3.1.

TABLE 3.1

#	$f(t)$	$F(s)$
1	$U(t)$	$\dfrac{1}{s}$
2	$A \cdot U(t)$	$\dfrac{A}{s}$
3	ε^{-at}	$\dfrac{1}{s+a}$
4	ε^{at}	$\dfrac{1}{s-a}$
5	$\varepsilon^{j\omega t}$	$\dfrac{1}{s-j\omega}$
6	$\varepsilon^{-j\omega t}$	$\dfrac{1}{s+j\omega}$
7	$\cos \omega t$	$\dfrac{s}{s^2+\omega^2}$
8	$\sin \omega t$	$\dfrac{\omega}{s^2+\omega^2}$
9	$\cosh \omega t$	$\dfrac{s}{s^2-\omega^2}$
10	$\sinh \omega t$	$\dfrac{\omega}{s^2-\omega^2}$
11	$\varepsilon^{(\alpha+j\omega)t}$	$\dfrac{1}{s-\alpha-j\omega}$
12	$\varepsilon^{(\alpha-j\omega)t}$	$\dfrac{1}{s-\alpha+j\omega}$
13	$\varepsilon^{-\alpha t} \sin \omega t$	$\dfrac{\omega}{(s+\alpha)^2+\omega^2}$
14	$\varepsilon^{-\alpha t} \cos \omega t$	$\dfrac{s+\alpha}{(s+\alpha)^2+\omega^2}$
15	t	$\dfrac{1}{s^2}$
16	$\dfrac{d\,f(t)}{dt}$	$sF(s)-f(0)$
17	$\int f(t)\,dt$	$\dfrac{1}{s}[F(s)+f^{-1}(0)]$

3.7. The Laplace transform of complex exponentials

Suppose one is given the time function

$$f(t) = \varepsilon^{(\alpha+j\omega)t} \tag{3.37}$$

We may let the complex coefficient of t correspond to the a in pair #4. Whereupon the $F(s)$ may be written as

$$F(s) = \frac{1}{s - \alpha - j\omega} \tag{3.38}$$

Similarly, if

$$f(t) = \varepsilon^{(\alpha-j\omega)t} \tag{3.39}$$

one can use the same form to obtain

$$F(s) = \frac{1}{s - \alpha + j\omega} \tag{3.40}$$

and these are listed as forms #11 and #12 in Table 3.1.

Other combinations of positive and negative real and complex exponentials can be transformed by similar reasoning.

3.8 Transforms of more complicated functions

A waveform often found in electronic equipment is the exponentially decaying sine wave, expressed as

$$f(t) = \varepsilon^{-\alpha t} \sin \omega t \tag{3.41}$$

The sine wave factor can be expressed with exponentials and the entire function written as

$$f(t) = \frac{\varepsilon^{-\alpha t}\varepsilon^{j\omega t}}{2j} - \frac{\varepsilon^{-\alpha t}\varepsilon^{-j\omega t}}{2j} \tag{3.42}$$

and the exponents combined to give

$$f(t) = \frac{1}{2j}\left[\varepsilon^{-(\alpha-j\omega)t} - \varepsilon^{-(\alpha+j\omega)t}\right] \tag{3.43}$$

For the first exponential term, let $(\alpha - j\omega)$ correspond to the a in pair #3 of Table 3.1, and for the second term let $(\alpha + j\omega)$ be the a in the same pair. Thus we can write

$$F(s) = \frac{1}{2j}\left[\frac{1}{(s + \alpha - j\omega)} - \frac{1}{(s + \alpha + j\omega)}\right] \tag{3.44}$$

One can find a least common denominator, and then simplify this last quantity to

$$F(s) = \frac{\omega}{(s + \alpha)^2 + \omega^2} \qquad (3.45)$$

This form is listed as pair #13 in Table 3.1.

PROBLEM

(1) Using any method, find the Laplace transform of

$$f(t) = \varepsilon^{-\alpha t} \cos \omega t$$

Check your answer with pair #14 in Table 3.1.

(2) Using the Laplace integral, find the transform of

$$f(t) = t$$

and check your answer with pair #15 in Table 3.1.

3.9. Additional practice with sinewaves

As one last item before we finish with simple functions, let us examine the function

$$f(t) = \sin (\omega t + \phi) \qquad (3.46)$$

We can expand the right-hand side trigonometrically to give

$$f(t) = \sin \omega t \cos \phi + \cos \omega t \sin \phi \qquad (3.47)$$

and note that $\cos \phi$ and $\sin \phi$ are constants which we can call b and a, respectively. Therefore

$$f(t) = b \sin \omega t + a \cos \omega t \qquad (3.48)$$

The transform may be written by pairs #7 and #8 as

$$F(s) = \frac{b\omega}{s^2 + \omega^2} + \frac{as}{s^2 + \omega^2} \qquad (3.49)$$

which is combined to give

$$F(s) = \frac{as + b\omega}{s^2 + \omega^2} \qquad (3.50)$$

where

$$\tan \phi = \frac{a}{b} \qquad (3.51)$$

The result shows that if ϕ becomes $90°$, for example, (3.51) requires that $b = 0$, and (3.50) becomes

$$F(s) = \frac{as}{s^2 + \omega^2} \tag{3.52}$$

which pair #7 shows to be a cosine wave. We can see by inspection that this is correct, as we know that a sine wave shifted $90°$ in phase would be the same as a cosine wave.

Another important fact to point out here is that the poles of this function of s do not depend upon the phase angle of the original function, that is, the poles of (3.50) occur at

$$\left.\begin{array}{c} s = j\omega \\[2mm] s = -j\omega \end{array}\right\} \tag{3.53}$$

and

and the location of the poles in the s-plane will be fixed, regardless of phase angle in the time domain. This characteristic will be of considerable importance later.

3.10. The Laplace transform of a derivative

It will be remembered from the first courses in circuit analysis that voltages appearing across capacities and inductances involve derivatives and integrals. Similar expressions for currents also involve integrals and derivatives, and therefore it will often be necessary to take the Laplace transforms of derivatives and integrals if the theory is to be of any worth for our future electronic research.

The reader is urged to study these last two articles carefully, as several important ideas are presented which are important as background information. It will be found that these operations are much simpler to perform in the s-plane than in the time domain. Let us assume the following three conditions:

(a) That $f(t) = 0$, for $t < 0$.

(b) That $f(t)$ is transformable; that is,

$$\mathscr{L}[f(t)] = F(s)$$

(c) That

$$\frac{d\,f(t)}{dt}\bigg|_{t=0} < \infty$$

We begin by looking at an elementary integral relation from calculus

$$\int u\, dv = uv - \int v\, du \qquad (3.54)$$

Suppose we let

$$u = f(t) \qquad \text{(a)} \qquad (3.55)$$

then

$$du = \frac{d\,f(t)}{dt}\, dt \qquad \text{(b)} \qquad (3.56)$$

Next, let

$$dv = \varepsilon^{-st}\, dt \qquad \text{(c)} \qquad (3.57)$$

then

$$v = \frac{-\varepsilon^{-st}}{s} \qquad \text{(d)} \qquad (3.58)$$

Now if we wish to take the Laplace transform of the derivative of $f(t)$, we have

$$\mathscr{L}[f'(t)] = F(s) = \int_0^\infty \left[\frac{d\,f(t)}{dt}\right] \varepsilon^{-st}\, dt \qquad (3.59)$$

by the usual definition. If we now write

$$F(s) = \int_0^\infty u\, dv = uv\, \Big|_0^\infty - \int_0^\infty v\, du \qquad (3.60)$$

we may replace the u and dv by the equivalents from (a), (b), (c), and (d).

$$F(s) = \frac{-f(t)\varepsilon^{-st}}{s}\, \Big|_0^\infty - \int_0^\infty -\frac{\varepsilon^{-st}}{s}\frac{d\,f(t)}{dt}\, dt \qquad (3.61)$$

Evaluating the first right-hand part, and rearranging the second,

$$F(s) = \frac{f(0)}{s} + \frac{1}{s}\int_0^\infty \left[\frac{d\,f(t)}{dt}\right] \varepsilon^{-st}\, dt \qquad (3.62)$$

where it is noted that the factor s has been brought outside the integral sign. This is permissible because t is the variable of integration in this case. Thus we now can write

$$sF(s) - f(0) = \int_0^\infty \left[\frac{d\,f(t)}{dt}\right] \varepsilon^{-st}\, dt \qquad (3.63)$$

It is now easy to see that the right-hand side is the Laplace transform of the derivative.

$$\mathscr{L}\left[\frac{d\,f(t)}{dt}\right] = sF(s) - f(0) \qquad (3.64)$$

and this pair is listed as #16 in Table 3.1.

The second term on the right is merely the value of $f(t)$ at $t = 0$. We see, therefore, that if we have a function of time, and the Laplace transform is already known, it may be differentiated merely by multiplying by s, and then subtracting the initial value of $f(t)$. We will have much use for this form in later work.

This transform illustrates again how a complicated operation (differentiation) in the time domain goes over into a simpler operation (multiplication and subtraction) in the s-domain.

EXAMPLE 1. Given the function

$$f(t) = \varepsilon^{-at} \qquad (3.65)$$

find the Laplace transform of the derivative of $f(t)$. We could differentiate the function first, and place into the Laplace integral, but we choose to use pair #3 in Table 3.1 to write

$$F(s) = \frac{1}{s+a} \qquad (3.66)$$

and perform our differentiation in the s-domain, which is much easier.   To differentiate, we multiply $F(s)$ by s, and subtract the value of (3.65) for $t = 0$. This gives

$$\mathscr{L}\left[\frac{d\varepsilon^{-at}}{dt}\right] = \frac{s}{s+a} - 1 \qquad (3.67)$$

PROBLEM 1. Check the validity of (3.67) by differentiating (3.65) first, and then taking the transform by previous methods.

PROBLEM 2. Find the Laplace transform of the derivative of

$$f(t) = \sin \omega t \qquad (3.68)$$

by differentiating in the s-domain.

3.11. The Laplace transform of an integral

As the last article in this chapter, we will now derive the Laplace transform of the integral of a function of time. We shall find that integration, like many other operations, is considerably simplified when performed in the s-plane. Let us begin by writing the general transform

$$F(s) = \int_0^\infty f(t)\varepsilon^{-st}\,dt \qquad (3.69)$$

which, to keep general, we now integrate by parts

$$F(s) = \int_0^\infty u\,dv = uv\Big|_0^\infty - \int_0^\infty v\,du \qquad (3.70)$$

This time, however, let

$$u = \varepsilon^{-st} \qquad \text{(a)} \qquad (3.71)$$

from which

$$du = -s\varepsilon^{-st}\,dt \qquad \text{(b)} \qquad (3.72)$$

Then we let

$$dv = f(t)\,dt \qquad \text{(c)} \qquad (3.73)$$

so that by integration

$$v = \int f(t)\,dt = \int_0^t f(t)\,dt + \left[\int f(t)\,dt\right]_{t=0} \qquad (3.74)$$

where the last term on the right is the value of the integral of $f(t)$ at $t = 0$. This could, for example, correspond to initial charge on a capacity. Using a fairly common terminology, we will denote this integration by a negative power, so that (3.74) may be written

$$v = \int_0^t f(t)\,dt + f^{-1}(0) \qquad \text{(d)} \qquad (3.75)$$

Note carefully that $f^{-1}(0)$ is the value of the integral at $t = 0$, and is not the same as $f(0)$ which we found in deriving the derivative transform in the last article.

If we now substitute the quantities (a), (b), (c) and (d) into (3.70) we have

$$F(s) = \left\{\varepsilon^{-st}\left[\int_0^t f(t)\,dt + f^{-1}(0)\right]\right\}_0^\infty -$$
$$-\int_0^\infty \left[\int_0^t f(t)\,dt + f^{-1}(0)\right](-s\varepsilon^{-st}\,dt) \qquad (3.76)$$

When the limits are substituted in the first integral expression, we have

$$F(s) = -f^{-1}(0) + s\int_0^\infty \left[\int_0^t f(t)\,dt + f^{-1}(0)\right]\varepsilon^{-st}\,dt \qquad (3.77)$$

where, in addition, the $-s$ in the second term has been brought outside the integral. This is permissible as the s is not the variable of integration. The last term in (3.77) is now rewritten as the sum of two integrals, as

$$F(s) = -f^{-1}(0) + s \int_0^\infty \left[\int_0^t f(t)\, dt \right] \varepsilon^{-st}\, dt + s \int_0^\infty f^{-1}(0) \varepsilon^{-st}\, dt \quad (3.78)$$

It will be noted that the last integral is merely the Laplace transform of a constant, which is the constant times $1/s$, and when multiplied by the factor s in the numerator, leaves the constant itself. Thus, canceling the first and last terms on the right, and dividing by s, gives

$$\frac{F(s)}{s} = \int_0^\infty \left[\int_0^t f(t)\, dt \right] \varepsilon^{-st}\, dt \quad (3.79)$$

Now we see that the term on the right is, by definition, the Laplace transform of the integral of $f(t)$, thus we may write

$$\mathscr{L} \left[\int_0^t f(t)\, dt \right] = \frac{F(s)}{s} \quad (3.80)$$

We note that the integral in (3.80) has limits, and thus is a definite integral. If we remove the limits, a constant of integration will appear when $f(t)$ is integrated. This constant may be Laplace transformed and added to the right-hand side of (3.80). Also, it will be noted that the value of the constant is the value of the integral at $t = 0$, thus

$$\mathscr{L} \left[\int f(t)\, dt \right] = \frac{F(s)}{s} + \frac{f^{-1}(0)}{s} \quad (3.81)$$

If the value of the integral is 0 at $t = 0$, i.e. if it is known that initial conditions are zero, the last term on the right will disappear. Equation (3.81) is listed as the last pair in Table 3.1.

EXAMPLE. Suppose we have a condenser which has an initial voltage a as shown in Fig. 3.1. This condenser is connected to a source of voltage $e(t)$ at time $t = 0$ as shown. We write the equation as

$$e(t) = \frac{1}{C} \int_0^t i\, dt + a$$

which is transformed term by term as

$$E(s) = \frac{I(s)}{Cs} + \frac{a}{s}$$

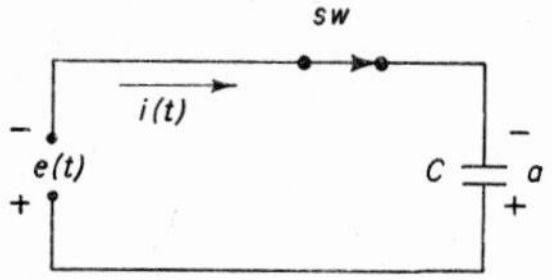

Fig. 3.1

NOTE. In this text we shall use the term current to be synonymous with electron flow. Although this differs from older terminology, the writer feels that the subject is too important to allow tradition or prejudice to interfere with the clearest possible presentation. The current, or electron flow, will in this text leave the negative terminal of the battery, will flow from cathode to plate in a tube, and from emitter to collector in an $N-P-N$ transistor.

CHAPTER IV

THE INVERSE LAPLACE TRANSFORMATION

4.1. Introduction

In the last chapter we developed a number of Laplace transforms of the more common functions. It was found that the transform of an exponential could be used to obtain practically all of the other pairs. Later on in the text we will develop a number of theorems which will prove useful in practical cases, but now it is desirable that we spend some time in learning how to take the inverse transforms of functions which arise in problems.

Speaking in general, one usually has a problem involving an excitation function applied to some network. The network, upon being thus excited, develops some response. The response is often in the form of an output voltage. Symbolically, we may illustrate this general definition as in Fig. 4.1.

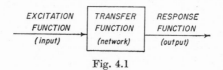

Fig. 4.1

In all future work, the transfer function will be defined as the ratio of output quantity to input quantity. If the input and output are voltages, we call the transfer function Z_t, and write the relation as

$$Z_t = \frac{e_0}{e_{\mathrm{IN}}} \tag{4.1}$$

If the transfer function of a given network is known, the output for a given excitation is then merely

$$e_0 = Z_t e_{\mathrm{IN}} \tag{4.2}$$

The difficulty which arises in practice is that when complicated networks are involved, the expression for e_0 usually involves combinations of derivatives, integrals, trigonometric terms, etc. By the use of our Laplace transform theory, these quantities are all converted to algebraic forms, whereupon the output voltage is obtained as a function of s. The problem is then one of transforming the output as a function of s back into a function of time.

EXAMPLE 1. As an example of how the Laplace transform theory is applied, let us consider the case shown in Fig. 4.2. The switch is

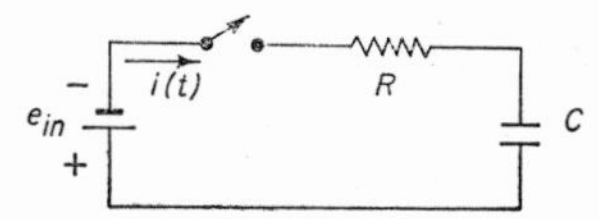

Fig. 4.2

closed at time $t = 0$, and it is required to find the resulting current as a function of time. By Kirchhoff's law, we can write the sum of the voltage drops as equal to the applied voltage, that is

$$e_{\text{IN}}(t) = Ri(t) + \frac{1}{C} \int i(t)\, dt \tag{4.3}$$

where we have specifically indicated that voltage and current are functions of time. There is no charge on the condenser prior to closing the switch.

We may transform (4.3) term by term as follows: $e_{IN}(t)$, being a battery, is constant, and by pair #2, Table 3.1, its transform is

$$e_{IN}(t) \rightarrow \frac{e_{\text{IN}}}{s} \tag{4.4}$$

where the arrow is read "transforms into". The second term is merely indicated by using a capital letter for the variable.

$$Ri(t) \rightarrow RI(s) \tag{4.5}$$

The last term requires the use of pair #17, which allows us to write

$$\frac{1}{C} \int i\, d(t) \rightarrow \frac{I(s)}{Cs} \tag{4.6}$$

The entire equation is now written as a function of s, and we have

$$\frac{e_{\text{IN}}}{s} = RI(s) + \frac{I(s)}{Cs} \tag{4.7}$$

Our problem called for $i(t)$ to be found. To do this we first solve (4.7) for current in the s domain, that is, I as a function of s.

$$\frac{e_{\text{IN}}}{s} = I(s)\left(R + \frac{1}{Cs}\right) \tag{4.8}$$

$$I(s) = \frac{e_{\text{IN}}}{s(R + 1/Cs)} \tag{4.9}$$

$$I(s) = \frac{e_{\text{IN}}}{Rs + 1/C} \tag{4.10}$$

and if we divide both numerator and denominator by R, we have

$$I(s) = \frac{e_{\text{IN}}}{R} \cdot \frac{1}{(s + 1/RC)} \tag{4.11}$$

The purpose of dividing by R was to get the part involving s into a familiar form. We see that the quantity multiplied by e_{IN}/R is, by pair #3, Table 3.1,

$$\frac{1}{(s + 1/RC)} \rightarrow \varepsilon^{-\frac{t}{RC}} \tag{4.12}$$

where the α corresponds to $1/RC$. Equation (4.11) is thus re-converted into a function of time

$$i(t) = \frac{e_{\text{IN}}}{R}\, \varepsilon^{-\frac{t}{RC}} \tag{4.13}$$

which the reader will recall from elementary work with circuit analysis as being correct.

In this example, the function of s to be transformed back into a function of time was very simple, and the transformation was accomplished by inspection. Such elementary forms are usually soon committed to memory. In most of the more advanced work, however, the function of s which results will be considerably more complex than this, and therefore we will spend the present chapter learning how to transform such functions back into the time domain.

EXAMPLE 2. After studying the above example, look at the problem in Fig. 4.3. This is the same problem as the previous example, except that the condenser now has a certain voltage v

prior to closing the switch. The Kirchhoff's law equations are the same, namely

$$e_{\text{IN}}(t) = Ri(t) + \frac{1}{C} \int i(t)\, dt \qquad (4.14)$$

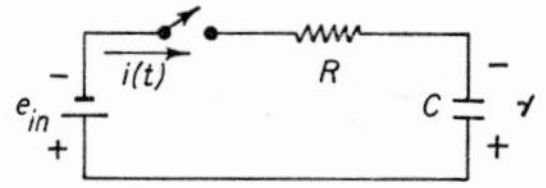

Fig. 4.3

but when we come to transform the integral term, note that the initial condition is not zero, and thus we must use the complete form as given in pair #17, Table 3.1.

$$\frac{e_{\text{IN}}}{s} = RI(s) + \frac{1}{Cs}[I(s) + i^{-1}(0)] \qquad (4.15)$$

$$\frac{e_{\text{IN}}}{s} = RI(s) + \frac{I(s)}{Cs} + \frac{i^{-1}(0)}{Cs} \qquad (4.16)$$

Now observe that the $i^{-1}(0)$ is the charge which was on the condenser prior to $t = 0$. Also note that this charge divided by capacity is the initial voltage v. Thus (4.16) becomes

$$\frac{e_{\text{IN}}}{s} = RI(s) + \frac{I(s)}{Cs} + \frac{v}{s} \qquad (4.17)$$

This last term is brought to the left-hand side, and factored as

$$\frac{e_{\text{IN}} - v}{s} = I(s)\left(R + \frac{1}{Cs}\right) \qquad (4.18)$$

Now in order to solve for $i(t)$, we first solve for $I(s)$, as

$$I(s) = \frac{(e_{\text{IN}} - v)}{s(R + 1/Cs)} \qquad (4.19)$$

As before this is factored into the form

$$I(s) = \frac{(e_{\text{IN}} - v)}{R} \cdot \frac{1}{(s + 1/RC)} \qquad (4.20)$$

We are now ready to take the inverse transform, which is the same as before, except that now the constant multiplier is $(e_{IN} - v)$ rather than e_{IN}

$$i(t) = \frac{(e_{IN} - v)}{R} \, \varepsilon^{-\frac{t}{RC}} \tag{4.21}$$

As we progress further into the book, it will be realized that Laplace transform technique automatically handles the problems of initial conditions, whereas the classical differential equation methods usually give trouble in this respect.

PROBLEM. Solve Example 1 by straight integration, and compare the time required with the time using Laplace transforms.

4.2. Functions of s from electronic networks

Linear networks are composed of various combinations of R, L and C. The basic relations between voltage and current in each of these elements is:
for a resistance

$$e = Ri \tag{4.22}$$

for an inductance

$$e = L \frac{di}{dt} \tag{4.23}$$

and for a capacity

$$e = \frac{1}{C} \int i \, dt \tag{4.24}$$

We may use our Laplace transform theory to transform each of these quantities into functions of s

$$E(s) = RI(s) \tag{4.25}$$

$$E(s) = sLI(s) \tag{4.26}$$

and

$$E(s) = \frac{I(s)}{sC} \tag{4.27}$$

Impedance, in either the time domain or the s-domain, is the ratio of voltage to current, and therefore:
for a resistance

$$Z(s) = R \tag{4.28}$$

for an inductance

$$Z(s) = sL \tag{4.29}$$

and for a capacity

$$Z(s) = \frac{1}{sC} \tag{4.30}$$

Note the similarity between impedance as a function of s, and impedance in a.c. circuit theory, where s was replaced by $j\omega$. We have defined s as a complex variable

$$s = \sigma + j\omega \tag{4.31}$$

We can see now that replacing s by $j\omega$, as in classical a.c. circuit theory, places a severe restriction on our solutions.

In any network, it will be just as easy to write the equations directly as a function of s. We can label each impedance as a function of s, as well as currents and voltages.

EXAMPLE. Using the conventional fictitious current notation, the loop equations of Fig. 4.4 are written as

$$\left(R + \frac{2}{sC}\right) I_1(s) - \frac{I_2(s)}{sC} = E_{\text{IN}}(s) \tag{4.32}$$

$$-\frac{I_1(s)}{sC} + \left(R + \frac{1}{sC}\right) I_2(s) = 0 \tag{4.33}$$

We solve for $I_2(s)$ by determinants

$$I_2(s) = \cfrac{\cfrac{E_{\text{IN}}(s)}{sC}}{\begin{vmatrix} \left(R + \dfrac{2}{sC}\right) & -\dfrac{1}{sC} \\ -\dfrac{1}{sC} & \left(R + \dfrac{1}{sC}\right) \end{vmatrix}} \tag{4.34}$$

which can be expanded and simplified to

$$I_2(s) = \frac{E_{\text{IN}}(s)Cs}{s^2 R^2 C^2 + 3sRC + 1} \tag{4.35}$$

We note that the output voltage is

$$E_0(s) = RI_2(s) \tag{4.36}$$

therefore, using (4.35) and (4.36)

$$E_0(s) = \frac{E_{\text{IN}}(s)RCs}{s^2R^2C^2 + 3sRC + 1} \tag{4.37}$$

By the definition given in art. 4.1, the transfer function is the ratio of output to input.

$$Z_t(s) = \frac{RCs}{R^2C^2s^2 + 3RCs + 1} \tag{4.38}$$

In many places, the t subscript is omitted if it is clear that the Z refers to a transfer function. The transfer function of the network

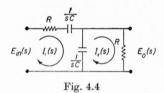

Fig. 4.4

shown in Fig. 4.4, and given by (4.38) can be factored by finding the roots of

$$R^2C^2s^2 + 3RCs + 1 = 0 \tag{4.39}$$

The roots are

$$s = -\frac{RC}{2}(3 + \sqrt{5}) \tag{4.40}$$

and

$$s = -\frac{RC}{2}(3 - \sqrt{5}) \tag{4.41}$$

The numbers are combined, and (4.38) is written in factored form as

$$Z_t(s) = \frac{RCs}{(s + 0.38RC)(s + 2.62RC)} \tag{4.42}$$

It will be observed that any transfer function can be written as the ratio of two polynomials, and can therefore be factored into a set of terms similar to (4.42). In some cases it will be necessary to solve cubic and higher order equations, but this can easily be done, graphically if necessary.

Recalling our complex variable theory from Chapter I, we note that (4.42) has one zero, and two poles. These are shown in Fig. 4.5. Except for the constant multiplier, the pole–zero diagram completely describes the transfer function. It will be obvious that two identical networks will have exactly the same pole–zero diagram, while two identical pole–zero diagrams may or may not represent the same network. This last statement will be demonstrated later.

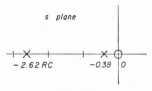

Fig. 4.5

If the transfer function $Z(s)$ is known, the response to any given stimulus can be written as

$$E_0(s) = Z(s)E_{\text{IN}}(s) \tag{4.43}$$

E_{IN} can be any signal; direct current, sine wave, pulses, etc. However, it can usually be written as a function of s. Observe that the pole–zero diagram of this product will have the same poles and zeros in the same locations as the transfer function alone, with various additional poles or zeros from $E_{\text{IN}}(s)$.

It should be apparent by now that one will often need to take inverse Laplace transforms of the form of (4.42) and (4.43). Thus it will be well if we concentrate for a while on taking the inverse of various abstract functions to become familiar with the technique.

After learning how to evaluate such terms with ease, we shall have a lot of interesting things to say about networks like Fig. 4.4, and others that are much more complex.

4.3. Functions of s involving simple poles

In many cases it will be found that the solution to a given problem in the s-domain results in an expression which is the product of several poles and zeros. In fact, this is the rule rather than the exception. The poles may be located at general points a and b, so that a general function of s having two poles is

$$F(s) = \frac{1}{(s + a)(s + b)} \tag{4.44}$$

Equation (4.42) had a zero of s in the numerator, as well as a constant multiplier. We will examine such cases shortly, but first we will begin with (4.44), which is made up of two factors only. The basic definition of the inverse Laplace transform is

$$f(t) = \frac{1}{2\pi j} \oint F(s)\varepsilon^{ts}\, ds \tag{4.45}$$

Placing (4.44), the function we wish to transform, into this definition gives

$$f(t) = \frac{1}{2\pi j} \oint \frac{\varepsilon^{ts}\, ds}{(s+a)(s+b)} \tag{4.46}$$

It is now necessary to recall (or review art. 1.15) that the integral of a function of s with respect to s is merely $2\pi j$ times the summation of the residues at the various poles of the function. It will be assumed from here on that we intend to integrate around all the poles. We note that the factor ε^{ts} in (4.46) is part of the function being integrated. We can call this entire quantity $G(s)$, to distinguish it from $F(s)$ alone. Thus we have

$$f(t) = \frac{1}{2\pi j} \oint G(s)\, ds \tag{4.47}$$

where

$$G(s) = F(s)\varepsilon^{ts} \tag{4.48}$$

In evaluating the residues of this integral, we find the residues at each of the two poles.

It will be recalled that within the confines of a very small circle about a pole, the function may be represented precisely by the product of the residue and the one factor which creates the pole. As an example, if K_a is the residue at the pole $s = -a$, then

$$G(s) = K_a \cdot \frac{1}{(s+a)} \tag{4.49}$$

or, as we wish to solve for the residue

$$K_a = (s+a)G(s) \tag{4.50}$$

Now note carefully that the $G(s)$ has a factor $(s+a)$, and that both terms cancel. This leads to the expression "removing a pole". We may indicate the value of the residue then, by evaluating (4.50) at $s = -a$.

$$K_a = (s + a)G(s)\big|_{s=-a} \qquad (4.51)$$

Since

$$G(s) = \frac{\varepsilon^{ts}}{(s + a)(s + b)} \qquad (4.52)$$

$$K_a = \frac{\varepsilon^{ts}}{(s + b)}\bigg|_{s=-a} \qquad (4.53)$$

or finally,

$$K_a = \frac{\varepsilon^{-at}}{b - a} \qquad (4.54)$$

In (4.53) we observe the removal of the pole at $s = -a$.

The residue K_b at pole $s = -b$ is found in the same manner, by removing this pole and evaluating the remainder of the function at $s = -b$. Therefore

$$K_b = \frac{\varepsilon^{ts}}{(s + a)}\bigg|_{s=-b} \qquad (4.55)$$

or

$$K_b = \frac{\varepsilon^{-bt}}{a - b} \qquad (4.56)$$

The total integral of $G(s)$ thus becomes

$$\oint G(s)\, ds = 2\pi j[K_a + K_b] \qquad (4.57)$$

We recall, however, that there was a $1/2\pi j$ constant multiplier in the definition of the inverse Laplace transform, and therefore the $2\pi j$ terms cancel, so that

$$f(t) = K_a + K_b \qquad (4.58)$$

Inserting the actual values of K_a and K_b, and simplifying, we have

$$f(t) = \frac{\varepsilon^{-bt} - \varepsilon^{-at}}{a - b} \qquad (4.59)$$

This article may tend to be confusing, but several examples will serve to clarify the idea.

EXAMPLE 1. Given

$$F(s) = \frac{1}{s + 2} \qquad (4.60)$$

find $f(t)$.

SOLUTION. There is only one pole, at $s = -2$, we therefore have only one residue. Set up $G(s)$, where

$$G(s) = \frac{\varepsilon^{ts}}{s + 2} \tag{4.61}$$

Remove the factor causing the pole, and evaluate at the pole.

$$K = \varepsilon^{ts}\big|_{s=-2} \tag{4.62}$$

and finally,

$$f(t) = \varepsilon^{-2t} \tag{4.63}$$

EXAMPLE 2. Given

$$F(s) = \frac{s}{s + 4} \tag{4.64}$$

find $f(t)$.

SOLUTION. Set up $G(s)$, where

$$G(s) = \frac{s\varepsilon^{ts}}{s + 4} \tag{4.65}$$

Again, there is one pole and therefore one residue. We remove the pole and evaluate

$$K = s\varepsilon^{ts}\big|_{s=-4} \tag{4.66}$$

which gives

$$K = -4\varepsilon^{-4t} \tag{4.67}$$

which is the function of time.

EXAMPLE 3. Given

$$F(s) = \frac{s + 6}{s - 3} \tag{4.68}$$

find $f(t)$.

SOLUTION. Set up the function $G(s)$, where

$$G(s) = \frac{(s + 6)\varepsilon^{ts}}{(s - 3)} \tag{4.69}$$

Solve for the one residue by removing the factor that creates the pole, and evaluating the remainder at $s = 3$.

$$K = (s + 6)\varepsilon^{ts}\big|_{s=3} \tag{4.70}$$

which, when evaluated, becomes $f(t)$

$$f(t) = (3 + 6)\varepsilon^{3t} = 9\varepsilon^{3t} \tag{4.71}$$

Summary of article: To use the definition of the inverse transform:

(a) Multiply the $F(s)$ by ε^{ts}. Call this product $G(s)$.

(b) Integrate around all the poles of $G(s)$ by finding the residue ⁻at each pole, and adding.

(c) The integral is the sum of residues times $2\pi j$.

(d) The $1/2\pi j$ multiplier in the definition cancels the $2\pi j$ arising from the integration, so that:

(e) The $f(t)$ is the summation of residues of $G(s)$.

The writer would mention at this point that he is departing radically from the methods used by most texts to evaluate inverse Laplace transforms. The usual approach is to break down functions that have several poles into a sum of partial fractions. Each fraction is then of a simple nature and the inverse is determined by inspection. Many books do not even mention the inverse Laplace integral.

The writer feels that the amount of work is about the same in either method, and feels also that once the reader grows accustomed to using the inverse integral, he will have no difficulty remembering the process. Chapter I provides a general discussion of line or circular integrals.

As a last comment, the writer wants each reader to become proficient in handling certain transcendental functions of s, rather than only algebraic functions. Such transcendental expressions arise often when other than direct current or sine wave input voltages are applied. Such transcendental functions cannot be expressed in partial fractions, yet the inverse Laplace integral is adequate for these types as well as the simple algebraic forms.

4.4. Functions of s involving both simple poles and zeros

In order to consolidate our understanding of the procedure in the previous article, let us examine a general algebraic function of s. General functions of s will arise when networks are analyzed, and will also be used to specify the properties of networks to be synthesized. At any rate, we usually find ourselves confronted with a ratio of polynomials in s, of the form

$$F(s) = \frac{a_0 s^n + a_1 s^{n-1} + a_2 s^{n-2} + \cdots a_n s^0}{b_0 s^{n+1} + b_1 s^n + b_2 s^{n-1} + \cdots b_{n+1} s^0} \qquad (4.72)$$

7

It is necessary to point out that some of the a and b coefficients may be complex as well as real; however, this will not usually cause difficulties.

Now our work at this point will depend upon what we want to do with the function of s that is given. If $F(s)$ represents an impedance, or perhaps a transfer function, we probably will want to keep it in the given form, but if $F(s)$ as given represents the output voltage of a network as a function of s, it will be necessary to dissect the numerator and denominator into their individual factors. The roots of the numerator and denominator may be found by analytical techniques, or by graphical methods, and (4.72) may be rewritten in factored form as

$$F(s) = \frac{(s - \alpha_1)(s - \alpha_2)(s - \alpha_3) \cdots (s - \alpha_n)}{(s - \beta_1)(s - \beta_2)(s - \beta_3) \cdots (s - \beta_n)} \qquad (4.73)$$

Once the function is in this factored form, the pole–zero diagram may be drawn by inspection.

Actually, since poles of the $F(s)$ are caused strictly by the factors in the denominator, it would not be necessary to factor the numerator. The only reason for doing so here is to bring out the point that if two factors, one in the numerator and one in the denominator, are equal, then they can be canceled at once and the function simplified.

We know that there will be one residue for every pole which remains, and for simple poles this residue can be found by removing the factor which causes the pole, and evaluating the remainder of the function at the value of s where the pole occurs. Regardless of the number of poles then, we can state that in general, the nth residue K_n is

$$K_n = [(s - \beta_n)F(s)]\big|_{s=\beta_n} \qquad (4.74)$$

It is pointed out again that this residue is a constant, which, when multiplied by the one factor which caused the pole, gives a perfect representation of $F(s)$ within a very small circle centered on the residue point.

The kernel, ε^{ts}, which occurs in the defining inverse Laplace integral, will always appear in the numerator of functions for which we want to find residues, thus it will not affect our factoring of the usual algebraic denominators. Denominators which involve exponential functions of s will be considered in the next article.

EXAMPLE. Suppose we are given the function

$$F(s) = \frac{(s - 3)\varepsilon^{ts}}{s^3 + 2s^2 + s + 2}$$

As a first step, it is necessary to solve the denominator to locate the poles of the function. The solution of the cubic can be had by formula or graphing the function. It will be found that the factors are

$$F(s) = \frac{(s - 3)\varepsilon^{ts}}{(s + 2)(s - j)(s + j)}$$

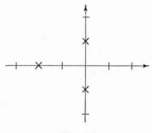

Fig. 4.6

The poles are shown in Fig. 4.6. At each pole there will be a residue. These are now found.

$$K_1\bigg|_{s=-2} = \frac{-5\varepsilon^{-2t}}{(-2 - j)(-2 + j)} = -\varepsilon^{-2t}$$

$$K_2\bigg|_{s=j} = \frac{(-3 + j)\varepsilon^{jt}}{(2 + j)(2j)}$$

$$K_3\bigg|_{s=-j} = \frac{(-3 - j)\varepsilon^{-jt}}{(2 - j)(-2j)}$$

The reader can show as an exercise that the sum of the three residues is

$$K_1 + K_2 + K_3 = \cos t - \sin t - \varepsilon^{-2t}$$

This would be the time response corresponding to the original function of s.

4.5. Functions of s having higher order poles

It will often happen that we are required to find the function of time from a function of s of the form

$$F(s) = \frac{(s + a)}{s(s + b)^n} \tag{4.75}$$

where n is an integer greater than 1. Such multiple poles can be indicated on the pole–zero diagram as a six-arm cross, as in Fig. 4.7.

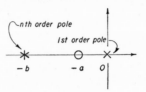

Fig. 4.7

In the chapters on "theorems" we will find easy ways of evaluating the time responses of such functions, but here it is desirable to develop a general formula for the residues. Equation (4.75) can be expanded in partial fractions as:

$$F(s) = \frac{B}{s} + \frac{A_1}{(s + b)} + \frac{A_2}{(s + b)^2} + \cdots \frac{A_k}{(s + b)^k} + \cdots \frac{A_n}{(s + b)^n} \tag{4.76}$$

Note that $k < n$. We can easily evaluate B as

$$B = sF(s)\Big|_{s=0} = \frac{s + a}{(s + b)^n}\Big|_{s=0} = \frac{a}{b^n} \tag{4.77}$$

Now let us multiply (4.76) by $(s + b)^n$,

$$(s + b)^n F(s) = \frac{B(s + b)^n}{s} + A_1(s + b)^{n-1}$$
$$+ A_2(s + b)^{n-2} + \cdots A_k(s + b)^{n-k} + \cdots A_n \tag{4.78}$$

We see that A_n can be determined by evaluating

$$(s + b)^n F(s)\big|_{s=-b} = A_n \tag{4.79}$$

and that the general term A_k can be found by differentiating both sides of (4.78) successively $(n - k)$ times, until A_k stands alone.

$$\frac{d^{n-k}[(s + b)^n F(s)]}{ds^{n-k}} = \lfloor n - k \, A_k \tag{4.80}$$

From which we write a general formula

$$A_k = \frac{1}{\underline{|n - k}} \cdot \frac{d^{n-k}[(s + b)^n F(s)]}{ds^{n-k}}\bigg|_{s=-b} \tag{4.81}$$

where k is the number of the particular term, and n is the highest exponent in $F(s)$.

EXAMPLE 1. Suppose we are given

$$F(s) = \frac{1}{s(s + 2)^2} \tag{4.82}$$

From (4.76) we write

$$F(s) = \frac{B}{s} + \frac{A_1}{s + 2} + \frac{A_2}{(s + 2)^2} \tag{4.83}$$

Here $n = 2$, and by (4.77)

$$B = sF(s)\big|_{s=0} = \tfrac{1}{4} \tag{4.84}$$

Now by (4.81), since $k = 1$,

$$A_1 = \frac{1}{\underline{|2 - 1}} \frac{d^{2-1}}{ds^{2-1}} \left[\frac{1}{s}\right]\bigg|_{s=-2} \tag{4.85}$$

$$A_1 = \frac{d\,\dfrac{1}{s}}{ds}\bigg|_{s=-2} = \left[-\frac{1}{s^2}\right]_{-2} = -\frac{1}{4} \tag{4.86}$$

and for the $k = 2$ term

$$A_2 = \frac{1}{\underline{|2 - 2}} \frac{d^{2-2}}{ds^{2-2}} \left[\frac{1}{s}\right] = \left[\frac{1}{s}\right]_{-2} = -\frac{1}{2} \tag{4.87}$$

so that

$$F(s) = \frac{\tfrac{1}{4}}{s} - \frac{\tfrac{1}{4}}{(s - 2)} - \frac{\tfrac{1}{2}}{(s - 2)^2} \tag{4.88}$$

We will finish taking the inverse of $F(s)$ shortly, but first, let us look at another example.

EXAMPLE 2. We are given that

$$F(s) = \frac{s+1}{s(s+2)^3} \tag{4.89}$$

We write

$$F(s) = \frac{B}{s} + \frac{A_1}{(s+2)} + \frac{A_2}{(s+2)^2} + \frac{A_3}{(s+2)^3} \tag{4.90}$$

Here $n = 3$. First

$$B = sF(s)\big|_{s=0} = \tfrac{1}{8} \tag{4.91}$$

Then by using (4.81) with $k = 3$

$$A_3 = \frac{1}{\underline{|3-3}} \cdot \frac{d^{3-3}}{ds^{3-3}} \left[\frac{s+1}{s} \right]\bigg|_{s=-2} = \frac{1}{2} \tag{4.92}$$

(It is easiest to do A_3 first, because this order, A_3, A_2, A_1, requires differentiation in normal order.) Where $k = 2$, then

$$A_2 = \frac{1}{\underline{|3-2}} \cdot \frac{d^{3-2}}{ds^{3-2}} \left[\frac{s+1}{s} \right]\bigg|_{s=-2} = -\frac{1}{4} \tag{4.93}$$

And finally, for $k = 1$,

$$A_1 = \frac{1}{\underline{|3-1}} \cdot \frac{d^{3-1}}{ds^{3-1}} \left[\frac{s+1}{s} \right]\bigg|_{s=-2} = -\frac{1}{8} \tag{4.94}$$

So the sum of the partial fractions is,

$$F(s) = \frac{\tfrac{1}{8}}{s} - \frac{\tfrac{1}{8}}{(s+2)} - \frac{\tfrac{1}{4}}{(s+2)^2} + \frac{\tfrac{1}{2}}{(s+2)^3} \tag{4.95}$$

This may be double-checked by multiplying out to see that the original $F(s)$ is obtained. Again, we will find the $f(t)$ shortly. The main pupose here is to develop facility with higher order poles.

The foregoing discussion of the inverse Laplace transform is complete enough to allow you to determine the function of time for any $F(s)$ whose denominator is algebraic. For cases where the denominator is not algebraic, it is necessary to have additional methods available. Such additional methods usually involve the application of a number of theorems.

The "theorems" are of such importance in practical evaluation of functions of s that a rather long chapter will now follow on this subject. Rigorous proofs will not be given in all cases, but the proof offered will be adequate to allow the reader to accept the theorem for use.

After finishing the chapter on theorems, we will be ready to begin some actual circuit analysis studies.

CHAPTER V

LAPLACE TRANSFORM THEOREMS

5.1. Introduction

IN this chapter we will study most of the important theorems of Laplace transforms. These theorems are rather simple, but it takes a fair amount of practice to use them in practical ways. A good working knowledge of the theorems is what takes the drudgery out of operations with Laplace transforms. Most of the theorems will relate operations in one plane to operations in the other plane.

In addition to their immediate value for taking inverse transforms, the theorems play a vital part in the development and extension of collected tables of Laplace transforms. The extensive tables in the back of this book have been developed from a few basic forms and repeated application of many theorems.

Each theorem has been given a definite name, and we will try to use the same names here as are common in the literature. Usually the names are descriptive of the operation involved, which makes them easy to remember.

5.2. Linear s-plane translation

We will begin our work with theorems by the study of shifting in the complex plane. This theorem, sometimes referred to as the "complex translation" theorem, tells us that if

$$F(s) = \mathscr{L}[f(t)] \tag{5.1}$$

then

$$F(s + a) = \mathscr{L}[\varepsilon^{-at}f(t)] \tag{5.2}$$

This theorem says then, that if we have some function of time which has a transformed function of s, and if we should multiply the original $f(t)$ by an exponential decay factor ε^{-at}, then the Laplace transform of the new time function could be found by merely shifting every point in the s-plane to the left by an amount a. A few examples will serve to clarify this concept.

EXAMPLE 1. Suppose we have a function of time

$$f(t) = \cos \omega t \qquad (5.3)$$

which we know from previous work has a transform

$$F(s) = \frac{s}{s^2 + \omega^2} \qquad (5.4)$$

Poles and zeros will be present at $\pm j\omega$, and 0, as shown in Fig. 5.1.

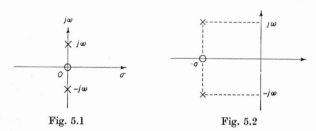

Fig. 5.1   Fig. 5.2

If now we should multiply (5.3) by an exponential factor so that a new $f(t)$ is

$$f(t) = \varepsilon^{-at} \cos \omega t \qquad (5.5)$$

then the shifting theorem says that we would replace each s in (5.4) by the factor $(s + a)$, to have the transform of (5.5), or

$$F(s) = \frac{s + a}{(s + a)^2 + \omega^2} \qquad (5.6)$$

The poles of this function, as well as the zero, will be shifted a units to the left, as shown in Fig. 5.2.

Since the location of the poles and zeros in the s-plane completely determines the function, we say in general that multiplying a function of time by ε^{-at} goes over into the s-plane as a shift of all points in the s-plane a units to the left. If we should multiply the time function by ε^{at}, we would then shift points in the s-plane in the opposite direction.

To prove the shifting theorem, let us use the definition of the Laplace transform to say that

$$\mathscr{L}[\varepsilon^{-at} f(t)] = \int_0^\infty [f(t)\varepsilon^{-at}]\varepsilon^{-st}\, dt \qquad (5.7)$$

$$= \int_0^\infty f(t)\varepsilon^{-(s+a)t}\, dt \qquad (5.8)$$

We can define

$$s + a = s_1 \tag{5.9}$$

so that

$$\mathscr{L}[\varepsilon^{-at}f(t)] = F(s_1) \tag{5.10}$$

or in other words

$$\mathscr{L}[\varepsilon^{-at}f(t)] = F(s + a) \tag{5.11}$$

EXAMPLE 2. Given

$$f(t) = \varepsilon^{-bt} \tag{5.12}$$

find the Laplace transform of $f(t)\varepsilon^{-at}$.

The Laplace transform of $f(t)$ alone is

$$\mathscr{L}[f(t)] = \frac{1}{s + b} \tag{5.13}$$

The shifting theorem says that we should merely shift all points in the s-plane a units to the left, or

$$\mathscr{L}[f(t)\varepsilon^{-at}] = \frac{1}{(s + a) + b} \tag{5.14}$$

This is easily shown to be true, because if we combine the two time functions before taking the Laplace transform, we have

$$\mathscr{L}[\varepsilon^{-(b+a)t}] = \frac{1}{s + (b + a)} \tag{5.15}$$

the same result as (5.14).

PROBLEMS

(a) Find the Laplace transforms of

(1) $$f(t) = \varepsilon^{-at} \cos \omega t$$

(2) $$f(t) = t\varepsilon^{-at}$$

ANS. $\dfrac{1}{(s + a)^2}$

(3) $$f(t) = \varepsilon^t \cosh \omega t$$

(4) $$f(t) = \varepsilon^{3t}U(t)$$

ANS. $\dfrac{1}{s - 3}$

(b) Find the inverse Laplace transforms of the following by applying the shifting theorem, and then recognizing the result.

(1)
$$F(s) = \frac{1}{s - 4}$$

Shift the points in the s-plane 4 units to the left, so that

$$F_1(s) = \frac{1}{s}$$

The function of time is therefore

$$f_1(t) = U(t)$$

and we can find the actual $f(t)$ by inserting the exponential factor

$$f(t) = \varepsilon^{at} f_1(t) = \varepsilon^{4t}$$

(2)
$$F(s) = \frac{1}{(s + a)^2}$$

(3)
$$F(s) = \frac{s - 6}{(s - 6)^2 + 16}$$

(4)
$$F(s) = \frac{2}{(s - 1)^2 - 4}$$

Ans. $\varepsilon^t \sinh 2t$.

This, and the following theorems to be developed in this chapter, will be numbered and collected into a table at the end of the book.

5.3. Final value theorem

In work with electronic circuits and networks (see Fig. 4.1), the transfer functions are often of such a nature that the output goes through certain variations, and finally approaches and settles down at some final, definite value. Final values of both current and voltage are often of interest, as in the example shown in Fig. 5.3. The transformed circuit diagram is (see art. 4.2) shown in Fig. 5.4. The equation for this simple one-loop network is seen by inspection to be

$$I(s) = \frac{E(s)}{sL + R} \tag{5.16}$$

Now under certain conditions $I(s)$ will have a final definite value, and under other conditions there will never be such a final value. For example, if the input voltage is a sine wave, then the current will never settle down to a steady value, but will continue indefinitely to oscillate between fixed limits as a sine wave of current. If $E(s)$ is a d.c. voltage, or step function, however, it is just as easy to see that the current does settle down to a definite final value (5.17).

$$i(t) = \frac{E}{R} \tag{5.17}$$

Having attempted to illustrate the meaning of the term "final value" as used in this article, we now proceed to state and prove the

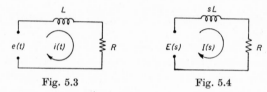

Fig. 5.3   Fig. 5.4

theorem. The final value theorem is stated as an equality of limits, which is written as

$$\lim_{s \to 0} sF(s) = \lim_{t \to \infty} f(t) \tag{5.18}$$

There are two limitations to be recognized immediately. First, we saw earlier that when $F(s)$ is multiplied by s, this represents a differentiation. Therefore both $f(t)$ and its first derivative must be Laplace transformable. Secondly, as we saw intuitively in the example of Fig. 5.3, there must actually be a final value. This last limitation states that the expression $sF(s)$ does not have poles on the $j\omega$ axis, or in the right-hand plane.

To prove the theorem, let us write the expression for the Laplace transform of a derivative, which is

$$\int_0^\infty f'(t)\varepsilon^{-st}\,dt = sF(s) - f(0) \tag{5.19}$$

Now observe that the parameter s is not a function of time, thus we can allow s to approach (0) before performing the integration if we wish. Thus considering only the left-hand side of (5.19) at first:

$$\lim_{s \to 0} \int_0^\infty f'(t)\varepsilon^{-st}\,dt = \int_0^\infty f'(t)\,dt = \lim_{t \to \infty} \int_0^t f'(t)\,dt \tag{5.20}$$

and the last integral in (5.20) becomes

$$\lim_{t \to \infty} \int_0^t f'(t)\, dt = \lim_{t \to \infty} [f(t) - f(0)] \qquad (5.21)$$

Since we have let $s \to 0$ for the left-hand side of (5.19), we must take the same limit on the right-hand side of (5.19), and combining this with the final result of (5.21),

$$\lim_{s \to 0} [sF(s) - f(0)] = \lim_{t \to \infty} [f(t) - f(0)] \qquad (5.22)$$

As the $f(0)$ is neither a function of s nor of t, it may be canceled from both sides, leaving

$$\lim_{s \to 0} sF(s) = \lim_{t \to \infty} f(t) \qquad (5.23)$$

and the theorem is proved.

Let us now apply this theorem to the function $I(s)$ of our example in (5.16). We choose $E(s)$ to be a step function of magnitude E, so that

$$I(s) = \frac{E}{s(sL + R)} \qquad (5.24)$$

The final value theorem requires that this function first be multiplied by s, to become

$$sI(s) = \frac{E}{sL + R} \qquad (5.25)$$

whereupon the limit becomes

$$\lim_{s \to 0} sI(s) = \frac{E}{R} \qquad (5.26)$$

which is simple enough to be apparent by inspection. Note that (5.24) has poles at $s = 0$, and $s = -R/L$. For other applied voltage functions, $I(s)$ could easily have poles on the $j\omega$ axis and thus make the theorem inapplicable.

Before going on to the next theorem, let us examine (5.24) in a slightly different way. Multiply out the denominator on the right-hand side, to get

$$I(s) = \frac{E}{s^2L + Rs} \qquad (5.27)$$

Now if we let s become very small, the s^2 term will become insignificant compared with the first power s term, so that

$$I(s) = \frac{E}{R} \cdot \frac{1}{s} \qquad (5.28)$$

and we recognize $1/s$ as being the transform of the unit step function $U(t)$, so that

$$i(t) = \frac{E}{R} \qquad (5.29)$$

this result, as before, being obtained by letting s approach zero.

PROBLEMS

(1) Find the final value of the output voltage in Fig. 5.5. Assume that the input is a unit step function.

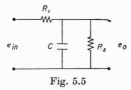

Fig. 5.5

(2) Assuming once more a unit step function, applied from a zero impedance source, state whether or not the final value theorem can be applied to find $e_0(t)$ in Fig. 5.6.

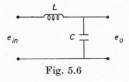

Fig. 5.6

5.4. Initial value theorem

Assume again as in the last article that both $f(t)$ and its derivative $f'(t)$ are Laplace transformable, and that the limit of the derivative of $F(s)$ exists as s approaches infinity. If these conditions hold, then the initial value theorem states that

$$\lim_{s \to \infty} sF(s) = \lim_{t \to 0} f(t) \qquad (5.30)$$

Thus the theorem says that the rate of change of $F(s)$ near infinity in the s-plane corresponds to the behavior of $f(t)$ near $t = 0$ in the time domain. The proof of the initial value theorem is straightforward, and proceeds as follows:

We have already derived the Laplace transform of a derivative which is

$$\int_0^\infty f'(t)\varepsilon^{-st}\,dt = sF(s) - f(0) \tag{5.31}$$

Now again, since s is a parametric variable and is not a function of time, we can allow s to approach infinity prior to the indicated integration.

$$\lim_{s\to\infty} \int_0^\infty f'(t)\varepsilon^{-st}\,dt = \lim_{s\to\infty} [sF(s) - f(0)] \tag{5.32}$$

Note that if $s \to \infty$, the exponential term becomes zero, making the entire left-hand side zero. Therefore

$$\lim_{s\to\infty} [sF(s) - f(0)] = 0 \tag{5.33}$$

As a final step, we note that

$$f(0) = \lim_{t\to 0} f(t) \tag{5.34}$$

and thus (5.33) becomes

$$\lim_{s\to\infty} sF(s) = \lim_{t\to 0} f(t) \tag{5.35}$$

whereupon the theorem is proved. Note carefully that this theorem is more general than the final value theorem as discussed in art. 5.3.

EXAMPLE. Consider Fig. 5.7.

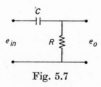

Fig. 5.7

If we let e_{IN} be $U(t)$, a unit step function, then the output as a function of s will be

$$E_0(s) = \frac{RC}{RCs + 1} \tag{5.36}$$

and it is required to find the initial value of $e_0(t)$ at the moment that the step voltage is applied to the input. Equation (5.36) is multiplied by s as the theorem requires:

$$sE_0(s) = \frac{sRC}{RCs + 1} = \frac{RC}{RC + 1/s} \tag{5.37}$$

and taking the limit

$$e_0(0) = \lim_{s \to \infty} sE_0(s) = 1 \text{ volt} \tag{5.38}$$

which is the unit step voltage which was applied.

PROBLEM. It should have been discovered by now that the final value theorem did not apply in the case of problem 2 of the last article. Using the same Fig. 5.6, first find the output voltage as a function of s; then, using the initial value theorem, find the initial value of $e_0(0)$ at the instant the step function is applied. Note that the $E_0(s)$ has conjugate poles on the $j\omega$-axis. The final value theorem cannot be used in such cases, although the initial value theorem has no such limitations.

5.5. Real translation

In real translation, a curve which represents a function of time is shifted to a new position along the time axis, without otherwise

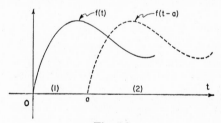

Fig. 5.8

changing the shape or characteristics of the function. For example, in Fig. 5.8. the function $f(t)$ which normally begins at $t = 0$ has been shifted intact by an amount a, whereupon it now becomes $f(t - a)$.

Now if the function $f(t)$ is not given as a curve, but is presented in tabular form, one could of course plot the curve from the given data. The position of such a curve would thus depend on the accuracy of the clock which was used to determine t.

Suppose for example that a function is measured by two independent observers, each having his own clock which he considers correct. But suppose that in reality clock (1) is correct, and that clock (2) is a sec too fast. Observer (1) will tabulate the beginning of the function at $t = 0$ sec, and observer (2) will state that the function begins at $t = a$ sec. Let us now say that t represents the correct clock, while τ represents the clock which is a sec fast. That is,

$$\tau = t - a \tag{5.39}$$

from which

$$d\tau = dt \tag{5.40}$$

Equation (5.40) indicates that each clock is running at the same rate, but that the clock keeping τ time is merely offset a sec from the clock which is keeping t time. The curve on the right in Fig. 5.8 can thus be labelled as $f(\tau)$.

Observer (2) will write the Laplace transform of his function in τ rather than t time, and his expression would be

$$F(s) = \int_0^\infty f(\tau)\varepsilon^{-s\tau}\, d\tau \tag{5.41}$$

However, because we know that his clock is in error by the amount a, we would correct his equation to read

$$F(s) = \int_a^\infty f(t-a)\varepsilon^{-s(t-a)}\, dt \tag{5.42}$$

Note that we have changed his lower limit from 0 to a, since from (5.39) when $\tau = 0$, $t = a$. Also if $f(t-a)$ is 0 from $t = 0$ to $t = a$, as shown in Fig. 5.8, we are permitted to make the lower limit of (5.42) equal 0, thus

$$F(s) = \int_0^\infty f(t-a)\varepsilon^{as}\varepsilon^{-st}\, dt \tag{5.43}$$

Notice also that as the exponential ε^{as} is not a function of time, it may be carried through the integral sign and to the other side as a negative exponent, the expression becoming

$$\varepsilon^{-as}F(s) = \int_0^\infty f(t-a)\varepsilon^{-st}\, dt \tag{5.44}$$

Having derived (5.44), we are now in a position to state the real translation theorem, which says that

$$\mathscr{L}[f(t-a)] = \varepsilon^{-as}F(s) \tag{5.45}$$

The theorem thus states generally that translation in the time domain goes over into multiplication by an exponential in the

8

s-domain. Note that the a is considered to be a non-negative real number.

EXAMPLE 1. To illustrate, let us take as a simple example the case where $f(t) = U(t)$, the step function. We now translate this curve

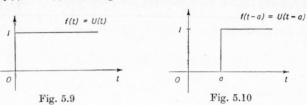

Fig. 5.9   Fig. 5.10

a units to the right, to have Fig. 5.10. By the use of theorem (5.45) we write immediately

$$\mathscr{L}[f(t-a)] = \varepsilon^{-as}F(s) = \varepsilon^{-as} \cdot \frac{1}{s} \qquad (5.46)$$

This can be checked by direct integration of $U(t-a)$.

$$\mathscr{L}[U(t-a)] = \int_0^\infty U(t-a)\varepsilon^{-st}\,dt \qquad (5.47)$$

$$= \int_0^a (0)\varepsilon^{-st}\,dt + \int_a^\infty (1)\varepsilon^{-st}\,dt \qquad (5.48)$$

or

$$\mathscr{L}[U(t-a)] = \frac{\varepsilon^{-as}}{s} \qquad (5.49)$$

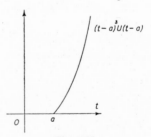

$(t-a)^3 U(t-a)$

Fig. 5.11

EXAMPLE 2. Consider Fig. 5.11. By the real translation theorem,

$$F(s) = \varepsilon^{-as}\mathscr{L}[t^3 U(t)] \qquad (5.50)$$

or, from the tables

$$F(s) = \frac{6\varepsilon^{-as}}{s^4} \qquad (5.51)$$

PROBLEM. Consider the time sampled step function shown in Fig. 5.12. Show that the transform is

$$F(s) = \frac{1}{s(1 + \varepsilon^{-s})} \qquad (5.52)$$

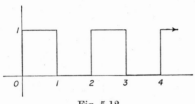

Fig. 5.12

HINT. Write the time function as a sum of displaced step functions, i.e.

$$f(t) = U(t) - U(t-1) + U(t-2) - U(t-3) \cdot \cdot \cdot \qquad (5.53)$$

and apply the theorem to each term, then simplify.

5.6. Complex differentiation

This theorem has limited usefulness in electronic circuit analysis, but is easy to prove and is quite valuable when used to extend a table of Laplace transforms. The mechanics of this theorem are compatible with those of the real differentiation, and also with real and complex integration theorems. The electronics engineer who eventually specializes in antennas, filter theory, network synthesis, and other branches of the art where s-plane operation is common will eventually find much use for this theorem.

In simple terms, the complex differentiation theorem states that if $F(s)$ is the Laplace transform of a function $f(t)$, then the derivative of $F(s)$ corresponds in the time world to multiplying the function of time by the variable t, as in (5.54)

$$\frac{dF(s)}{ds} = -\mathscr{L}[tf(t)] \qquad (5.54)$$

Note that there is a sign change involved.

To prove this theorem, let us write the basic equation of the Laplace transform, which is:

$$F(s) = \int_0^\infty f(t)\varepsilon^{-st} \, dt \qquad (5.55)$$

and differentiate with respect to s,

$$\frac{dF(s)}{ds} = \frac{d}{ds} \int_0^\infty f(t)\varepsilon^{-st}\, dt \tag{5.56}$$

Now we can rearrange the right-hand side of (5.56) somewhat, because s and t are not functions of each other.

$$\frac{dF(s)}{ds} = \int_0^\infty f(t)\, dt \, \frac{d\varepsilon^{-ts}}{ds} \tag{5.57}$$

$$= \int_0^\infty f(t)\, dt \, (-t)\varepsilon^{-ts} \tag{5.58}$$

$$= \int_0^\infty -tf(t)\varepsilon^{-st}\, dt \tag{5.59}$$

and finally,

$$\frac{dF(s)}{ds} = -\mathscr{L}[tf(t)] \tag{5.60}$$

which proves the theorem.

EXAMPLES

(1) Consider the pair of functions

$$F(s) = \frac{1}{s}; \qquad f(t) = U(t) = 1$$

Applying the complex differentiation theorem,

$$\frac{dF(s)}{ds} = -\frac{1}{s^2}; \qquad -tf(t) = -t$$

we find that

$$\frac{1}{s^2} = \mathscr{L}(t) \tag{5.61}$$

The new function of s in (5.61) can be differentiated again,

$$\frac{d\, 1/s^2}{ds} = -\frac{2}{s^3} \tag{5.62}$$

or

$$\frac{2}{s^3} = \mathscr{L}(t^2) \tag{5.63}$$

and we see that this process could go on indefinitely, leading us to a general form for powers of the original step function transform.

(2) Consider the pair

$$F(s) = \frac{s}{s^2 + a^2}; \qquad f(t) = \cos at$$

Applying the theorem

$$\frac{dF(s)}{ds} = \frac{a^2 - s^2}{(s^2 + a^2)^2}; \qquad -tf(t) = -t \cos at$$

we have the new pair

$$\mathscr{L}(-t \cos at) = \frac{a^2 - s^2}{(s^2 + a^2)^2} \qquad (5.64)$$

Note in passing that the derived function of s has higher order poles on the imaginary axis.

PROBLEMS

(1) With $f(t) = \sin \omega t$, apply the theorem twice in succession to derive two new functions of s.

(2) With $f(t) = \varepsilon^{-at}$, derive a new pair of transforms by using the theorem developed in this article.

(3) For an $F(s) = \varepsilon^{-as}$, apply the complex differentiation theorem to derive a new function of time, and graph the first part of the resulting waveform.

5.7. Complex integration

This theorem, like the complex differentiation theorem developed in art. 5.6, is easy to prove, and serves among other things to extend and check tables of Laplace transforms, in addition to furthering our understanding of operations in the complex plane. Formally, the theorem states that

$$\int_s^\infty F(s)\, ds = \mathscr{L}\left[\frac{f(t)}{t}\right] \qquad (5.65)$$

This is subject to the same conditions that apply throughout this chapter, namely that $f(t)$ is Laplace transformable, and obviously, from the way (5.65) is written, that $f(t)/t$ is also Laplace transformable, and that the left-hand integral exists.

To begin our development of this theorem, we write the original definition of the Laplace transform, which is, as always

$$F(s) = \int_0^\infty f(t)\varepsilon^{-st}\, dt \tag{5.66}$$

Both sides are now integrated with respect to s, from s to ∞.

$$\int_s^\infty F(s)\, ds = \int_s^\infty \int_0^\infty f(t)\varepsilon^{-st}\, dt\, ds \tag{5.67}$$

It is permissible to rearrange the double integral as follows:

$$\int_s^\infty f(t) \left[\int_s^\infty \varepsilon^{-ts}\, ds \right] dt = \int_0^\infty \frac{f(t)\varepsilon^{-ts}}{t}\, dt \tag{5.68}$$

wherein the integral within the brackets has been reduced to ε^{-st}/t. Using this result, (5.67) becomes

$$\int_s^\infty F(s)\, ds = \int_0^\infty \frac{f(t)\, \varepsilon^{-st}}{t}\, dt \tag{5.69}$$

or, by definition

$$\int_s^\infty F(s)\, ds = \mathscr{L}\left[\frac{f(t)}{t} \right] \tag{5.70}$$

and the proof is complete.

EXAMPLES

(1) Consider the pair of transforms

$$2s^{-3} \rightarrow t^2 \tag{5.71}$$

If the theorem is applied,

$$2\int_s^\infty s^{-3}\, ds = \frac{2 \cdot s^{-2}}{-2} = \frac{1}{s^2}, \quad \text{and} \quad \frac{t^2}{t} = t \tag{5.72}$$

We have developed the new pair

$$\frac{1}{s^2} \rightarrow t \tag{5.73}$$

which may be checked by using the tables.

(2) Consider the pair

$$\frac{2as}{(s^2 + a^2)^2} \rightarrow t \sin at \tag{5.74}$$

Again applying the theorem

$$2a \int_s^\infty \frac{s \, ds}{(s^2 + a^2)^2} = \frac{a}{s^2 + a^2}, \quad \text{and} \quad \frac{t \sin at}{t} = \sin at \quad (5.75)$$

Thus we have the new pair

$$\frac{a}{s^2 + a^2} \rightarrow \sin at \quad (5.76)$$

which is a pair we remember from earlier work.

PROBLEMS

(1) Apply the complex integration theorem to (5.64) in the last article, to develop the original pair used in example (2) of that article.

(2) Using the function of time

$$f(t) = \varepsilon^{j\omega_1 t} - \varepsilon^{j\omega_2 t} \quad (5.77)$$

show that application of the theorem leads to the new function of s

$$F(s) = \ln \left(\frac{s - j\omega_1}{s - j\omega_2} \right) \quad (5.78)$$

What limitations must be imposed upon ω_1 and ω_2?

(3) Considering the basic definition of natural logarithms, (5.78) says that

$$\varepsilon^{F(s)} = \frac{s - j\omega_1}{s - j\omega_2} \quad (5.79)$$

Is there any meaningful interpretation of this expression?

5.8. Sectioning a function of time

It often happens in electronic work that we wish to examine a function of time which has been "sampled". This sampling can occur in many ways, such as the electronic or mechanical switching in chopper-stabilized amplifiers, in telemetry, or in coded data transmission systems.

It is intended in this article to digress briefly for a short discussion of sectioning a function of time. The ideas presented will be simple, but will perhaps clarify one or two points that will arise in the next theorem which we shall develop.

The Faltung integral, or convolution theorem to be developed in the following article will involve one or two rather tricky limit changes, and it is best to prepare for them in advance, so as to avoid having to interrupt a development which will be somewhat tedious at best.

Let us consider some relatively simple function of time, such as the exponentially decaying wave in Fig. 5.13. Note that this

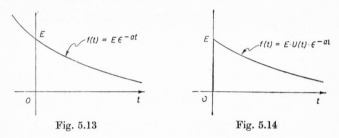

Fig. 5.13   Fig. 5.14

function has values for both positive and negative values of t. If we multiply this function by a unit step function, we "slice off" the entire portion to the left of $t = 0$, to obtain the section shown in Fig. 5.14. Now let us take the original function, Fig. 5.13, and multiply it by a displaced step function, $U(t - b)$.

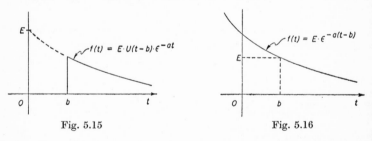

Fig. 5.15   Fig. 5.16

The result is shown in Fig. 5.15. It is seen that part of the original function has been removed, but that the portion remaining has not been altered in any way.

Now let us start again with the function shown in Fig. 5.13. This time we shall first translate the curve to the right by an amount b, letting it become a function of $(t - b)$, as in Fig. 5.16.

After translating, the curve is now sectioned by multiplying by a displaced unit step function which begins at $t = b$. This is shown in Fig. 5.17. Notice the difference between Figs. 5.17 and 5.15.

Let us examine one or two more relations using step functions, and then we shall proceed to the next article. In most of our work in the time domain, we use t as the independent variable. If we choose some constant value of time (τ), we can call τ a parametric variable. We have spoken of parametric variables earlier. As

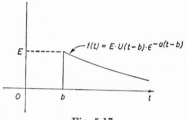

Fig. 5.17

another example, suppose we have current i flowing in an R–L–C circuit. Normally we would consider L to be a constant, but we could find i, change L and find i again, change L and find i once more, etc. (this would result in a frequency response curve), here the L would be the parametric variable, or "selective" variable.

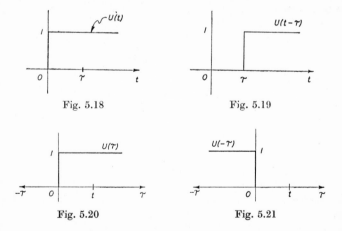

Fig. 5.18   Fig. 5.19

Fig. 5.20   Fig. 5.21

Consider Fig. 5.18. Choose some value $t = \tau$ as a constant, and shift by an amount τ to have Fig. 5.19. Now, however, let us choose τ as the variable, and pick t as a fixed value of τ (see Fig. 5.20). Or, for $U(-\tau)$, we have in Fig. 5.21. We now shift by an amount t to have $U(t - \tau)$, as in Fig. 5.22.

In Fig. 5.22 τ has been replaced by $(t - \tau)$, which has folded the function around the vertical axis, and then translated by an amount t. This folding (Faltung) operation is used in the next section where we treat the Faltung integral.

These relations between t and τ will be used in the next article freely, without stopping then to show their graphical relations or

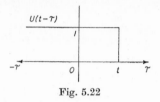

Fig. 5.22

directions. Thus, having prepared these curves for reference, we proceed now to the next theorem.

5.9. The convolution theorem

The theorem to be developed in this article deals with the complex multiplication of functions, and is also referred to as Borel's theorem, or the Faltung integral. This theorem will provide an additional way to take inverse Laplace transforms of functions of s when the $F(s)$ can be separated into factors whose inverse transforms are known. For ordinary algebraic functions of s, the previous methods usually require less work, but the convolution theorem can also be employed for transcendental functions of s, thus expanding our ability to deal with complex waveforms such as are found in modern electronic systems.

The development of this theorem is somewhat more involved than those undertaken previously, so in order not to become confused by excessive details, we shall define certain operations and refer back to art. 5.8. for ideas on sectioning.

To begin, if we multiply two functions of time, and then integrate the product between the limits of 0 and t, we perform a process which we define as convolution. That is

$$f(t) \triangleq \int_0^t f_1(t - \tau) \cdot f_2(\tau)\, d\tau \tag{5.80}$$

Here τ is the variable of integration, and t is constant while integrating. Do not attempt to see the reason for choosing this particular integral now. Let us merely work with it to see if we can arrive at any worthwhile result. The Laplace transform of (5.80) can be written as

$$F(s) = \int_0^\infty \left[\int_0^t f_1(t - \tau) \cdot f_2(\tau) d\tau \right] \varepsilon^{-st} dt \qquad (5.81)$$

The upper limit t can be changed to ∞ if we first multiply the product by $U(t - \tau)$. See Fig. 5.22, as this will make the over-all function zero from t to ∞ anyway. Equation (5.81) then becomes

$$F(s) = \int_0^\infty \int_0^\infty f_1(t - \tau) \cdot f_2(\tau) \cdot U(t - \tau) d\tau \, \varepsilon^{-st} dt \qquad (5.82)$$

Now at this point, it is felt best to state that the order of integration can be changed, without giving a rigorous proof. Writing (5.82) in slightly different form gives

$$F(s) = \int_0^\infty f_2(\tau) \left[\int_0^\infty f_1(t - \tau) \cdot U(t - \tau) \cdot \varepsilon^{-st} dt \right] d\tau \qquad (5.83)$$

Note that the integral in the bracketed term contains the product $f(t - \tau) \, U(t - \tau)$, which can be shown in Fig. 5.23.

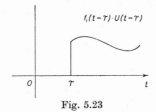

$$f_1(t - \tau) \cdot U(t - \tau)$$

Fig. 5.23

In Fig. 5.23 it is evident that the function is zero from 0 to τ, and thus the lower limit in the bracketed term of (5.83) can be changed from 0 to τ, to give

$$F(s) = \int_0^\infty f_2(\tau) \left[\int_\tau^\infty f_1(t - \tau) \varepsilon^{-st} dt \right] d\tau \qquad (5.84)$$

We have dropped the displaced step function term in (5.84), as it is of no importance after we change the lower limit.

If one now recalls the real translation theorem, (5.45) in art. 5.5, the entire bracketed term in (5.84) goes over into the s-plane as

$$\int_\tau^\infty f_1(t - \tau) \varepsilon^{-st} dt = \varepsilon^{-s\tau} F_1(s) \qquad (5.85)$$

(the lower limit can be τ or 0, because we remember that the function is zero to the left of $t = \tau$ anyway).

Placing (5.85) back into (5.84), and bringing $F_1(s)$ outside the integral gives

$$F(s) = F_1(s) \cdot \int_0^\infty f_2(\tau)\varepsilon^{-s\tau}\,d\tau \tag{5.86}$$

which, in view of our recent discussion of t-time and τ-time, we recognize as

$$F(s) = F_1(s) \cdot F_2(s) \tag{5.87}$$

Using (5.87) in combination with (5.81), it can be stated that

$$F_1(s) \cdot F_2(s) = \mathscr{L}\left[\int_0^t f_1(t-\tau) \cdot f_2(\tau)\,d\tau\right] \tag{5.88}$$

This equation (5.88) is the usual way of expressing the real convolution theorem. It is evident of course that

$$\mathscr{L}^{-1}[F(s)] = \mathscr{L}^{-1}[F_1(s) \cdot F_2(s)] = \int_0^t f_1(t-\tau) \cdot f_2(\tau)d\tau \tag{5.89}$$

It should be possible to use this theorem to find the inverse Laplace transform of any $F(s)$ which can be factored into two parts, if each part has an $f(t)$ which can be recognized. The procedure for using the theorem will be illustrated by examples.

EXAMPLES

(1) Using the real convolution theorem, find the inverse of

$$F(s) = \frac{1}{(s+\alpha)(s+\nu)} \tag{5.90}$$

Choose the two factors as

$$F_1(s) = \frac{1}{s+\alpha}; \quad \text{so that } f_1(t) = \varepsilon^{-\alpha t}; \quad \text{or} \quad f_1(t-\tau) = \varepsilon^{-\alpha(t-\tau)}$$

$$F_2(s) = \frac{1}{s+\nu}; \quad \text{so that } f_2(t) = \varepsilon^{-\nu t}; \quad \text{or} \quad f_2(\tau) = \varepsilon^{-\nu\tau}$$

Then

$$\mathscr{L}^{-1}[F(s)] = \int_0^t \varepsilon^{-\alpha(t-\tau)}\varepsilon^{-\nu\tau}\,d\tau \tag{5.91}$$

$$= \varepsilon^{-\alpha t}\int_0^t \varepsilon^{-(\alpha-\nu)\tau}\,d\tau \tag{5.92}$$

$$= \frac{\varepsilon^{-\alpha t}}{\alpha-\nu}\left[\varepsilon^{(\alpha-\nu)\tau}\right]_0^t \tag{5.93}$$

or finally

$$\mathscr{L}^{-1}[F(s)] = \frac{\varepsilon^{-\nu t} - \varepsilon^{-\alpha t}}{\alpha - \nu} \tag{5.94}$$

which is known to be correct.

(2) Apply the theorem to find the inverse of

$$F(s) = \frac{1}{(s + \alpha)s^2} \tag{5.95}$$

Note that this function has a double pole at $s = 0$.

Choose the two factors as

$$F_1(s) = \frac{1}{s + \alpha}; \quad \text{or} \quad f_1(t) = \varepsilon^{-\alpha t}, \quad \text{and} \quad f_1(t - \tau) = \varepsilon^{-\alpha(t-\tau)}$$

$$F_2(s) = \frac{1}{s^2}; \quad \text{or} \quad f_2(t) = t, \quad \text{and} \quad f_2(\tau) = \tau$$

Then

$$\mathscr{L}^{-1}[F(s)] = \int_0^t \varepsilon^{-\alpha(t-\tau)}\, \tau\, d\tau \tag{5.96}$$

$$= \varepsilon^{-\alpha t} \int_0^t \tau \varepsilon^{-\alpha \tau}\, d\tau \tag{5.97}$$

Which may be completed by reference to a table of integrals, so that

$$\mathscr{L}^{-1}[F(s)] = \frac{\varepsilon^{-\alpha t} + \alpha t - 1}{\alpha^2} \tag{5.98}$$

Note that in both examples the functions which were integrated could have been drawn graphically, so that if it had not been possible to integrate analytically, at least we could have found the inverse by graphical means.

This makes it possible to set up mechanized computers to perform certain calculations related to Laplace transforms.

The convolution theorem developed in this article is quite general, and can be used to obtain some of the simpler theorems.

PROBLEM. Letting the s-plane function be $F(s)/s$, use the convolution theorem to prove that

$$\mathscr{L}^{-1}\left[\frac{F(s)}{s}\right] = \int_0^t f(t)\, dt$$

5.10. Scale change theorem

The time scale theorem to be developed in this article is useful for forming new transform pairs, for simplifying the arithmetical work when the transform contains unwieldy factors, and for work with partial differential equations.

We first state the scale change theorem in (5.99) as follows, assuming as usual that $f(t)$ is Laplace transformable:

$$\mathscr{L}\left[f\left(\frac{t}{a}\right)\right] = aF(as) \tag{5.99}$$

If the t-plane variable is divided by the constant a, then both the s-plane variable and the entire s-transform are multiplied by the constant.

The proof of the theorem is relatively straightforward and begins by writing the definition of the Laplace transform, which is

$$\mathscr{L}[f(t)] = \int_0^\infty f(t)\varepsilon^{-st}\,dt = F(s) \tag{5.100}$$

Let us next divide $f(t)$ by the constant a, so that

$$\mathscr{L}\left[f\left(\frac{t}{a}\right)\right] = \int_0^\infty f\left(\frac{t}{a}\right)\varepsilon^{-st}\,dt \tag{5.101}$$

The right-hand integral can be slightly altered as

$$\mathscr{L}\left[f\left(\frac{t}{a}\right)\right] = \int_0^\infty f\left(\frac{t}{a}\right)\varepsilon^{-\frac{sat}{a}}\frac{dat}{a} \tag{5.102}$$

$$= a\int_0^\infty f\left(\frac{t}{a}\right)\varepsilon^{-as\left(\frac{t}{a}\right)}d\left(\frac{t}{a}\right) \tag{5.103}$$

In the past, when variations in t have been necessary, the time as measured by a τ-clock has proved useful. Let us therefore make the substitution

$$\frac{t}{a} = \tau, \quad \text{and} \quad as = z \tag{5.104}$$

Using these new variables, (5.103) becomes

$$\mathscr{L}\left[f\left(\frac{t}{a}\right)\right] = a\int_0^\infty f(\tau)\varepsilon^{-z\tau}\,d\tau \tag{5.105}$$

As far as the integration is concerned, one can as well measure time with a τ-clock as with a t-clock, and therefore the only thing which appears unusual in (5.105) is that the transform variable is z rather than s. It seems then that

$$\mathscr{L}\left[f\left(\frac{t}{a}\right)\right] = aF(z) \qquad (5.106)$$

but if z is replaced by its equivalent from (5.104),

$$\mathscr{L}\left[f\left(\frac{t}{a}\right)\right] = aF(as) \qquad (5.107)$$

which is a proof of the scale change theorem.

The theorem is easy to use. If an original $f(t)$ has a transform $F(s)$, then one can change the t to t/a merely by replacing each s in the function of s by (as), and multiplying the entire new s-plane function by a.

EXAMPLES

(1) If there exists the transform pair

$$\varepsilon^{-4t} \to \frac{1}{s+4} \qquad (5.108)$$

then for $a = 2$,

$$\varepsilon^{-4\left(\frac{t}{2}\right)} \to \frac{2}{2s+4} = \frac{1}{s+2} \qquad (5.109)$$

which is easy to see by inspection.

(2) If a more complicated transform pair is chosen, such as

$$\frac{t \sin \beta t}{2\beta} \to \frac{s}{(s^2 + \beta^2)^2} \qquad (5.110)$$

it would not be quite so easy to determine the function of s if t were to be replaced by some new value, say, $t/5$. Using the scale change theorem, however, one writes by inspection

$$\frac{t/5 \sin (\beta t/5)}{2\beta} \to \frac{5(5s)}{[(5s)^2 + \beta^2]^2} \qquad (5.111)$$

Because it is so easy to use, this theorem will find numerous applications in chapters to follow.

PROBLEMS

(1) Make free use of the table in Appendix III, and find the inverse Laplace transform of

$$F(s) = \frac{4}{(16s^2 + \beta^2)^2}$$

(2) Choose some function of s which has several symmetrical poles in the s-plane, and show that a radial contraction of the poles in the s-plane corresponds to a time expansion or stretching of the function in the t-domain in the same ratio. Discuss.

(3) Examine the pole–zero diagram, Fig. 5.24, which has two symmetrical poles on the $j\omega$-axis.

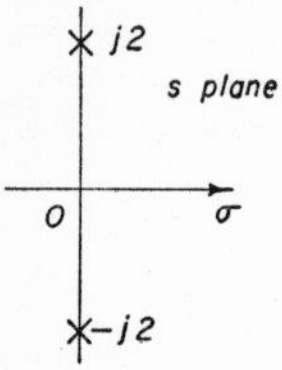

The function of s is

$$F(s) = \frac{1}{(s + j2)(s - j2)} = \frac{1}{s^2 + 4}$$

from which

$$f(t) = \frac{\sin 2t}{2}$$

Fig. 5.24

Suppose now that these two poles were moved uniformly toward the center of the s-plane, until they finally merged into a double pole at $s = 0$, whereupon the function would become

$$F(s) = \frac{1}{s^2}$$

Show that $f(t) = t$ by the use of the scale change theorem. Do not use the tables, or prior knowledge of what $f(t)$ would be.

5.11. Summary of chapter V

The objective of this chapter has been not merely to derive transforms, but to develop and illustrate more subtle relations between the s- and the t-domains. These various relations have been collected and discussed as theorems, and form what are called "operational transform pairs." Once one has done a certain amount of practice work with the theorems, their use becomes more and more automatic, and it will be found that complicated forms can be simplified greatly through a good understanding of the theorems presented here. One will find additional theorems in more advanced texts, but it is felt that the eight principle theorems here will suffice for all practical applications.

It is difficult, if not impossible, to assess any one of the theorems as being of more value, or more commonly used than any other. This depends entirely upon the problem at hand.

The linear s-plane translation theorem, dealing as it does with an exponential factor in the time domain, is certainly one of the more useful in electronics work, as we deal with decaying voltage waveforms, current discharges, attenuation, etc., almost every day.

The final and initial value theorems, although perhaps not quite so useful in an original analysis, nevertheless serve as guides for checking solutions, and in numerous cases allow a specific formula to be derived at a glance.

The real translation theorem begins an introduction into numerous problems concerning complex waveshapes. In fact this theorem, or concepts closely related to it, will be used in some way with almost every problem which involves other than sinusoidal voltages and currents.

The complex differentiation and integration theorems are of great value to extending and modifying tables of Laplace transforms, and also for increasing our general familiarity with operation in the time and complex frequency domains.

Although not in itself a theorem, the ideas on sectioning a function of time have been included as general subject matter, as these concepts are used throughout the structure of our electronics analyses.

The convolution theorem has been included to illustrate an entirely different way to take inverse Laplace transforms. This theorem may provide the only means of performing such inverse transformations if transcendental functions of s are included as factors. The convolution theorem also suggests a procedure for finding inverse transforms by graphical methods if the function of s cannot be handled analytically.

At this point, enough formal material has been covered to begin its application to network analysis. Many details and fine points will be brought out in the examination of the various circuits.

CHAPTER VI

NETWORK ANALYSIS BY MEANS OF THE LAPLACE TRANSFORMATION

6.1. Introduction

IT is usually agreed that most theories are of little worth unless they can be applied to promote or serve some useful purpose. One of the most desirable features of the Laplace transform is its ability to promote more general and detailed understanding of the basic nature of network analysis problems. It also serves in most practical ways to let us furnish answers to network problems where transient or non-sinusoidal waveshapes are involved.

Most technicians and many engineers have, through long use, come to regard the concept of reactance, as expressed by $2\pi f L$ or $1/2\pi f C$, as all that it was necessary to know about network impedances, especially if the j-operator was used to indicate "direction" of the R–L–C terms.

The concept of "reactance" served for most analytical work in the early days of electronics and radio. Then one dealt usually with d.c., or sinewaves. Today, however, square waves, pulses, triangles, sawteeth and a host of other exotic waveshapes are every bit as common in our daily experiences as are sinewaves. Yet through habit and long association with the term "reactance", one is sometimes taken by surprise upon realizing that the concept of reactance breaks down entirely, indeed is meaningless, when other than sinusoidal waveforms are being considered.

In this chapter, we shall work with newer and more general concepts of impedance, which will not depend on waveshape. These new concepts will permit much deeper insight into the true working of network analysis, and will serve as background for the chapter on the fundamentals of network synthesis to follow. This chapter will be concerned entirely with specific networks. We shall attempt to choose for each article a network which is commonly used in a particular instrument, electronic system or situation.

6.2. Writing network equations for multiple loop circuits

Let us review briefly the procedure usually employed to write the equations of a multiple loop network. The reader is assumed to be familiar with Kirchhoff's laws, the theory of determinants, mutual impedances, etc. Rather than use n-meshes, we will choose a three loop circuit of general impedances, as in Fig. 6.1, and the reader can extend the ideas to more loops by inspection.

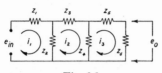

Fig. 6.1

From elementary work, using Maxwell's fictitious current notation, the reader will recall that the three loop equations are:

$$e_{IN} = z_{11}i_1 + z_{12}i_2 + z_{13}i_3 \qquad (6.1)$$

$$0 = z_{21}i_1 + z_{22}i_2 + z_{23}i_3 \qquad (6.2)$$

$$0 = z_{31}i_1 + z_{32}i_2 + z_{33}i_3 \qquad (6.3)$$

Here it is noted that z_{11} represents the self-impedance of loop 1, z_{12} is the common, or mutual impedance between loop 1 and loop 2, etc., i.e.

$$z_{11} = z_1 + z_2 \qquad (6.4)$$

$$z_{12} = -z_2 \qquad (6.5)$$

$$z_{13} = 0 \qquad (6.6)$$

$$z_{22} = z_2 + z_3 + z_4 \qquad (6.7)$$

$$z_{21} = -z_2 \qquad (6.8)$$

Note that since each element in Fig. 6.1 is labeled as a general impedance, it may actually be a resistor, inductor or condenser.

Having written the network equations in standard form, it is now possible to use them to solve for the various required quantities, such as input impedance, or output voltage. By way of further review, if it is desired to solve for input impedance of the network in Fig. 6.1, we first solve for current i_1, using determinants.

$$i_1 = \frac{\begin{vmatrix} e_{IN} & z_{12} & z_{13} \\ 0 & z_{22} & z_{23} \\ 0 & z_{32} & z_{33} \end{vmatrix}}{\begin{vmatrix} z_{11} & z_{12} & z_{13} \\ z_{21} & z_{22} & z_{23} \\ z_{31} & z_{32} & z_{33} \end{vmatrix}} \tag{6.9}$$

and expanding the numerator by minors

$$i_1 = \frac{e_{IN}\begin{vmatrix} z_{22} & z_{23} \\ z_{32} & z_{33} \end{vmatrix}}{\begin{vmatrix} z_{11} & z_{12} & z_{13} \\ z_{21} & z_{22} & z_{23} \\ z_{31} & z_{32} & z_{33} \end{vmatrix}} \tag{6.10}$$

At this point we can set up the ratio for the input impedance z_{IN} by inspection, as

$$z_{IN} = \frac{e_{IN}}{i_1} = \frac{\begin{vmatrix} z_{11} & z_{12} & z_{13} \\ z_{21} & z_{22} & z_{23} \\ z_{31} & z_{32} & z_{33} \end{vmatrix}}{\begin{vmatrix} z_{22} & z_{23} \\ z_{32} & z_{33} \end{vmatrix}} \tag{6.11}$$

and it is then only necessary to insert the algebraic or numerical values of the impedances into (6.11) to have the input impedance.

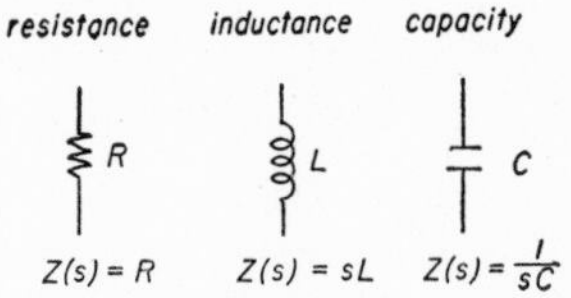

resistance   inductance   capacity

R L C

$Z(s) = R$ $Z(s) = sL$ $Z(s) = \frac{1}{sC}$

Fig. 6.2

It is necessary at this point to review art. 4.2, where the impedance of resistors, inductors and condensers was developed as a function of s. This information is shown in Fig. 6.2.

In equations (6.1), (6.2) and (6.3), i_1 goes at once into $I(s)$, and e_{IN} becomes $E_{\mathrm{IN}}(s)$, thus these equations become

$$E_{\mathrm{IN}}(s) = Z_{11}(s)I_1(s) + Z_{12}(s)I_2(s) + Z_{13}(s)I_3(s) \qquad (6.12)$$

$$0 = Z_{21}(s)I_1(s) + Z_{22}(s)I_2(s) + Z_{23}(s)I_3(s) \qquad (6.13)$$

$$0 = Z_{31}(s)I_1(s) + Z_{32}(s)I_2(s) + Z_{33}(s)I_3(s) \qquad (6.14)$$

where the use of the lower case letters in the time world, and capital letters in the s-domain is consistent with our previous usage.

Note that the $Z(s)$ terms and $I(s)$ terms are usually written by inspection or direct conversion, but that the $E_{\mathrm{IN}}(s)$ usually requires that a transformation from $e_{\mathrm{IN}}(t)$ be effected.

Having defined our standard way of writing the network equations in terms of s or t, we now begin the study of typical network problems.

6.3. Relay damping problems

As a relatively simple problem to illustrate the use of the s-plane, and its pole–zero diagram, let us consider Fig. 6.3, where a relay L

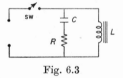

Fig. 6.3

is to be damped in such a manner that it will appear non-oscillatory to the contact points, thereby minimizing arcing. Someone has suggested that a series R–C circuit connected directly across the relay may do the job.

The problem to be analyzed then, is whether an R–C connection across L can make the entire combination appear to be non-oscillatory to the switch contacts.

Let us examine Fig. 6.4, where we show the impedance of each component as a function of s. By the usual rule of combining such a series–parallel impedance configuration, we have

$$Z_{\mathrm{IN}}(s) = \frac{\left(R + \dfrac{1}{sC}\right) \cdot sL}{\left(R + \dfrac{1}{sC}\right) + sL} \qquad (6.15)$$

or

$$Z_{\text{IN}}(s) = \frac{RLs + \dfrac{L}{C}}{R + \dfrac{1}{sC} + sL} \tag{6.16}$$

Clearing of fractions by multiplying both numerator and denominator by sC gives

$$Z_{\text{IN}}(s) = \frac{RLCs^2 + Ls}{LCs^2 + RCs + 1} \tag{6.17}$$

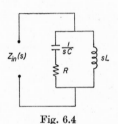

Fig. 6.4

Let us now draw the pole–zero diagram of this function of s. The zeros can be found by setting the numerator equal to 0.

$$s(RLCs + L) = 0 \tag{6.18}$$

from which the zeros are

$$\left. \begin{aligned} s &= 0 \\ s &= -\frac{1}{RC} \end{aligned} \right\} \tag{6.19}$$

The poles can be found by setting the denominator of (6.17) equal to 0.

$$LCs^2 + RCs + 1 = 0 \tag{6.20}$$

and by the use of the quadratic formula, the two poles are

$$\left. \begin{aligned} s &= \frac{-RC + \sqrt{(R^2C^2 - 4LC)}}{2LC} \\ s &= \frac{-RC - \sqrt{(R^2C^2 - 4LC)}}{2LC} \end{aligned} \right\} \tag{6.21}$$

Equation (6.21) can be manipulated slightly to give

$$\left.\begin{aligned} s &= -\frac{R}{2L} + \sqrt{\left(\frac{R^2}{4L^2} - \frac{1}{LC}\right)} \\ s &= -\frac{R}{2L} - \sqrt{\left(\frac{R^2}{4L^2} - \frac{1}{LC}\right)} \end{aligned}\right\} \tag{6.22}$$

A j may be removed from the radical if the signs are reversed inside, thus

$$s = -\frac{R}{2L} \pm j\sqrt{\left(\frac{1}{LC} - \frac{R^2}{4L^2}\right)} \tag{6.23}$$

The complete pole–zero diagram now appears as in Fig. 6.5.

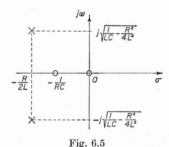

Fig. 6.5

We now come to the realization that the circuit of Fig. 6.3 (or 6.4) is completely described by the pole–zero diagram. That is, this pole–zero diagram gives all the information about the input impedance $Z_{IN}(s)$. In fact, having nothing more than the pole–zero diagram of Fig. 6.5, one could form the proper factors and recombine them to get (6.17). This is obvious, since the diagram was developed from (6.17) in the first place.

Now let us return to the problem at hand, that of making this total impedance appear non-oscillatory so that there will be minimum arcing at the contact points.

Examining the pole-zero diagram of $Z_{IN}(s)$, it is easily seen that the function $Z_{IN}(s)$ can be made non-oscillatory by reducing the $j\omega$-component of the pole locations to 0, i.e. let us move both poles toward each other until they are both on the σ-axis.

All that we have to do to move the poles so, is to let their j-components become 0, that is,

$$\sqrt{\left(\frac{1}{LC} - \frac{R^2}{4L^2}\right)} = 0 \qquad (6.24)$$

or

$$\frac{1}{LC} = \frac{R^2}{4L^2} \qquad (6.25)$$

or

$$R = 2\sqrt{\left(\frac{L}{C}\right)} \qquad (6.26)$$

Knowing the value L of the relay, and having derived (6.26) from the pole–zero diagram, we can now choose a suitable value of C and use the required value of R called for in (6.26). Since both poles now rest on the σ-axis, there are no j frequency components, and the circuit is thus completely non-oscillatory as required.

PROBLEM. Derive the relations between the parameters shown in Fig. 6.6, draw the pole–zero diagram, and show values of R and C which will make the circuit non-oscillatory.

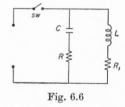

Fig. 6.6

6.4. The Wien-bridge oscillator

Oscillators of the Wien-bridge type are often used when it is necessary to generate frequencies of the order of from 1 c/s to 1 Mc/s. This wide range, some six orders of magnitude, together with the fact that this type of oscillator is by far the most commonly used in this range, regardless of cost, indicates that every electronics engineer should be thoroughly familiar with its operation.

Fig. 6.7 shows the essential features of the Wien-bridge oscillator. Actually, the series–parallel R–C arms shown represent only one-half the bridge circuit. The other half consists of a combination linear and non-linear negative feedback circuit whose only function is to automatically adjust the amplifier gain to the precise value required.

In this article we shall be concerned with an analysis of the frequency determining network, and the gain and phase requirements of the amplifier. Let us examine the R–C network as shown in Fig. 6.8.

In this network, the voltage e_0 goes to the amplifier input, while the amplifier output feeds voltage back into the network input.

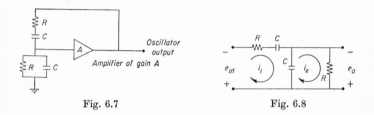

Fig. 6.7   Fig. 6.8

Using the customary notation, we now write the Kirchhoff's law equations around both loops. We express all voltages, currents and impedances as functions of s.

$$E_{\text{IN}}(s) = \left(R + \frac{2}{sC} \right) I_1(s) - \frac{1}{sC} I_2(s) \qquad (6.27)$$

$$0 = - \frac{1}{sC} I_1(s) + \left(R + \frac{1}{sC} \right) I_2(s) \qquad (6.28)$$

The next step indicated is to solve this set of equations for $I_2(s)$, as follows:

$$I_2(s) = \frac{\begin{vmatrix} \left(R + \dfrac{2}{sC} \right) & E_{\text{IN}}(s) \\[2mm] - \dfrac{1}{sC} & 0 \end{vmatrix}}{\begin{vmatrix} \left(R + \dfrac{2}{sC} \right) & - \dfrac{1}{sC} \\[2mm] - \dfrac{1}{sC} & \left(R + \dfrac{1}{sC} \right) \end{vmatrix}} \qquad (6.29)$$

The determinants are now expanded and like terms combined to give

$$I_2(s) = \frac{E_{\text{IN}}(s) \cdot \dfrac{1}{sC}}{R^2 + \dfrac{3R}{sC} + \dfrac{1}{s^2C^2}} \qquad (6.30)$$

which is cleared of fractions by multiplying both numerator and denominator by s^2C^2

$$I_2(s) = \frac{E_{\text{IN}}(s)sC}{R^2C^2s^2 + 3RCs + 1} \qquad (6.31)$$

This value for $I_2(s)$ can now be multiplied by R to obtain the output voltage $E_0(s)$, thus

$$E_0(s) = \frac{E_{\text{IN}}(s)RCs}{R^2C^2s^2 + 3RCs + 1} \qquad (6.32)$$

We are now in a position to solve for the transfer function very easily (see art. 4.1).

$$Z_T(s) = \frac{E_0(s)}{E_{\text{IN}}(s)} = \frac{RCs}{R^2C^2s^2 + 3RCs + 1} \qquad (6.33)$$

Equation (6.33) is the transfer function of the network shown in Fig. 6.8. It contains all the information that we need to know about both frequency and amplitude.

Both poles of (6.33) lie on the negative σ-axis in the s-plane, with no $j\omega$-components present. If we were to take the inverse Laplace transform of this function we would get a pair of exponentially decreasing time functions. Thus the pole locations should indicate that this network alone can have no oscillatory properties. It is therefore incorrect to compare it in any way with similarly arranged L–C networks which actually can oscillate alone.

To make this R–C network oscillate, we can make up for all losses by means of the amplifier of gain A, setting the tandem combination for the network and amplifier equal to unity, i.e.

$$Z_T(s) \cdot A = 1 \qquad (6.34)$$

or

$$RCsA = R^2C^2s^2 + 3RCs + 1 \qquad (6.35)$$

or

$$R^2C^2s^2 + RCs(3 - A) + 1 = 0 \qquad (6.36)$$

Now by inspection of (6.36) it is found that when the amplifier has zero phase shift, and when

$$A = 3 \tag{6.37}$$

then

$$R^2C^2s^2 = -1 \tag{6.38}$$

which makes

$$s^2 = -\frac{1}{R^2C^2} \tag{6.39}$$

or

$$s = \pm \frac{j}{RC} \tag{6.40}$$

But the general definition of s is

$$s = \sigma + j\omega = \frac{j}{RC} \tag{6.41}$$

and when we equate real terms to real terms and imaginary to imaginary, it is found that

$$\sigma = 0 \tag{6.42}$$

$$\omega = \frac{1}{RC} \tag{6.43}$$

or, since $\omega = 2\pi f$,

$$f = \frac{1}{2\pi RC} \tag{6.44}$$

Summarizing then, we observe that when the amplifier gain was set at 3 (6.37) and combined with the network of Fig. 6.8, the net result was to create a new function with new poles at $\pm 1/RC$ on the $j\omega$-axis (6.40), as in Fig. 6.9.

These poles have no σ-component, and hence the inverse transform, or oscillator output is

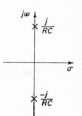

Fig. 6.9

$$e_0(t) \simeq \sin\left(\frac{t}{RC}\right) = \sin \omega t \tag{6.45}$$

Equation (6.45) indicates that the output waveshape is a pure sinewave, with no distortion. Equations (6.37) and (6.44) give the results which should be retained for actual design use.

This particular method of working with the transfer function was used to give the reader more practice in reasoning in the s-plane alone. A practice problem will now bring out an alternate method.

PROBLEM

(1) Write the transfer function (6.33) upside down, as

$$\frac{E_{IN}(s)}{E_0(s)} = \frac{R^2C^2s^2 + 3RCs + 1}{RCs} \tag{6.46}$$

Substitute $j\omega$ for s throughout, and observe that to have zero phase shift between output and input, the j-term must be set to zero. Use this fact to solve for frequency of oscillation. Find the required oscillator gain from the remaining real part of (6.46).

(2) Using the previous results of this article, give the output voltage (magnitude), and state what the phase shift would be for the network shown in Fig. 6.10. Assume no loading on the output.

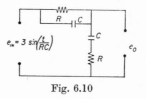

Fig. 6.10

6.5 A phase-shift oscillator

The Wien-bridge oscillator discussed in the previous article used an R–C network which had zero phase shift, together with an amplifier whose gain was 3 and whose phase shift was also zero. The zero phase shift requirement ordinarily would require two amplifying stages in cascade. The present objective is to discuss another

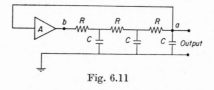

Fig. 6.11

network which will shift phase by 180° at the oscillating frequency, and which will therefore require only a single stage, that is, one which has an additional 180° of phase shift.

Let us examine Fig. 6.11, which shows a three-section R–C network, together with an amplifier stage of gain A. The oscillator output is assumed to be unloaded, so that a cathode follower or some other type of buffer stage must be used.

The reason for taking the output from the point a rather than the point b will be apparent shortly. The three-section network to be

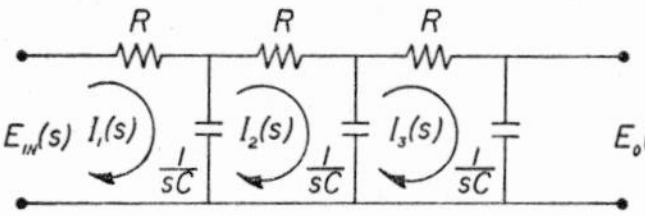

Fig. 6.12

analyzed is redrawn in Fig. 6.12, where each impedance is given as a function of s. The three network equations are

$$E_{\text{IN}}(s) = \left(R + \frac{1}{sC} \right) I_1(s) - \frac{1}{sC} I_2(s) + 0I_3(s) \qquad (6.47)$$

$$0 = -\frac{1}{sC} I_1(s) + \left(R + \frac{2}{sC} \right) I_2(s) - \frac{1}{sC} I_3(s) \qquad (6.48)$$

$$0 = 0I_1(s) - \frac{1}{sC} I_2(s) + \left(R + \frac{2}{sC} \right) I_3(s) \qquad (6.49)$$

It is suggested at this point that the reader perform the algebra necessary to solve for $I_3(s)$, then multiply this by the final impedance in Fig. 6.12, which is $1/sC$, and simplify to obtain the transfer function, which is then shown to be

$$Z_T(s) = \frac{1}{R^3 C^3 s^3 + 5R^2 C^2 s^2 + 6RCs + 1} \qquad (6.50)$$

Every electronics engineer should derive this result at least once, to satisfy himself that it is correct, straightforward, and that he can do it. After having once gone through the tedious job of obtaining $Z_T(s)$ for this network, he can thereafter look up the transfer function in Appendix I, which is a table of transfer functions of networks such as this one.

It is now most conventional and convenient to invert the transfer function, to obtain

$$\frac{E_{\text{IN}}}{E_0}(s) = 1 + 5R^2 C^2 s^2 + 6RCs + R^3 C^3 s^3 \qquad (6.51)$$

The variable s can then be replaced by its imaginary component $j\omega$ (we assume for the moment that the input is a sine wave), this gives

$$\frac{e_{IN}}{e_0} = 1 - 5R^2C^2\omega^2 + j(6RC\omega - R^3C^3\omega^3) \qquad (6.52)$$

Now for the input and output voltages to be displaced 180° in phase, the imaginary term must be exactly zero, thus

$$6RC\omega - R^3C^3\omega^3 = 0 \qquad (6.53)$$

or, solving for ω

$$\omega = \frac{\sqrt{6}}{RC} \qquad (6.54)$$

from which

$$f = \frac{\sqrt{6}}{2\pi RC} \qquad (6.55)$$

Equation (6.55) thus gives the frequency of oscillation in terms of R and C. After letting the j-term in (6.52) become zero, there remains

$$\frac{e_{IN}}{e_0} = 1 - 5R^2C^2\omega^2 \qquad (6.56)$$

If we square (6.54) we have

$$\omega^2 = \frac{6}{R^2C^2} \qquad (6.57)$$

which can be substituted into (6.56) to give

$$\frac{e_{IN}}{e_0} = 1 - \frac{5R^2C^2 \cdot 6}{R^2C^2} \qquad (6.58)$$

or

$$\frac{e_{IN}}{e_0} = -29 \qquad (6.59)$$

Equation (6.59) thus shows that there is a 29 to 1 voltage reduction in the network, and that the amplifier A must have exactly this gain A for the oscillator to be successful. Equations (6.59) and (6.55) are the key results to be retained from this analysis. The minus sign in (6.59) shows that there is indeed a 180° phase shift between e_{IN} and e_0.

One could interchange the R and C values in Fig. 6.12, and the circuit operation would be unchanged except that the formula for frequency would be

$$f = \frac{1}{2\pi\sqrt{(6)}RC} \tag{6.60}$$

The gain would still have to be 29.

To be successful as an oscillator, there must be some non-linearity in the amplifier which will standardize the gain at precisely 29. This non-linear quantity, however introduced, will create some distortion in the otherwise pure sinewave output. We will show in the next article that the network of Fig. 6.12 will act as a low-pass filter, greatly attenuating any harmonics which may occur as a result of the non-linearity. Interchanging R and C would allow proper oscillator action, but would accentuate any harmonic distortion. These same considerations make it desirable to take the output from the network, where distortion is small, rather than from the amplifier output, where the distortion is not only present, but amplified twenty-nine times.

This type of phase-shift oscillator can be made exceptionally stable with respect to B plus variations, temperature and tube parameter changes. With good attention to design it represents one of the most simple and satisfactory oscillators possible.

6.6. Harmonic Discrimination in a three-section phase shift oscillator

In the phase-shift oscillator described in the last article, probably the simplest form of non-linearity is clipping in the vacuum tube amplifier. Such clipping is usually symmetrical, and thus will create third harmonics (and higher odd harmonics) as distortion. Fortunately, however, the network itself (Fig. 6.12) acts as a low-pass filter to remove a large part of any such distortion. We should now determine the ratio of third harmonic reduction to fundamental signal reduction. Fifth and higher order harmonics will usually not be strong enough to prove troublesome.

Let us begin with the network input to output voltage ratio already given by (6.52)

$$\frac{e_{\mathrm{IN}}}{e_0} = 1 - 5R^2C^2\omega^2 + j(6RC\omega - R^3C^3\omega^3) \tag{6.61}$$

At the fundamental frequency ω_0, the j-term is equal to zero, from which

$$\omega_0 = \frac{\sqrt{6}}{RC} \tag{6.62}$$

Now the various harmonic frequencies ω are

$$\omega = n\omega_0 = \frac{n\sqrt{6}}{RC} \tag{6.63}$$

so that (6.61) becomes

$$\frac{e_{IN}}{e_0} = 1 - 5n^2 6 + j(6^{\frac{3}{2}}n - 6^{\frac{3}{2}}n^3) \tag{6.64}$$

or

$$\frac{e_{IN}}{e_0} = 1 - 30n^2 + j6^{\frac{3}{2}}(n - n^3) \tag{6.65}$$

As an absolute magnitude, (6.65) can be written as

$$\left| \frac{e_{IN}}{e_0} \right| = \sqrt{\{(1 - 30n^2)^2 + 6^3(n - n^3)^2\}} \tag{6.66}$$

or

$$\left| \frac{e_{IN}}{e_0} \right| = \sqrt{(216n^6 + 468n^4 + 156n^2 + 1)} \tag{6.67}$$

Considering (6.63) and (6.67), when $n = 1$, we have for the fundamental

$$\left| \frac{e_{IN}}{e_0} \right| = \sqrt{(216 + 468 + 156 + 1)} = 29 \tag{6.68}$$

A result which we recall from the last article.

Now for the third harmonic, $n = 3$, and (6.67) gives

$$\left| \frac{e_{IN}}{e_0} \right| = 444 \tag{6.69}$$

Assume the highly unlikely case where the fundamental and the third harmonic inputs are identical in magnitude. The actual reduction is

$$\frac{n_3}{n_1} = \frac{444}{29} = 15.3 \text{ to } 1 \tag{6.70}$$

which in itself would be relatively good discrimination against the third harmonic. Let us now assume that our worst possible case could occur if the input to the network should become a square wave. If this should happen, the third harmonic would be one-third the amplitude of the fundamental, and the discrimination would be

$$\frac{444 \times 3}{29} \simeq 46 \text{ to } 1 \tag{6.71}$$

In practical oscillators, the non-linearity necessary to stabilize the gain at exactly 29 would be nowhere near enough to even approach square wave clipping, thus we can see that the third harmonic distortion for this oscillator can easily be only a very small fraction of 1%.

6.7. The R–C cathode follower oscillator

The R–C oscillator to be discussed in this article was patented some years ago by the writer,* and is somewhat unusual in that no voltage amplification is required. Most oscillators require a cathode follower or some other type of isolation between the actual oscillating network and the load. If a cathode follower is employed to achieve

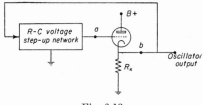

Fig. 6.13

a low output impedance for driving heavy loads, it seems only logical to use it to drive the R–C network as well, thus eliminating one tube. The general arrangement is shown in Fig. 6.13, which the writer has named the "R–C cathode follower oscillator".

It is required that no inductance be used in the frequency determining network, only resistance and capacity are allowed. One observes that if a voltage is applied to the grid of the cathode follower in Fig. 6.13, that the same voltage, with no change in phase, will appear at the cathode, slightly reduced in amplitude. Now if this cathode follower is to be made to oscillate, it will be necessary to take the output voltage from the cathode, feed it through some

* *Amer. Pat.* 2769088.

type of voltage step-up device, having no phase shift, and re-apply it to the grid.

An easy way to provide the required voltage step-up would be to use a transformer or a resonant tuned circuit, but since no inductance is permitted, it is necessary to choose a network which employs only resistance and capacity.

Now the writer has heard a great many engineers express the opinion that one cannot step up a voltage with a network which has only R and C elements. The reader can easily show that there is no basis for such thinking, by analyzing the network shown in Fig. 6.14.

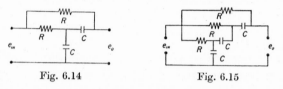

Fig. 6.14   Fig. 6.15

It will be found upon analysis that the output voltage e_0 can exceed the input voltage considerably. Unfortunately, although the network in Fig. 6.14 has adequate voltage step-up, it is not suitable for use as the network required in Fig. 6.13 because the over-all phase shift cannot be made zero.

The slightly more involved network shown in Fig. 6.15 meets both the voltage step-up and the zero phase shift requirements, and is used in the circuit as the basis for the R–C cathode follower oscillator. If all R's and all C's are identical, it will be found that for a frequency

$$f = \frac{1}{2\pi\sqrt{(6)}RC} \tag{6.72}$$

the phase shift will be zero, and the voltage step-up will be adequate so that this network can be used in Fig. 6.13 to allow the cathode follower to oscillate. Since the output of the cathode follower is at a very low impedance, it is not ordinarily necessary to provide further isolation between oscillator and load. For additional practice in determining transfer functions, the reader is urged to work the following three problems.

PROBLEMS

(1) Show graphically that the network in Fig. 6.14 can have a voltage step-up greater than unity. Estimate the voltage gain, and phase shift for the condition $R = X_c$.

(2) Analyze the network of Fig. 6.15 and determine its transfer function.

Ans. $$Z_T(s) = \frac{1 + 5RCs + 6R^2C^2s^2}{1 + 5RCs + 6R^2C^2s^2 + R^3C^3s^3}$$

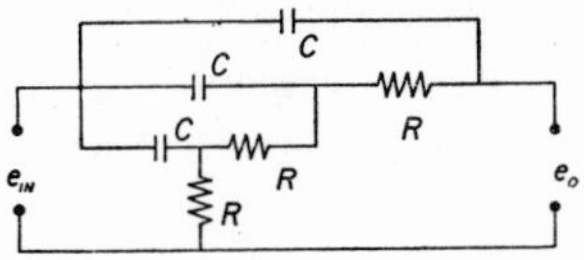

Fig. 6.16

(3) Consider the voltage step-up network of Fig. 6.16. Show that the transfer function is

$$Z_T(s) = \frac{6RCs + 5R^2C^2s^2 + R^3C^3s^3}{1 + 6RCs + 5R^2C^2s^2 + R^3C^3s^3}$$

Show further that when the complex frequency s is

$$s = \frac{j\sqrt{6}}{RC}$$

that the phase shift is zero. Find the exact voltage gain for this value of s. (*Note*. The gain for this circuit is only a few per cent.)

6.8. R–C oscillator, single section variable capacity

The entire purpose of the Laplace transformation is to assist in the solution of problems, and the electronics engineer is regularly concerned with the problems of solving new and unusual networks. It is therefore felt necessary to include a discussion of at least one "non-standard" oscillator network problem for additional practice with transfer functions.

The oscillators covered earlier can be either fixed or variable frequency types. If the frequency is to be variable, one must resort to double or triple-section variable condensers for tuning. It would certainly be desirable if one could accomplish the same results with only a single-section variable condenser. That such is possible, at least in some cases, is brought out in the discussion of the oscillator network in Fig. 6.17. This network will be recognized as similar to that used in the Wien-bridge oscillator already considered. We expect therefore, that an amplifier of zero phase shift, and of gain A, where

$$A = \frac{e_{\text{IN}}}{e_0}$$

will be required as the active element.

In the network of Fig. 6.17, the goal is to use only a single variable capacity C. The condenser C_1 is to remain fixed. Another obvious requirement is that the magnitude of the network gain (e_0/e_{IN})

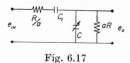

Fig. 6.17

remain relatively constant over the entire frequency range, otherwise the feedback amplifier gain will have to be continuously varied, which is neither practical nor desirable.

The amplifier employed can be either a vacuum tube or transistor device. If a transistor amplifier is used, the input impedance will be finite and can be included as a portion of aR. If the amplifier input value is $R_{\text{IN}} \, \Omega$ (ohms), then the increased gain A_1 will be

$$A_1 = \frac{aR}{R_{\text{IN}}} \cdot \frac{e_{\text{IN}}}{e_0} \tag{6.73}$$

Realizing that such is the case, let us ignore loading at this time, and proceed to analyze the network as shown.

The first step in this sort of analysis is, as usual, to write the network equations and then solve for the transfer function. The reader should do so at this point and show that (6.74) is correct.

$$Z_T(s) = \frac{saRC_1}{s^2 R^2 CC_1 + sR(Ca + C_1 a + C_1/a) + 1} \tag{6.74}$$

As has been done before, the reader can now determine $z(\omega)$ by substituting $j\omega$ for each s in (6.74). The resulting equation takes the form

$$\frac{e_{\text{IN}}}{e_0} = \left(1 + \frac{1}{a^2} + \frac{C}{C_1}\right) + j\left(\frac{\omega CR}{a} - \frac{1}{\omega aRC_1}\right) \tag{6.75}$$

For zero phase shift, the imaginary term must be set to zero, which gives us information about the frequency, i.e.

$$\left(\frac{\omega C R}{a} - \frac{1}{\omega a R C_1}\right) = 0 \qquad (6.76)$$

from which

$$f = \frac{1}{2\pi R\sqrt{(CC_1)}} \qquad (6.77)$$

From (6.77) we note that if C_1 is a constant value, while C is the variable, we can lump all of the constants together as k and write

$$f = \frac{k}{R\sqrt{C}} \qquad (6.78)$$

Provided that the network is otherwise satisfactory as a basis for the oscillator, this informs us that the frequency of oscillation is inversely proportional to the square root of the tuning capacity C. This recalls a similar formula for resonance in a parallel L–C circuit, which is

$$f = \frac{1}{2\pi\sqrt{(LC)}} \qquad (6.79)$$

but the two circuits have nothing in common.

Assuming zero phase shift, the real part of (6.75) becomes

$$\frac{e_{\text{IN}}}{e_0} = 1 + \frac{1}{a^2} + \frac{C}{C_1} \qquad (6.80)$$

Now let us choose C_1, the fixed capacity, to be much larger than C. Then (6.80) becomes

$$\frac{e_{\text{IN}}}{e_0} = 1 + \frac{1}{a^2} \qquad (6.81)$$

Such a choice of C_1 will allow the oscillator gain to remain essentially constant over the band. It is quite likely that we shall be using a transistor input stage, and the required total amplifier gain was given for that case by (6.73)

$$A_1 = \frac{aR}{R_{\text{IN}}} \cdot \frac{e_{\text{IN}}}{e_0} \qquad (6.82)$$

where $A_1 = $ over-all amplifier gain

$R_{\text{IN}} = $ amplifier input resistance

$\left(\dfrac{e_{\text{IN}}}{e_0}\right) = $ network loss

Substituting (6.81) into (6.82) gives

$$A_1 = \frac{aR}{R_{\text{IN}}} \cdot \left(1 + \frac{1}{a^2}\right) \tag{6.83}$$

or

$$A_1 \propto a + \frac{1}{a} \tag{6.84}$$

Differentiating A_1 gives

$$\frac{dA_1}{da} = 1 - \frac{1}{a^2} \tag{6.85}$$

and setting to zero,

$$1 - \frac{1}{a^2} = 0 \tag{6.86}$$

which shows that when

$$a = 1 \tag{6.87}$$

the minimum amplifier gain is needed.

If there is no loading on the network, a suitable value for a can be chosen by inspection from (6.81). For the assumed transistor amplifier, we will require an optimum gain of 2, along with zero phase shift.

This sort of problem, with all its ramifications, is typical of an everyday network analysis which the engineer could be called upon to make at any time.

6.9. Active integrating and differentiating networks

We shall shortly become involved in filters, and an introduction to network synthesis. The two circuits to be discussed in this article are

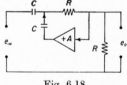

Fig. 6.18

special cases of such active networks. They have long been used where it is necessary to perform integration or to differentiate signals with greater flexibility and accuracy than can be done with simple R–C passive elements. (Consider the circuit shown in Fig. 6.18.)

For purposes of analysis, it is convenient to replace the amplifier of gain A by a voltage source Ae_0, so that the new circuit will appear as in Fig. 6.19.

As usual, the first step is to write the network equations, which in this case are:

$$\frac{2}{sC}\,i_1 - \frac{1}{sC}\,i_2 = e_{\text{IN}} - Ae_0 \qquad (6.88)$$

$$-\frac{1}{sC}\,i_1 + \left(2R + \frac{1}{sC}\right) i_2 = Ae_0 \qquad (6.89)$$

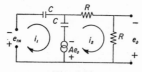

Fig. 6.19

Note that because of the feedback, a voltage source appears in loop 2, so that the equation about loop 2 is not zero, as has been the case in previous articles. The next step in the orderly process of deriving the transfer function is to solve for i_2. (Note also that it does not matter in cases such as these whether we write the i and e as functions of s or t, since we plan to form a ratio. The ratio will be a function of s in either case.)

$$i_2 = \frac{\dfrac{e_{\text{IN}}}{sC} - \dfrac{Ae_0}{sC} + \dfrac{2Ae_0}{sC}}{\dfrac{4R}{sC} + \dfrac{2}{s^2C^2} - \dfrac{1}{s^2C^2}} \qquad (6.90)$$

and the output voltage is this value multiplied by R.

$$e_0 = \frac{\dfrac{e_{\text{IN}}R}{sC} + \dfrac{Ae_0R}{sC}}{\dfrac{4R}{sC} + \dfrac{1}{s^2C^2}} \qquad (6.91)$$

$$e_0 = \frac{e_{\text{IN}}R + ARe_0}{4R + \dfrac{1}{sC}} \qquad (6.92)$$

or

$$4Re_0 + \frac{e_0}{sC} - ARe_0 = Re_{\text{IN}} \tag{6.93}$$

so that

$$\frac{e_0}{e_{\text{IN}}} = \frac{R}{4R + 1/sC - AR} \tag{6.94}$$

This may be put into the form

$$Z_T(s) = \frac{RCs}{1 + RCs(4 - A)} \tag{6.95}$$

Now let us set the gain of the feedback amplifier to exactly 4. The amplifier is to have zero phase shift so that gain will be plus rather than minus. Equation (6.95) then becomes

$$Z_T(s) = RCs \tag{6.96}$$

Let us further stipulate that the product $RC = 1$. We then have

$$Z_T(s) = s \tag{6.97}$$

Equation (6.97) thus indicates that for the imposed conditions, $RC = 1$; $A = +4$, that the transfer function of this network is the perfect derivative operator s. Or, as far as time functions are concerned,

$$e_0 = \frac{de_{\text{IN}}}{dt} \tag{6.98}$$

We see that within the frequency range and output limits of the amplifier, perfect differentiation can be performed. Also, the reader who is familiar with operational amplifiers connected as differentiators, will note that whereas the process discussed here requires a gain of exactly 4, the technique using operational amplifiers requires infinite, or, in practice, very large gains. The low gain of this circuit makes it possible to use enormous amounts of feedback to stabilize the gain at exactly the required value of 4.

PROBLEM. Using the same technique, step by step, as has been discussed here, analyze the circuit in Fig. 6.20.

Show that the transfer function of this circuit is

$$Z_T(s) = \frac{1}{s} \tag{6.99}$$

This result shows that within the frequency and amplitude limitations of the amplifier, that the circuit performs perfect integration such that

$$e_0 = \int_0^t e_{\mathrm{IN}}(t) \, dt \tag{6.100}$$

These two useful circuits are merely special cases of general active ladder networks which will be covered in detail later in the text.

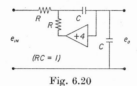

Fig. 6.20

6.10. Operational amplifiers

The last article discussed integration and differentiation through the process of using an amplifier of low gain, together with the appropriate network. Here we shall discuss briefly a more common method of doing the same job.

Consider the circuit shown in Fig. 6.21. If we assume that the amplifier presents no load to the voltage e_2, then e_2 represents a

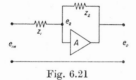

Fig. 6.21

single unknown voltage node, and we may write a single nodal equation to represent the circuit operation, which is

$$\frac{(e_2 - e_{\mathrm{IN}})}{Z_1} + \frac{(e_2 - e_0)}{Z_2} = 0 \tag{6.101}$$

Now e_2 is seen by inspection to be

$$e_2 = \frac{e_0}{A} \tag{6.102}$$

and placing this into (6.101) gives

$$\frac{(e_0/A - e_{\mathrm{IN}})}{Z_1} + \frac{(e_0/A - e_0)}{Z_2} = 0 \tag{6.103}$$

or

$$\frac{e_0}{AZ_1} - \frac{e_{IN}}{Z_1} + \frac{e_0}{AZ_2} - \frac{e_0}{Z_2} = 0 \qquad (6.104)$$

from which

$$\frac{e_0}{e_{IN}} = \frac{1}{1/A + Z_1/AZ_2 - Z_1/Z_2} \qquad (6.105)$$

Now observe that if the gain A is made very large, ideally approaching infinity, the first two denominator terms drop out, and if Z_1 and Z_2 are given as functions of s; we can write the transfer function of Fig. 6.21 as

$$Z_T(s) = -\frac{Z_2(s)}{Z_1(s)} \qquad (6.106)$$

If it is desired to perform integration with this network, one can choose

$$Z_1(s) = \frac{1}{sC}; \qquad Z_2(s) = R \qquad (6.107)$$

whereupon the transfer function becomes

$$Z_T(s) = -\frac{R}{sC} \qquad (6.108)$$

and we see that the transfer function is proportional to the integral operator $1/s$. Also, the proportionality constant R/C can easily be much greater than unity, thus giving amplification as well.

Should one choose to use the circuit as a differentiating network, the conditions

$$Z_1(s) = R; \qquad Z_2(s) = sL \qquad (6.109)$$

will provide an over-all transfer function

$$Z_T(s) = -\frac{Ls}{R} \qquad (6.110)$$

It is to be noted, however, first that it will be difficult in practice to make the ratio L/R greater than unity, and second that since it is very difficult to construct high-Q inductances, the quality of the differentiation will suffer. Amplifier A must be of the inverting type.

PROBLEM. If the amplifier should be a transistor device, the input impedance would be finite, and we could not assume zero loading at the point e_2 in Fig. 6.21. Showing a third impedance, Z_3, from this point to ground, derive the transfer function.

ANS. $$Z_T(s) = \frac{1}{1/A - Z_1/Z_2 + Z_1/AZ_2 + Z_1/AZ_3} \qquad (6.111)$$

6.11. Single section low-pass R–C filter

In this article we shall discuss the fundamental properties of a single section low-pass R–C filter. This is almost the simplest type of electrical filter which can be built, yet several characteristics of the single, double, and triple section R–C filters are not widely known.

Let us examine the simple network in Fig. 6.22. The transfer function of this network can easily be shown to be

$$Z_T(s) = \frac{1}{1 + RCs} \qquad (6.112)$$

or, if we replace s by $j\omega$,

$$Z_T(s) = \frac{1}{1 + jRC\omega} \qquad (6.113)$$

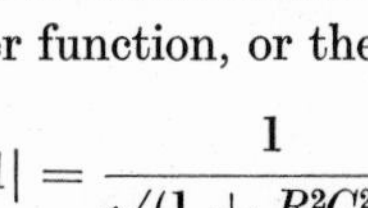

Fig. 6.22

Assume that the input to the network is unity, then the absolute magnitude of the transfer function, or the gain, becomes:

$$|A| = \frac{1}{\sqrt{(1 + R^2C^2\omega^2)}} \qquad (6.114)$$

It is customary to refer to the upper cut-off frequency as the "half power point", the "3 dB down point", or the frequency where the gain is down to $1/\sqrt{2}$ times the low frequency gain. Therefore, if the cut-off frequency is denoted by ω_0, (6.114) gives

$$\frac{1}{\sqrt{2}} = \frac{1}{\sqrt{(1 + R^2C^2\omega_0^2)}} \qquad (6.115)$$

and this can be solved to give

$$\omega_0 = \frac{1}{RC} \qquad (6.116)$$

We note also that this result placed into (6.113) shows the output voltage lags the input voltage by 45°. This phase shift is called ϕ_0.

$$\phi_0 = -45° \tag{6.117}$$

Now in order to graph the magnitude as a function of frequency, we can say that any general frequency may be written as

$$\omega = n\omega_0 \tag{6.118}$$

where ω is in radians. This can be placed into the general expression for gain, (6.114), to give

$$|A| = \frac{1}{\sqrt{(1 + n^2)}} \tag{6.119}$$

For graphing phase, we may use the same information and (6.113) to state that the phase gain is

$$\phi = -\tan^{-1} n \tag{6.120}$$

It is instructive to determine the rate of cut-off at the frequency ω_0, or at the point on the gain-frequency curve where $n = 1$. Equation (6.119) can be differentiated to give

$$\frac{d|A|}{dn} = -\tfrac{1}{2}(1 + n^2)^{-3/2}2n \tag{6.121}$$

and the slope at $n = 1$ is

$$\frac{d|A|}{dn}\bigg|_{n=1} = -\tfrac{1}{2}(2)^{-3/2} \cdot 2 = -0.3535 \text{ V/rad} \tag{6.122}$$

This value for the slope at the cut-off frequency will be compared with that obtained for the two- and three-section low-pass filters to be discussed next. Thus we shall determine whether or not there is any particular advantage in breaking a given filter up into more sections.

6.12. Two-section non-tapered R–C low-pass filter

A tapered network is one in which the input impedance of each added section is high enough that it does not appreciably load the preceding network. Thus, if we have a network which consists of two cascaded sections, each the same as the section just analyzed in art. 6.11, the resulting network is non-tapered. Such a two-section network is shown in Fig. 6.23.

At this point the reader should write and solve the equations of this network, to ascertain that the transfer function is

$$Z_T(s) = \frac{1}{R^2C^2s^2 + 3RCs + 1} \tag{6.123}$$

The reader may wonder why the transfer function is always solved first as a function of s. It is mentioned again that one does not always work with sine waves, and it is best to learn the most general

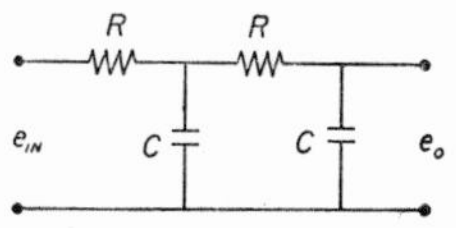

Fig. 6.23

method, which will work for any type of input waveshape. Thus, if we wish to catalog a set of transfer functions, it is most appropriate to show them as functions of s. Special cases where the exclusive use of sinewaves permit s to be replaced by $j\omega$ are easily handled if one has the general form to begin with. If in (6.123) we insert $j\omega$ for s, we have

$$A = \frac{1}{1 - R^2C^2\omega^2 + j3RC\omega} \tag{6.124}$$

The magnitude of this expression is

$$|A| = \frac{1}{\sqrt{(1 + 7R^2C^2\omega^2 + R^4C^4\omega^4)}} \tag{6.125}$$

As in the previous article, the radical is set equal to $\sqrt{2}$ to find ω_0, the cut-off frequency.

$$\omega_0 = \frac{\sqrt{(-7 + \sqrt{53})}}{\sqrt{(2)}RC} \tag{6.126}$$

This simplifies numerically to

$$\omega_0 = \frac{0.374}{RC} \tag{6.127}$$

We can now let the general frequency $\omega = n\omega_0$, as in the previous article, thus

$$\omega = \frac{0.374n}{RC} \tag{6.128}$$

which can now be substituted back into (6.125) to obtain

$$|A| = \frac{1}{\sqrt{(1 + 0.98n^2 + 0.0196n^4)}} \tag{6.129}$$

Comparing this result with (6.119) in the last article, we see clearly that for values of n from 0 to 1.0, which is the normal pass-band, the gain curve is practically identical for both networks. We see from this analysis that there is no practical advantage in using a two-section network rather than a single-section network for low-pass filters. As far as phase shift is concerned, we note from (6.124) that

$$\phi = -\tan^{-1}\left(\frac{3RC\omega}{1 - R^2C^2\omega^2}\right) \tag{6.130}$$

or, at cut-off, where $\omega = \omega_0$

$$\phi_0 = -51.5° \tag{6.131}$$

which is slightly greater than the $-45°$ for the single section.

We shall now examine the three-section non-tapered case. This last will allow us to draw conclusions on the worth of using many sections rather than a single section for R–C low-pass filter networks.

6.13. Three-section non-tapered R–C low-pass filter

Following the trend of the two previous sections, we shall now derive the cut-off frequency and phase shift for a three-section low-pass R–C filter network. The network under consideration is shown in Fig. 6.24.

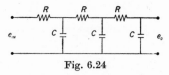

Fig. 6.24

If the reader has not done so already, it is suggested at this point that he write the network equations and determine that the transfer function is

$$Z_T(s) = \frac{1}{R^3C^3s^3 + 5R^2C^2s^2 + 6RCs + 1} \tag{6.132}$$

The next step is to substitute $j\omega$ for s, to give

$$A = \frac{1}{1 - 5R^2C^2\omega^2 + j(6RC\omega - R^3C^3\omega^3)} \tag{6.133}$$

Following the same pattern which has been established in the last two articles, we now write the magnitude of A as

$$|A| = \frac{1}{\sqrt{(R^6C^6\omega^6 + 13R^4C^4\omega^4 + 26R^2C^2\omega^2 + 1)}} \quad (6.134)$$

As before, the quantity inside the radical is set equal to 2.0. This gives

$$R^6C^6\omega^6 + 13R^4C^4\omega^4 + 26R^2C^2\omega^2 - 1 = 0 \quad (6.135)$$

Now physical reasoning (and the trend established by (6.127) and (6.116) earlier), shows us that the term $RC\omega_0$ will be much less than unity. This makes it easy to solve (6.135) by using only the last two terms. Thus

$$\omega_0 = \frac{1}{\sqrt{(26)}RC} \quad (6.136)$$

or

$$\omega_0 = \frac{0.2}{RC} \quad (6.137)$$

Next, we let

$$\omega = n\omega_0 = \frac{0.2n}{RC} \quad (6.138)$$

and insert this term into (6.134) to have

$$|A| = \frac{1}{\sqrt{(1 + 1.04n^2 + 0.021n^4 + 0.000068n^6)}} \quad (6.139)$$

It will be observed that over the normal pass-band, i.e. where n is between 0 and 1.0, that (6.139) is essentially the same value as the gain function for both the single and double section networks. In fact, if one differentiates (6.139) and determines the slope of the curve at $n = 1$, the increase over a single section will be negligible. The phase shift is given by

$$\phi = -\tan^{-1}\left(\frac{6RC\omega - R^3C^3\omega^3}{5R^2C^2\omega^2 - 1}\right) \quad (6.140)$$

or at $\omega = \omega_0$,

$$\phi_0 = -124° \quad (6.141)$$

The results of the last three sections can be summarized in Table 6.1.

TABLE 6.1. R–C non-tapered low-pass filter data

Number of sections	ω_0	ϕ_0	Amplitude curve (practical, approximate)
1	$\dfrac{1}{RC}$	$-45°$	$\dfrac{1}{\sqrt{(1 + n^2)}}$
2	$\dfrac{0.374}{RC}$	$-53°$	$\dfrac{1}{\sqrt{(1 + 0.98n^2)}}$
3	$\dfrac{0.2}{RC}$	$-124°$	$\dfrac{1}{\sqrt{(1 + 1.04n^2)}}$

It would appear that the reader who requires a low-pass filter with a sharp cut-off at ω_0 should use some other type than the cascaded R–C sections. We shall develop filters with sharper cut-off characteristics shortly.

The non-tapered n-section R–C network, although of doubtful value as a quality filter, serves admirably for many phase shift problems and purposes. The next article will develop a general method of finding the transfer function of such non-tapered n-section networks.

6.14. Iterative networks

The reader who has faithfully worked all problems up to this point will have discovered that the solution of a three-mesh network such as discussed in the last article requires considerable work. The writer suspects that any suggestion on his part to work out transfer functions for five or six-mesh networks would make the reader consider switching his interests to medicine or carpentry for a livelihood. To avoid this unpleasant state of events, let us now develop an easy way to determine the transfer function when the network consists of many L-shaped cascaded sections.

Consider the general network shown in Fig. 6.25. Let $Z(s)$ be the series impedance of the network (one section), and let $Y(s)$ be the shunt admittance arms. These may individually be any combination of impedances. (Note only that the sections must be L-shaped, as shown in Fig. 6.25.)

Write a general model for the transfer function as shown in (6.142) below.

$$Z_T(s) = \frac{1}{a + bZY + cZ^2Y^2 + dZ^3Y^3 + \cdots nZ^nY^n} \quad (6.142)$$

To make the problem easy, the coefficients a, b, c, etc., may be taken from Pascal's triangle, as shown in Fig. 6.26. Pascal's triangle of binomial coefficients is constructed as follows. Draw the two

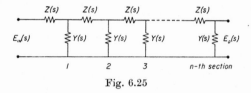

Fig. 6.25

boundary lines of ones, and then note that any number inside the boundary is formed by adding together the number x immediately above it, and x's neighbor on the right, i.e.

$$\begin{array}{cc} 3 & 3 \\ 6 & \end{array} \quad ; \ 6 = 3 + 3$$

Fig. 6.26 illustrates the preferred construction.

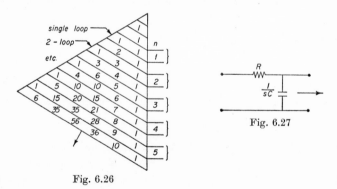

Fig. 6.26

Fig. 6.27

As an example, if one has a five-section, cascaded R–C network, all sections identical, merely choose the downward sloping row of coefficients that corresponds to the number of loops in the network, where each section is as shown in Fig. 6.27. That is

$$Z = R; \ Y = sC; \ ZY = RCs \quad (6.143)$$

Looking at Fig. 6.26, we note that there are six coefficients

$$\left. \begin{matrix} a & b & c & d & e & f \\ 1 & 15 & 35 & 28 & 9 & 1 \end{matrix} \right\} \tag{6.144}$$

and placing these into the general form

$$Z_T(s) = \frac{1}{1 + 15RCs + 35R^2C^2s^2 + 28R^3C^3s^3 + 9R^4C^4s^4 + R^5C^5s^5} \tag{6.145}$$

The obvious ease of using this method should make it the number one approach whenever identical n-section cascaded networks are encountered. It is noted that $Z(s)$ and $Y(s)$ can both be more involved than shown, without affecting the generality of the method.

PROBLEMS.

(1) Find the transfer function for Fig. 6.24 (in the previous article) by this method. Compare the times required for solution.

(2) Using the Pascal triangle method, find the transfer function of the network shown in Fig. 6.28.

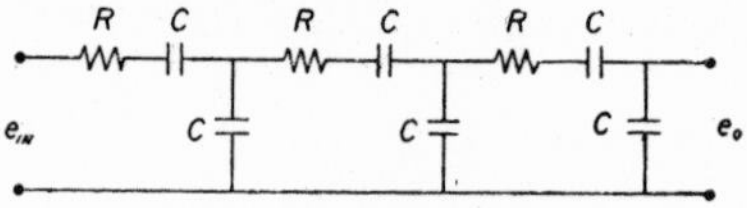

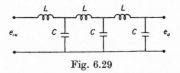

Fig. 6.28

ANS.

$$Z_T(s) = \frac{1}{13 + 19RCs + 8R^2C^2s^2 + R^3C^3s^3} \tag{6.146}$$

(3) Consider the network in Fig. 6.29. Assuming sine wave input, will there be any phase shift in this network? Justify your answer

Fig. 6.29

by showing the presence or absence of j-terms in the transfer function.

6.15. Initial conditions in network parameters

When using the Laplace transform as a means of circuit analysis, we consider the action to begin at time $t = 0$. This follows from the basic defining integral. Excitation functions are tacitly assumed to begin at $t = 0$ even though we do not always say so in specific terms. Of course this situation is good, as the Laplace transform method of analysis will give us transient responses as well as the steady state response.

There are several situations which occur that we have not discussed formally up to this time. We refer here to the problems of initial conditions, and to the subject of mutual inductance.

It has been considered better to omit these topics during the formal development of the abstract material, and to present them at this point, since we are now working with actual networks in this chapter, and initial conditions usually are of importance only in practice.

The subject of mutual inductance and how to handle it mathematically is very hazy to many electronic engineers. One of the difficulties probably lies in the numerous definitions, special handbook formulas, and available methods of working problems where mutual inductance is involved. We shall attempt in the next few articles to present the most simple method of dealing with mutual inductance problems in networks.

First, however, let us examine some cases where initial conditions occur. Since this book is written for electronics people, we shall attempt to cover initial conditions by means of practical electronic examples, rather than to develop an isolated abstract theory.

6.16. Initial charge or voltage on condenser.

Earlier in the text we discussed the relation between capacity, voltage and current. Suppose, however, that we now have the condenser charged to some fixed voltage α at the time we begin our analysis. This is shown in Fig. 6.30. Now by the most basic definition, we have the relation

$$i(t) = C \frac{de(t)}{dt} \tag{6.147}$$

We now take the Laplace transform of this equation, making certain that we use the complete form for the transform of the derivative, as given in (3.64). This general form is

$$\mathscr{L}\left[\frac{df(t)}{dt}\right] = sF(s) - f(0) \tag{6.148}$$

where we recall that the $f(0)$ was the value of $f(t)$ at time $t = 0$, when approached from the right. Using this form, (6.147) transforms into

$$I(s) = C[sE(s) - \alpha] \tag{6.149}$$

where we see that α is $e(t)$ at $t = 0$, i.e. the initial voltage on the condenser. (One could deal with initial charge just as easily by

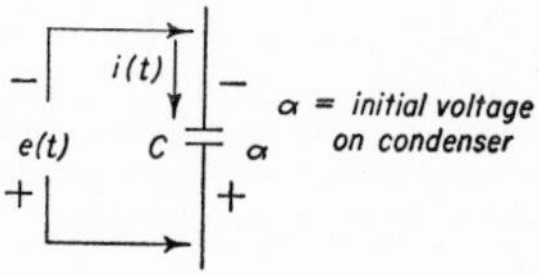

Fig. 6.30

noting that charge is voltage times capacity.) Let us multiply out (6.149) to obtain

$$I(s) = sC \cdot E(s) - \alpha C \tag{6.150}$$

Each item in (6.150) should be labeled as follows:

$I(s) = $ transformed current

$sC = $ transformed admittance (Y)

$E(s) = $ transformed voltage

$\alpha C = $ current.

The only term which might be questioned is the last, αC. Note, however, that αC must have the dimension of current to be consistent with the other two terms in (6.150). We know, of course, that in the time domain the term αC (voltage times capacity) always equals charge. Thus we must remember that charge in the time-world goes over into voltage in the s-world.

Equation (6.150) can best be illustrated circuit-wise by the single node diagram shown in Fig. 6.31.

Somehow or other, many electronics engineers seem to prefer to deal with mesh equations rather than node equations. We should therefore also examine the integral equivalent of (6.147) to develop a diagram suitable for mesh analysis. Observe that in general

$$e(t) = \frac{1}{C} \int_0^t i(t)\, dt + \alpha \qquad (6.151)$$

and that this transforms into

$$E(s) = \frac{I(s)}{sC} + \frac{\alpha}{s} \qquad (6.152)$$

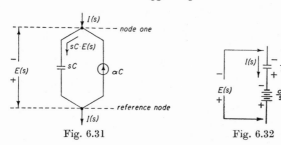

Fig. 6.31   Fig. 6.32

Further, observe that since the left-hand side is a voltage, the right-hand side must be the sum of two voltages, i.e. two voltages connected in series. This leads us to the transformed diagram shown in Fig. 6.32. We shall use some examples to further illustrate these concepts after we consider initial current in an inductance.

6.17. Initial current in an inductance

Let us consider the inductance shown in Fig. 6.33, which carries a current ρ at time $t = 0$. The most basic way of relating the parameters is

$$e(t) = L \frac{di(t)}{dt} \qquad (6.153)$$

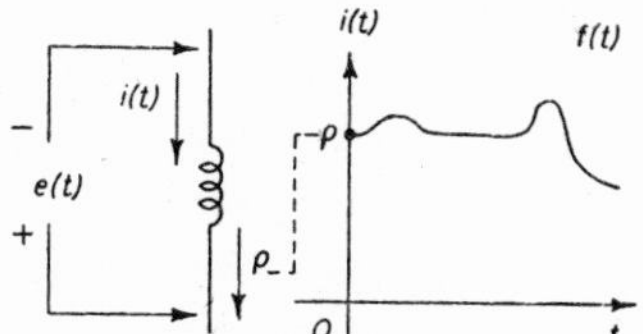

Fig. 6.33

Performing the transformation, and keeping the complete derivative we have

$$\mathscr{L}[e(t)] = L\mathscr{L}\left[\frac{di(t)}{dt}\right] \qquad (6.154)$$

which becomes

$$E(s) = L[sI(s) - \rho] \qquad (6.155)$$

This is next multiplied out to give

$$E(s) = sL \cdot I(s) - \rho L \qquad (6.156)$$

It is to be noted that, dimension-wise

$E(s)$ = transformed voltage

sL = transformed impedance

$I(s)$ = transformed current

ρL = voltage.

The term ρL must be called a voltage to be consistent with the other two terms. We observe with interest that

$$e = L\frac{di}{dt} = N\frac{d\phi}{dt} \qquad (6.157)$$

and for a linear inductance, that

$$L = N \cdot \frac{\phi}{i} \qquad (6.158)$$

Now ρ was defined as a current, and if we multiply (6.158) by ρ we have

$$\rho L = \frac{\rho N\phi}{i} \qquad (6.159)$$

which, dimension-wise, is

$$\rho L = \frac{\text{current} \cdot N\phi}{\text{current}} \qquad (6.160)$$

Thus we can say, if someone should press us for details, that ρL represents the flux linkages in the coil at time $t = 0$.

Fig. 6.34

Equation (6.156) can be illustrated circuit-wise as shown in Fig. 6.34, where ρL is shown in the transformed circuit as a "transformed" battery.

Whenever an initial current appears in an inductance which is part of a network to be analyzed, the new network in the s-plane can show a voltage source ρL in series with the inductance. The circuit then can be treated as any other simple network that contains numerous voltage sources.

EXAMPLE. Let us now consider a series R–L–C circuit, to illustrate both cases of initial conditions. This is shown in Fig. 6.35. In this example, ρ represents an initial current flowing in the coil at $t = 0$, and α represents an initial voltage on the condenser at $t = 0$.

By the use of our "transformed battery" concept, it is easy to draw the s-plane equivalent circuit, shown in Fig. 6.36. It should

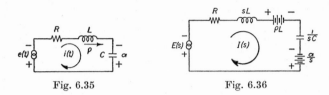

Fig. 6.35   Fig. 6.36

now be easy to write the one Kirchhoff's law equation around this loop, and this equation is

$$\left(R + sL + \frac{1}{sC} \right) I(s) = E(s) + \rho L - \frac{\alpha}{s} \qquad (6.161)$$

The desired response, $I(s)$, is then

$$I(s) = \frac{E(s) + \rho L - \alpha/s}{R + sL + 1/sC} \qquad (6.162)$$

Now observe that (6.162) can be written in the form

$$I(s) = \frac{E(s)}{R + sL + 1/sC} + \frac{(\rho L - \alpha/s)}{R + sL + 1/sC} \qquad (6.163)$$

or

$$I(s) = I_1(s) + I_2(s) \qquad (6.164)$$

Note that $I_1(s)$ is the component of I due to the driving function. This yields both steady-state and transient solutions. $I_2(s)$ is the current component due to the initial conditions, and can only yield a transient solution.

To continue our example, suppose we should choose a specific input voltage

$$e(t) = U(t) \qquad (6.165)$$

so that

$$E(s) = \frac{1}{s} \qquad (6.166)$$

Let us look first at $I_1(s)$, which becomes

$$I_1(s) = \frac{1}{Ls^2 + Rs + 1/C} \tag{6.167}$$

$I_1(s)$ will have no zeros, but will have poles at

$$s = \frac{-R \pm j\sqrt{(4L/C - R^2)}}{2L} \tag{6.168}$$

or in other words, $I_1(s)$ has the form

$$I_1(s) = \frac{1}{(s + \alpha + j\beta)(s + \alpha - j\beta)} \tag{6.169}$$

This has a pole–zero diagram shown in Fig. 6.37. Thus, by merely inspecting Fig. 6.37, we see that the application of $U(t)$ creates an exponentially decaying sinewave of current.

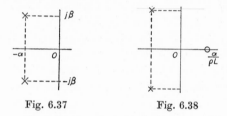

Fig. 6.37   Fig. 6.38

We can now examine the $I_2(s)$ component. In this case

$$I_2(s) = \frac{\rho L - \alpha/s}{R + sL + 1/sC} \tag{6.170}$$

Multiplying both numerator and denominator by s gives

$$I_2(s) = \frac{(\rho Ls - \alpha)}{Ls^2 + Rs + 1/C} \tag{6.171}$$

The pole–zero diagram for $I_2(s)$ is now shown in Fig. 6.38.

We see here that in addition to the same two complex conjugate poles, we now have a zero on the positive σ-axis. Notice that the zero location does not determine the response, but only the magnitude and phase of the response. Since there are no poles on the vertical axis, or at the origin, there is no steady-state response.

It will be recalled again that a single pole at the origin represents a steady d.c.; complex poles on the $j\omega$-axis represent a steady a.c. sinewave; and complex conjugate poles in the left half-plane represent an exponentially decaying sinewave.

PROBLEM. Using the same symbols that we have employed in the last two articles, draw the transformed network of Fig. 6.39. Write the two loop equations as functions of s.

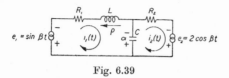

Fig. 6.39

6.18. Mutual inductance

It has been the writer's experience that many electronics engineers have a somewhat nebulous understanding of mutual inductance. In fact, some circuit design engineers have been observed to devise alternate, more elaborate networks just to avoid coupling two coils together. In a few such cases, the feeling seemed to be that mutual inductance was some uncertain, troublesome, unfriendly characteristic which should be avoided if at all possible.

It is unfortunate that such hesitancy should ever occur, but perhaps it is the result of lack of attention to the concept of mutual inductance in the engineer's early formulative courses in circuit theory. At any rate, to quote a more famous author, "circuit analysis is the engineer's bread and butter", so in this article we want to develop a logical, consistent and easily remembered way to handle mutual inductance in circuit analysis problems.

One more comment before we proceed: in view of the known facts about atoms and their behavior which were not available a century ago, the writer finds it most difficult to consider a "current" in a conductor which is something other than an electron flow. It is gratifying then, to observe that more and more authors are coming to accept "current" and "electron flow" to be one and the same thing. This in spite of much opposition from science teachers and engineering professors who should know better.

Having expressed the foregoing views, it is easy to see that if we label the inductance shown in Fig. 6.40 as an impedance sL, then application of a voltage e as shown will cause a current i to flow through the impedance as shown in Fig. 6.40.

The same signs and directions apply for any impedance. Many years ago, before much was understood about impedance, one had to invent devices such as "back e.m.f." to explain part of the relation between e and i. This "induced back voltage" was supposed to be opposite in sign from the applied voltage, and to this day causes no end of confusion.

The reader who has successfully studied the preceding portion of this text will assert that sL is a completely general impedance,

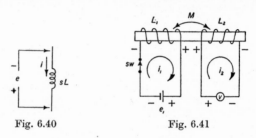

Fig. 6.40   Fig. 6.41

expressing exactly and at all times the ratio e/i. This makes it unnecessary to consider such terms as "back e.m.f." further.

Suppose we redraw the coil pictorially, showing a mutually coupled coil and a switch to initiate a current in L_1 (see Fig. 6.41). The reader should now determine to his satisfaction that the meter

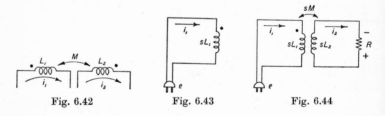

Fig. 6.42   Fig. 6.43   Fig. 6.44

will read up-scale immediately following closure of the switch, and that all polarities are correct as shown.

On a schematic, or network diagram, it is customary to employ small dots to indicate the ends of two or more coils which have the same instantaneous polarity. Thus Fig. 6.41 could be shown as in Fig. 6.42. L_1 might be the primary of a power transformer as shown in Fig. 6.43, with L_2 far removed and not loaded, that is, $i_2 = 0$.

If we should now place a load R across L_2 and move it close to L_1, then M assumes a value, as in Fig. 6.44. We see that the induced current in the secondary loop reduces the total impedance in the primary loop, because where in Fig. 6.43 we had

$$e = sL_1 i \tag{6.172}$$

or

$$Z_{\text{IN}} = sL_1 \tag{6.173}$$

in Fig. 6.44 we have

$$\left.\begin{array}{ll} e = sL_1 i_1 - sM i_2 & (a) \\ 0 = -sM i_1 + (sL_2 + R)i_2 & (b) \end{array}\right\} \tag{6.174}$$

Assume a turns-ratio of one to one, in which case $L_2 = L_1$ and $i_2 = i_1$, then (6.174(a)) becomes

$$e = s(L_1 - M)i_1 \tag{6.175}$$

This says that the input impedance e/i_1 is

$$Z_{\text{IN}} = s(L_1 - M) \tag{6.176}$$

M appears then to reduce the value of primary impedance, which we know to be a fact in actual reality. In writing the loop equations around loop one in Fig. 6.44 then, we consider the mutual current to be minus in the mathematical sense, as M does not, of course, represent a negative inductance.

RULE. We may formulate a general rule from the foregoing, as follows:

(a) If the current in loop j enters the dot end of an inductance in loop j, and a current in loop k leaves the dot end of an inductance in loop k, then i_{jk} is considered minus for combining with a mutual inductance M_{jk}.

(b) If the current in loop j enters the dot end of an inductance in loop j, and a current in loop k enters the dot end of an inductance in loop k, then the mutual current i_{jk} is considered plus for combining with a mutual inductance M_{jk}.

The rule is somewhat awkward when stated in words, but is easy to understand and memorize when illustrated with several examples.

EXAMPLE 1. Note that we sometimes write e and i as functions of time, while expressing impedances as functions of s. This is permissible if we recall that s is an operator, and provided we transform e and i into functions of s before doing anything else with such "mixed" equations. The equations for the network shown in Fig. 6.45 are, using the above rules,

$$\left.\begin{array}{l} e_1 = sL_1i_1 - sMi_2 \\ -e_2 = -sMi_1 + sL_2i_2 \end{array}\right\} \qquad (6.177)$$

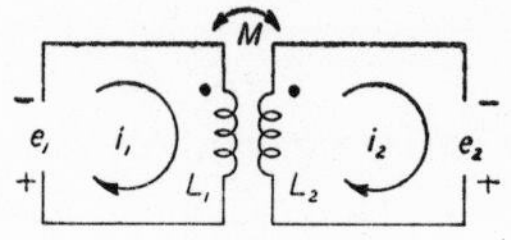

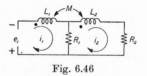

Fig. 6.45

EXAMPLE 2. Using the given rules, the equations for the circuit shown in Fig. 6.46 are:

$$e_1 = (sL_1 + R_1)i_1 - (R - sM)i_2 \qquad (6.178)$$

$$0 = -(R - sM)i_1 + (R_1 + R_2 + sL_2)i_2 \qquad (6.179)$$

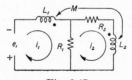

Fig. 6.46

EXAMPLE 3. (See Fig. 6.47.) The equations are:

$$e_1 = (sL_1 + R_1)i_1 - (R_1 + sM)i_2 \qquad (6.180)$$

$$0 = -(R_1 + sM)i_1 + (R_1 + R_2 + sL_2)i_2 \qquad (6.181)$$

Fig. 6.47

Short digression on flux-linkages. Note carefully that an initial current in one loop will combine through any mutual inductance to form a transformed battery in the other loop (in addition to combining with inductance in its own loop).

We have shown that the transformed battery can be considered as a flux linkage. This fact can be used to determine which way to how polarities. Let us examine Fig. 6.48. The physical shape of the coil determines the placement of the dots. The initial current $_1$ in L_1 generates the transformed battery $\rho_1 L_1$ with polarity as hown. This direction is not obvious by inspection, but was etermined from (6.156) and the use of Fig. 6.34 as a model.

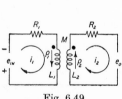

Fig. 6.48

If we now realize that flux linkages which are mutual to both coils vill affect both coils in the same way, we observe that the current $_1$ which causes flux linkages $\rho_1 L_1$ in coil L_1 must, by sharing flux nkage with L_2, set up a transformed battery $\rho_1 M$ of the same olarity with respect to the dots. We are now in a position to onsider example 4.

EXAMPLE 4. Fig. 6.49 shows a somewhat more involved situation vhere initial currents are present in the inductances. Writing the

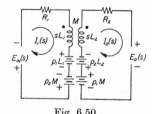

Fig. 6.49   Fig. 6.50

quations as functions of s will be simple if we plan the approach arefully. First, let us draw the transformed circuit, using the transformed battery" concept of art. 6.17. First, we note that the ule for mutual currents shows that

$$i_{12} = i_{21} = \text{(minus)} \qquad (6.182)$$

Then we proceed to write the equations directly as functions of s. These are

$$(R_1 + sL_1)I_1(s) - sMI_2(s) = E_{\text{IN}}(s) + \rho_1 L_1 - \rho_2 M \qquad (6.183)$$

$$-sMI_1(s) + (R_2 + sL_2)I_2(s) = E_0(s) + \rho_2 L_2 - \rho_1 M \qquad (6.184)$$

EXAMPLE 5. Let us consider the network shown in Fig. 6.51. We will assume that the switch closes at $t = 0$.

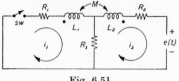

Fig. 6.51

As initial conditions, let us further assume that at time $t = 0$

$$\left.\begin{array}{l} i_1(0) = 0 \\ i_2(0) = -\rho \end{array}\right\} \quad (6.185)$$

It will be noted that by the rule, the mutual current i_{12} and i_{21} will be minus for M (also the mutual current in R_3 will be minus by inspection). The transformed diagram is drawn in Fig. 6.52. Note

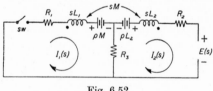

Fig. 6.52

that there is no transformed battery ρM in loop 2 as $i_1(0) = 0$, but the transformed ρM does appear in loop 1, due to M and the initial current ρ in loop 2. The equations are:

$$(R_1 + R_3 + sL_1)I_1(s) - (R_3 + sM)I_2(s) = \rho M \quad (6.186)$$

$$-(R_3 + sM)I_1(s) + (R_2 + R_3 + sL_2)I_2(s) = E(s) - \rho L_2 \quad (6.187)$$

Application of the concepts presented in this chapter should permit the reader to undertake rigorous analyses of almost any of the networks in general use, and allow him to begin work on special configurations for his own special requirements as time goes by.

CHAPTER VII

TRANSFORMS OF SPECIAL WAVESHAPES AND PULSES

7.1. Introduction

Up to this point in the text we have been concerned primarily with developing the mathematical theory of the Laplace transformation, presenting the various theorems which make the theory useful in practice, and learning to work with transfer functions in the s-plane. Except for having taken the transforms of sine waves and the unit step function, there has been little discussion of the wide variety of possible excitation functions which are encountered in everyday work.

In this chapter we will develop the transforms for a number of such waveshapes and pulses. We will also develop a few new theoretical concepts as appropriate. It will obviously not be possible to give detailed examples of the application of each waveshape transform developed here to every transfer function that has been discussed, but several selected examples will illustrate typical applications to electronic engineering problems.

7.2. Laplace transform of a displaced step function

It was found in Chapter V that the transform of the unit step function $U(t)$ is

$$\mathscr{L}[U(t)] = \frac{1}{s} \tag{7.1}$$

It was also observed that such a function of s, having a pole at the origin, always inserts a d.c. component of voltage or current into the time function output. The displaced step function shown in Fig. 7.1 was also discussed briefly in Chapter V.

The corresponding function of s was written as

$$F(s) = \int_0^\infty U(t-a)\varepsilon^{-st}\,dt = \int_a^\infty \varepsilon^{-st}\,dt \tag{7.2}$$

which then became

$$\mathscr{L}[U(t - a)] = \frac{\varepsilon^{-as}}{s} \qquad (7.3)$$

This result can now be employed to find the Laplace transform of the rectangular pulse shown in Fig. 7.2. This pulse can be expressed as

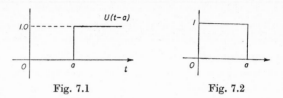

Fig. 7.1   Fig. 7.2

a function of time by writing

$$f(t) = U(t) - U(t - a) \qquad (7.4)$$

and by using (7.1) and (7.3) it is easily seen that

$$F(s) = \frac{1}{s} - \frac{\varepsilon^{-as}}{s} = \frac{1 - \varepsilon^{-as}}{s} \qquad (7.5)$$

EXAMPLE. In the design of small mechanical and electronic devices for use in guided missiles, it is usually necessary to know whether or not the device will successfully withstand the high shock during acceleration when the missile is launched.

Actual shock patterns present during a launching are usually available for numerous points on the missile structure. Such patterns are obtained by recording the electrical output of accelerometers that have been placed at the selected points on the structure, and accumulating the data for the entire structure over a period involving many launchings.

An individual shock pattern, for a particular location of interest, is played back from a tape recording (with instantaneous voltage corresponding to instantaneous acceleration in g's) into a shock spectrum computer. The shock spectrum computer then furnishes four separate functions of acceleration v. frequency, namely:

(1) positive during the shock
(2) negative during the shock
(3) positive after the shock
(4) negative after the shock

Now the electronics engineer may wish to mount a small wiring assembly, bracket, switch or vacuum tube device at this particular point on the missile. Suppose the item is a small, simple bracket. The engineer either knows the resonant frequency of the bracket assembly or he can find it by a simple test. Knowing the resonant frequency, the engineer merely looks at the shock spectrum chart and reads the acceleration which would occur on the part at the frequency involved, if the part should indeed be mounted at the location involved. He can thus decide prior to actually mounting the part and making a test whether the arrangement would be suitable, or whether it would shear off and fail in practice.

In this somewhat lengthy example, we will limit our interest to such a shock spectrum computer. The computer is, in essence, the electronic equivalent of a mechanical mass-spring oscillating system, which can be adjusted in steps to resonate over the entire frequency range of interest. It is thus the equivalent also of an entire set of vibrating reed type accelerometers, except that such reeds can give only very limited information from brief shock impulses.

An actual shock spectrum computer is synthesized from R–C networks and active feedback elements, but in principle, we can use

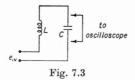

Fig. 7.3

a pure inductance and capacity to illustrate the problem, as shown in Fig. 7.3.

If the system is excited by the recorded shock pattern, the response will be presented on the oscilloscope screen, which is calibrated in g units. Now by using form 5, Appendix I(b), we see that the transfer function for the network of Fig. 7.3 is

$$Z_T(s) = \frac{1}{LCs^2 + 1} \tag{7.6}$$

It is necessary for the electronics engineer to have some standard test to determine whether or not the computer is working properly, and for use in calibration. Such a test often involves the application of a rectangular acceleration (voltage) input to the computer. Thus, the task in this example is to find the computer response to the voltage pulse shown in Fig. 7.2. By definition, it is seen that

$$E_0(s) = Z_T(s)E_{\text{IN}}(s) \tag{7.7}$$

or

$$E_0(s) = \frac{1 - \varepsilon^{-as}}{LCs\left(s^2 + \dfrac{1}{LC}\right)} \tag{7.8}$$

The denominator can be factored to give

$$E_0(s) = \frac{1}{LC} \cdot \frac{(1 - \varepsilon^{-as})}{s\left(s + j\dfrac{1}{\sqrt{(LC)}}\right)\left(s - j\dfrac{1}{\sqrt{(LC)}}\right)} \tag{7.9}$$

or

$$E_0(s) = \frac{\omega^2(1 - \varepsilon^{-as})}{s(s + j\omega)(s - j\omega)} \tag{7.10}$$

where we let

$$\omega = \frac{1}{\sqrt{(LC)}} \tag{7.11}$$

We are now ready to determine $e_0(t)$, which may be found by using the line integral of the inverse transformation.

$$e_0(t) = \frac{\omega^2}{2\pi j} \oint \frac{(1 - \varepsilon^{-as})\varepsilon^{ts}\, ds}{s(s + j\omega)(s - j\omega)} \tag{7.12}$$

This is separated into two integrals as

$$e_0(t) = \underbrace{\frac{\omega^2}{2\pi j} \oint \frac{\varepsilon^{ts}\, ds}{s(s + j\omega)(s - j\omega)}}_{f(t)} - \underbrace{\frac{\omega^2}{2\pi j} \oint \frac{\varepsilon^{-as}\varepsilon^{ts}\, ds}{s(s + j\omega)(s - j\omega)}}_{f(t-a)U(t-a)} \tag{7.13}$$

Only single order poles are involved, and it is easily found that the two integrals give

$$e_0(t) = [1 - \cos \omega t] - [1 - \cos \omega(t - a)] \tag{7.14}$$

or

$$e_0(t) = \cos \omega(t - a) - \cos \omega t \tag{7.15}$$

This is the time response to a unit shock of duration a, where ω is the frequency to which the computer is tuned. Equation (7.15) can be manipulated into the form

$$e_0(t) = 2 \sin\left(\frac{\omega a}{2}\right) \cdot \sin\left(\omega t - \frac{\omega a}{2}\right) \qquad (7.16)$$

Note that since the second integral in (7.13) gives a function multiplied by $U(t - a)$, equation (7.16) must be interpreted as the response of the computer after the shock. The response during the shock is given by the first bracketed term in (7.14).

Examining (7.16), we see that for shocks which are narrow compared with period T of the computer, the maximum acceleration after removal of the shock is

$$|e_0(t)|_{\max} = \frac{2\pi a}{T} \qquad (7.17)$$

while for other applied shocks, the highest acceleration after the shock is finished is given by

$$|e_0(t)|_{\max} = 2 \sin\left(\frac{\pi a}{T}\right) \qquad (7.18)$$

It is interesting to note that if the input pulse represents say, 100 g, up to 200 g may be applied to small parts mounted at the location in question. Equation (7.18) shows that the negative slope of the excitation at $t = a$ can remove all or part of the acceleration on the component, or leave it unchanged.

7.3. Transform of the dirac delta function

The delta function $\delta(t)$ is useful for many purposes. It may be defined by

$$\left.\begin{aligned} &\delta(t) = 0, \; t \neq 0 \\ &\int_{-\infty}^{\infty} \delta(t) \, dt = 1 \end{aligned}\right\} \qquad (7.19)$$

An equally valid definition is

$$\left.\begin{aligned} &\delta(t) = 0, t < 0 \\ &\delta(t) = \lim_{\alpha \to \infty} \alpha \varepsilon^{-\alpha t}, t > 0 \end{aligned}\right\} \qquad (7.20)$$

Still another definition, used often in connection with sampling electronic functions is

$$\delta(t) = \lim_{a \to 0} \frac{1}{a}[U(t) - U(t - a)] \qquad (7.21)$$

This last definition is illustrated in Fig. 7.4.

It will be noted that (7.5), the transform of the rectangular pulse of unit height, can be multiplied by $1/a$ to give the transform of Fig. 7.4 directly thus

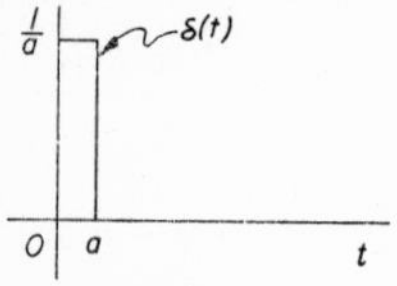

$$\mathscr{L}[\delta(t)] = \lim_{a \to 0} \frac{1 - \varepsilon^{-as}}{as} \qquad (7.22)$$

or

$$\mathscr{L}[\delta(t)] = 1 \qquad (7.23)$$

Fig. 7.4

The delta function is also sometimes called the unit impulse.

PROBLEM. Find $\mathscr{L}[\delta(t - a)]$.

7.4. Derivatives of infinite slopes expressed as δ-functions

Suppose we are given $f_a(t)$ as in Fig. 7.5. This is essentially the same function as $f(t)$ shown in Fig. 7.6 if τ is made very small. The

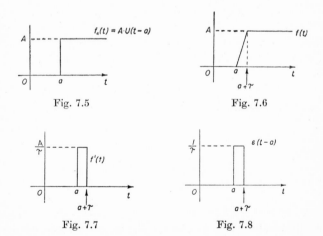

Fig. 7.5

Fig. 7.6

Fig. 7.7

Fig. 7.8

derivative of $f(t)$ is illustrated in Fig. 7.7. Now let us examine the delta function $\delta(t - a)$ shown in Fig. 7.8. By comparing Fig. 7.8 with Fig. 7.7, it is noted that the height of $f'(t)$ is A times the height of the δ-function, and since both are the same width τ, it follows that

$$f'(t) = A\delta(t - a) \tag{7.24}$$

and since A is the value of $f(a)$ from Fig. 7.5, (7.24) becomes

$$f'(t) = f(a)\delta(t - a) \tag{7.25}$$

Now $f(a)$ will be some constant, and thus we can differentiate any step function and express the result as a constant times a δ-function,

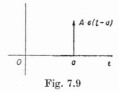

Fig. 7.9

as in (7.25). The derivative in Fig. 7.1 is usually drawn and labeled as in Fig. 7.9. For the unit δ-function, the A in Fig. 7.9 would be 1.0.

7.5. Sampling another function with a δ-function

Suppose we have a function $f(t)$ as shown in Fig. 7.10, and sample it by the δ-function also shown. (This means that the functions are

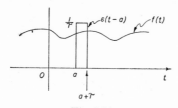

Fig. 7.10

multiplied point by point along the t-axis.) Having multiplied the two functions point by point, we observe that the integral of the result is

$$\int_{\phi_1}^{\phi_2} f(t)\delta(t - a)\, dt = \int_{\phi_1}^{a} 0 \cdot dt + \int_{a}^{a+\tau} f(a)\delta(t - a)\, dt + \int_{a+\tau}^{\phi_2} 0 \cdot dt \tag{7.26}$$

or, since the first and last terms on the right are zero, and since the $f(a)$ in the center term is a constant and can be brought outside the integral, then

$$\int_{\phi_1}^{\phi_2} f(t)\delta(t - a)\, dt = f(a) \int_{a}^{a+\tau} \delta(t - a)\, dt = f(a) \tag{7.27}$$

ϕ_1 and ϕ_2 can be any values, infinite or finite, as long as they are on opposite sides of $t = a$.

7.6. Fourier coefficients ascertained by means of δ-functions

Let us assume that we have an even periodic waveshape, that is, one which is symmetrical about the j-axis. Such a function will be composed of harmonics which are cosine terms. We can express such even functions as

$$f(x) = \sum_{n=0}^{\infty} a_n \cos nx \qquad (7.28)$$

Both sides can now be multiplied by $\cos mx$ to give

$$f(x) \cos mx = \cos mx \sum_{n=0}^{\infty} a_n \cos nx \qquad (7.29)$$

If both sides are now integrated over one period of the waveform, that is, from $-\pi$ to π,

$$\int_{-\pi}^{\pi} f(x) \cos mx \, dx = \int_{-\pi}^{\pi} \cos mx \sum_{n=0}^{\infty} a_n \cos nx \, dx \qquad (7.30)$$

it is shown in texts on circuit analysis that the right-hand integral will be zero except where $n = m$, in which case the integral becomes equal to $a_n\pi$. Therefore

$$a_n = \frac{1}{\pi} \int_{-\pi}^{\pi} \cdot f(x) \cos nx \, dx \qquad (7.31)$$

This formula allows us to find any Fourier coefficient a_n if the function $f(x)$ is known. It is also possible to solve for a_n in terms of derivatives of $f(x)$. Thus, starting with (7.28), we can differentiate to obtain

$$f'(x) = -\sum_{n=0}^{\infty} na_n \sin nx \qquad (7.32)$$

which is next multiplied by $\sin mx$, and then integrated over a full period as before.

$$\int_{-\pi}^{\pi} f'(x) \sin mx \, dx = -\int_{-\pi}^{\pi} \sin mx \sum_{n=0}^{\infty} na_n \sin nx \, dx \qquad (7.33)$$

The reader can easily show, as in the case before, that the right-hand integral is zero for every value of n except $n = m$, and that for this case the integral is $-na_n\pi$. Thus (7.33) becomes

$$a_n = -\frac{1}{n\pi}\int_{-\pi}^{\pi}f'(x)\sin nx\,dx \qquad (7.34)$$

Starting again with (7.28), we can differentiate twice to obtain

$$f''(x) = -\sum_{n=0}^{\infty}n^2 a_n\cos nx \qquad (7.35)$$

This can be multiplied by $\cos mx$ and integrated as before to solve for a_n, which is

$$a_n = -\frac{1}{n^2\pi}\int_{-\pi}^{\pi}f''(x)\cos nx\,dx \qquad (7.36)$$

These formulas are now consolidated in Table 7.1.

TABLE 7.1

$$a_n = \frac{1}{\pi}\int_{-\pi}^{\pi}f(x)\cos nx\,dx$$

$$a_n = -\frac{1}{n\pi}\int_{-\pi}^{\pi}f'(x)\sin nx\,dx$$

$$a_n = -\frac{1}{n^2\pi}\int_{-\pi}^{\pi}f''(x)\cos nx\,dx$$

$$a_n = \frac{1}{n^3\pi}\int_{-\pi}^{\pi}f'''(x)\sin nx\,dx, \text{ etc.}$$

Now observe that if we can express $f(x)$ or any of its derivatives as a sum of δ-function, we can use (7.27) to write

$$\int_{-\pi}^{\pi}f^n(x)\delta(x-\tau)\,dx = \left|\begin{array}{l}f(\tau) \text{ if } -\pi < \tau < \pi\\ 0 \text{ for } \tau \text{ otherwise}\end{array}\right\} \qquad (7.37)$$

Thus, for example, (7.36) can be written as

$$a_n = -\frac{1}{n^2\pi}[\cos n\tau_1\cdot\delta(x-\tau_1) + \cos n\tau_2\cdot\delta(x-\tau_2) + \cdots] \qquad (7.38)$$

where each cosine term is caused by one δ-function.

EXAMPLE. Let us apply the concepts presented in this article to find the Fourier coefficients of the waveform, one period of which is

shown in Fig. 7.11. In order to use one of the forms shown in
Table 7.1, it will first be necessary to see if we can express some
derivative of $f(x)$ as a set of δ-functions. Let us draw the first
derivative of $f(x)$ as shown in Fig. 7.12.

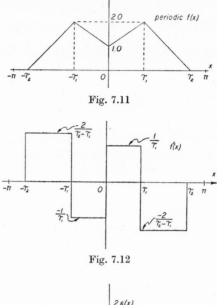

Fig. 7.11

Fig. 7.12

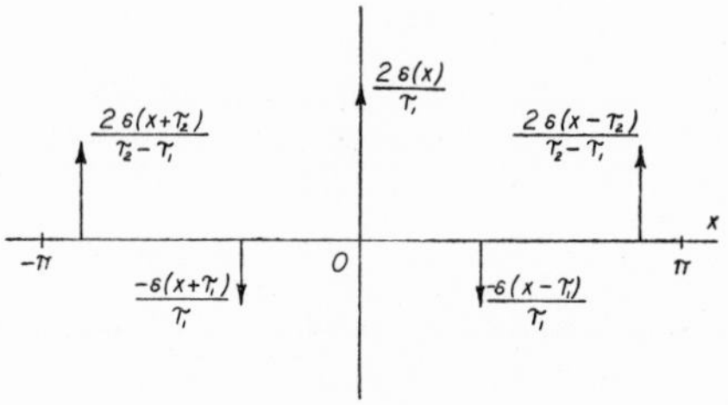

Fig. 7.13

Thus far no delta functions have appeared, but taking the second
derivative will result in a set of δ-functions, as shown in Fig. 7.13.
We may now choose the form given by (7.36) or (7.38) and write

$$a_n = -\frac{1}{n^2\pi}\left[\frac{2}{(\tau_2-\tau_1)}\cos(-n\tau_2) - \frac{1}{\tau_1}\cos(-n\tau_1) + \frac{2}{\tau_1}\cos(0)\right.$$
$$\left. -\frac{1}{\tau_1}\cos(n\tau_1) + \frac{2}{(\tau_2-\tau_1)}\cos(n\tau_2)\right] \quad (7.39)$$

It will be recalled that the cosine of minus angles equals the cosine of the same positive angles, which allows several simplifications, therefore

$$a_n = \frac{2}{n^2\pi} \left[\frac{\cos n\tau_1}{\tau_1} - \frac{2\cos n\tau_2}{\tau_2 - \tau_1} - \frac{1}{\tau_1} \right] \tag{7.40}$$

This allows any coefficient to be found directly.

PROBLEM. The reader is now requested to analyze Fig. 7.11 by the usual Fourier transform method to determine the coefficients of the resulting series; reduce the results to (7.40), compare the time and labor required, and decide the merits of articles 7.5 and 7.6.

7.7. The Laplace transform of a series of pulses

Consider the periodic pulse train illustrated in Fig. 7.14, where the period is T, pulse width is a, and height is unity. The entire train

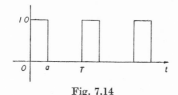

Fig. 7.14

of pulses, $f(t)$, can be expressed as a sum of displaced step functions, and is written as

$$f(t) = U(t) - U(t - a)$$

$$+ U(t - T) - U(t - T - a)$$

$$+ U(t - 2T) - U(t - 2T - a)$$

$$+ \cdots \tag{7.41}$$

By the use of equation (7.3), we can transform term by term into $F(s)$, so that

$$F(s) = \frac{1}{s} - \frac{\varepsilon^{-as}}{s} + \frac{\varepsilon^{-Ts}}{s} - \frac{\varepsilon^{-(T+a)s}}{s} + \frac{\varepsilon^{-2Ts}}{s} - \frac{\varepsilon^{-(2T-a)s}}{s} + \cdots \tag{7.42}$$

By grouping alternate terms, this can be factored as follows:

$$F(s) = \frac{1}{s} [1 + \varepsilon^{-Ts} + \varepsilon^{-2Ts} + \varepsilon^{-3Ts} + \cdot \cdot \cdot]$$

$$- \frac{\varepsilon^{-as}}{s} [1 + \varepsilon^{-Ts} + \varepsilon^{-2Ts} + \varepsilon^{-3Ts} + \cdot \cdot \cdot] \quad (7.43)$$

It is observed that both bracketed terms are identical, so these may now be factored out to give

$$F(s) = \frac{1}{s} [1 - \varepsilon^{-as}][1 + \varepsilon^{-Ts} + \varepsilon^{-2Ts} + \varepsilon^{-3Ts} + \cdot \cdot \cdot] \quad (7.44)$$

It is further recognized that the infinite series on the right is an expansion of the form

$$\frac{1}{1 - x} = 1 + x + x^2 + x^3 + x^4 + \cdot \cdot \cdot \quad (7.45)$$

hence, (7.44) simplified, is

$$F(s) = \frac{1 - \varepsilon^{-as}}{s(1 - \varepsilon^{-Ts})} \quad (7.46)$$

which is the compact expression for the Laplace transform of the periodic train of pulses. Equation (7.46) is general, as pulses of any height A can be transformed simply by carrying the A through as a constant multiplier.

PROBLEM 1. Show that the square wave having amplitudes 0 and A, and period T, has for its transform

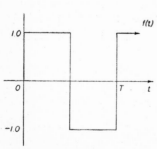

Fig. 7.15

$$F(s) = \frac{A}{s\left(1 + \varepsilon^{-\frac{Ts}{2}}\right)} \quad (7.47)$$

PROBLEM 2. Show that the square wave pictured in Fig. 7.15 has the transform

$$F(s) = \frac{\tanh\left(\frac{Ts}{4}\right)}{s} \quad (7.48)$$

Note: It would appear from (7.48) that we have a pole at $s = 0$, but notice that for small values of s, the tanh of the argument approaches the argument, thus

$$F(0) = \frac{T}{4} \qquad (7.49)$$

and not ∞, as would be required for a pole. Since no pole exists at zero, no d.c. term is present, as is obvious from looking at Fig. 7.15.

.8. The Laplace transform of a general periodic wave

Suppose that a given waveform is periodic, with period T. We can then say with perfect generality that

$$f(t) = f(t + T) \qquad (7.50)$$

and that the transform

$$F(s) = \int_0^\infty f(t)\varepsilon^{-st}\, dt \qquad (7.51)$$

If we wish, we may perform the integration in steps of one period, that is, from 0 to T, T to $2T$, $2T$ to $3T$, etc., to infinity. We can do this by using the shifting theorem to shift the entire function one period at a time, thus

$$\int_0^\infty f(t)\varepsilon^{-st}\, dt = \int_0^T f(t)\varepsilon^{-st}\, dt + \int_T^{2T} f(t + T)\varepsilon^{-s(t+T)}\, dt + \cdots$$

$$+ \int_{nT}^{(n+1)T} f(t + nT)\varepsilon^{-s(t+nT)}\, dt \qquad (7.52)$$

However, because $f(t)$ is periodic, $f(t)$ will suffice for each term.

$$\int_0^\infty f(t)\varepsilon^{-st}\, dt = \sum_{n=0}^\infty \int_{nT}^{(n+1)T} f(t)\varepsilon^{-st}\varepsilon^{-nTs}\, dt \qquad (7.53)$$

The exponential term ε^{-nTs} is not a function of t, and can be brought through the integral sign, thus

$$\mathscr{L}[f(t)] = \sum_{n=0}^\infty \varepsilon^{-nTs} \int_{nT}^{(n+1)T} f(t)\varepsilon^{-st}\, dt \qquad (7.54)$$

The integral is evaluated over one period, and since $f(t)$ is the same over any period we choose, we may just as well choose the first period from 0 to T. Therefore

$$F(s) = \sum_{n=0}^{\infty} \varepsilon^{-nTs} \int_0^T f(t) \varepsilon^{-st}\, dt \qquad (7.55)$$

Finally, we observe that

$$\sum_{n=0}^{\infty} \varepsilon^{-nTs} = \frac{1}{1 - \varepsilon^{-Ts}} \qquad (7.56)$$

which reduces (7.55) to the simple form

$$F(s) = \frac{1}{(1 - \varepsilon^{-Ts})} \int_0^T f(t) \varepsilon^{-st}\, dt \qquad (7.57)$$

Equation (7.57) is thus a general result and can be applied to any type of periodic waveshape. Its use greatly simplifies the determination of the Laplace transform in many cases.

EXAMPLE 1. Let us find the Laplace transform of the pulse train shown in Fig. 7.14 by this technique.

Since the wave train is periodic, it is no longer necessary for us to integrate to infinity, but only from 0 to T. In fact, since we observe by inspection that the function is zero from a to T, it is really only necessary to integrate out to a. The simple result, using (7.57) as a guide, is

$$\mathscr{L}[f(t)] = \frac{1}{(1 - \varepsilon^{-Ts})} \int_0^a \varepsilon^{-st}\, dt \qquad (7.58)$$

which simplifies almost by inspection to the answer

$$F(s) = \frac{1 - \varepsilon^{-as}}{s(1 - \varepsilon^{-Ts})} \qquad (7.59)$$

As the reader can see, it is of little value for an engineer merely to know the definition of the Laplace transform. It is a good working knowledge of all the theorems, little tricks and manipulations which make the theory of real use.

EXAMPLE 2. It is not always expedient to use this periodicity theorem. As an example of a poor application, suppose that

$$f(t) = \sin \omega t$$

ne of the first functions used in the text. Here the period is $T = 2\pi/\omega$, and the periodicity theorem shows that

$$F(s) = \frac{1}{\left(1 - \varepsilon^{-\frac{2\pi s}{\omega}}\right)} \int_0^{\frac{2\pi}{\omega}} \sin \omega t \varepsilon^{-st}\, dt \qquad (7.60)$$

The reader should work this out as a separate test of the theorem. t will indeed reduce to the familiar form

$$F(s) = \frac{\omega}{s^2 + \omega^2} \qquad (7.61)$$

ut considerably more effort is required than merely to integrate rom 0 to ∞ in the first place.

EXAMPLE 3. Let us find the Laplace transform of the sawtooth vave shown in Fig. 7.16

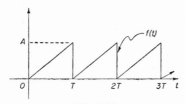

Fig. 7.16

Over the first period, the formula for $f(t)$ is

$$f(t) = \frac{At}{T} \qquad (7.62)$$

The second and following periods will all have different constants added which would complicate things should we try to take the ransform conventionally. However, we can use the periodicity heorem and state directly that

$$\mathscr{L}[f(t)] = \frac{A}{T(1 - \varepsilon^{-Ts})} \int_0^T t\varepsilon^{-st}\, dt \qquad (7.63)$$

The integral is a standard form which is found in any set of ntegral tables. After inserting the limits and simplifying algebraic-lly, one has

$$F(s) = A\left[\frac{1}{Ts^2} - \frac{\varepsilon^{-Ts}}{s(1 - \varepsilon^{-Ts})}\right] \qquad (7.64)$$

EXAMPLE 4. We saw that for a sine wave, it was easier to take the transform directly, rather than trying to use the periodicity theorem.

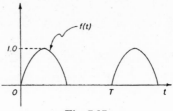

Fig. 7.17

Suppose, however, that one has a half-wave rectified sine wave as shown in Fig. 7.17. Using the periodicity theorem, we write

$$F(s) = \frac{1}{(1 - \varepsilon^{-Ts})} \int_0^{\frac{T}{2}} \sin \omega t \; \varepsilon^{-st} \, dt \qquad (7.65)$$

$$F(s) = \frac{1}{(1 - \varepsilon^{-Ts})} \left[\frac{\varepsilon^{-st}s \sin \omega t - \omega \varepsilon^{-st} \cos \omega t}{s^2 + \omega^2} \right] \qquad (7.66)$$

and since $T = 2\pi/\omega$, (7.66) reduces to

$$F(s) = \frac{\omega}{(s^2 + \omega^2)\left(1 - \varepsilon^{-\frac{\pi s}{\omega}}\right)} \qquad (7.67)$$

7.9. The Laplace transform of a single sawtooth pulse

Let us consider the case of a single sawtooth pulse, which occurs only once and does not repeat itself. This appears in Fig. 7.18. Using the direct approach, we write

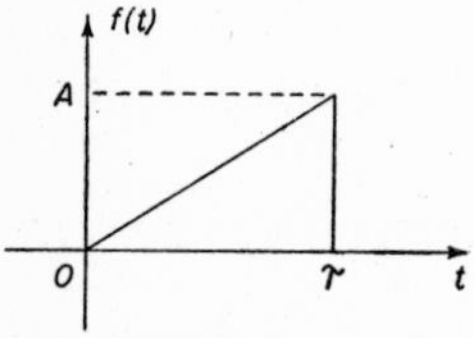

$$f(t) = \frac{At}{\tau} \bigg|_{t < \tau} \qquad (7.68)$$

and

$$F(s) = \frac{A}{\tau} \int_0^\tau t\varepsilon^{-st} \, dt \qquad (7.69)$$

Fig. 7.18

After using a standard form for the integral, and inserting limits, we have

$$F(s) = \frac{A}{\tau s^2} \left[1 - (1 + as)\varepsilon^{-as} \right] \qquad (7.70)$$

PROBLEM. Apply the single pulse shown in Fig. 7.18 to a network which has the transfer function

$$Z_T(s) = \frac{1}{LCs^2 + 1} \tag{7.71}$$

and solve for the output voltage as a function of time. What conclusions can be drawn (a) during the pulse? (b) after the pulse is finished?

7.10. Pulsed periodic functions

It often happens in electronics and radio work that one has short bursts or pulses of periodic functions. In radio telegraphy, for example, the R–F carrier, which has its own particular frequency, is keyed on and off in accordance with the dot and dash sequence of the international code. In missile range timing systems, and in many types of data transmission systems, the signals are in the form of keyed sinewaves.

Inasmuch as these pulsed periodic functions play an important part in practical electronics, we should examine a typical waveform and determine its Laplace transform for addition to our list of reference transforms. Such a waveform is shown in Fig. 7.19.

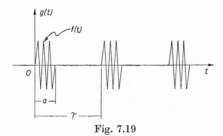

Fig. 7.19

Notice that $f(t)$ represents a continuous periodic function. This could be a sinewave, but we will keep it a general function until we finish the analysis; $g(t)$ represents the pulses of $f(t)$ after keying, and will involve the pulse length a and the keying period τ.

Let us first write an expression for $g(t)$ that is correct within the first period. The undesired portion of $f(t)$ can be blanked out by using two step functions, as

$$g(t) = f(t)[U(t) - U(t - a)] \tag{7.72}$$

Note again that this expression is only valid for the first period τ. However, the same format occurs for each succeeding period, and we learned in art. 7.8 that it was only necessary to integrate the Laplace transform over one period for such functions. We can therefore use (7.57) to write

$$G(s) = \frac{1}{(1 - \varepsilon^{-\tau s})} \int_0^\tau g(t)\varepsilon^{-st}\,dt \qquad (7.73)$$

If we now replace $g(t)$ in the integral with its actual value taken from (7.72), we have

$$G(s) = \frac{1}{(1 - \varepsilon^{-\tau s})} \int_0^a f(t)\varepsilon^{-st}\,dt \qquad (7.74)$$

The portion of the integral from a to τ is zero, and is omitted.

If the original function $f(t)$ had not been pulsed, we could have written its transform by using the periodicity theorem as

$$F(s) = \frac{1}{(1 - \varepsilon^{-as})} \int_0^a f(t)\varepsilon^{-st}\,dt \qquad (7.75)$$

In integrating from 0 to a, we may cover several actual periods of $f(t)$, but the exponential in the multiplier involves the same a, and makes the actual number of periods of $f(t)$ immaterial. We can use (7.75) to write

$$\int_0^a f(t)\varepsilon^{-st}\,dt = (1 - \varepsilon^{-as})F(s) \qquad (7.76)$$

and finally, this result is placed into (7.74) to give

$$G(s) = \frac{(1 - \varepsilon^{-as})F(s)}{1 - \varepsilon^{-\tau s}} \qquad (7.77)$$

or

$$G(s) = \frac{(1 + \varepsilon^{-as})F(s)}{1 - \varepsilon^{-\tau s}}; \qquad \text{if } f(t + a) = -f(t) \qquad (7.77a)$$

When using (7.77), make certain that $f(t + a) = f(t)$. If $f(t + a) = -f(t)$, reverse the sign on the exponential term in the numerator as shown in (7.77a). $F(s)$, of course, is the transform of $f(t)$, the original waveform before it was keyed. If the reader wishes to call the final transform $F(s)$ rather than $G(s)$, he can merely substitute some other letter for $f(t)$ and $F(s)$ above.

EXAMPLE. A telegraph key is used to modulate an R–F carrier with a series of dots. The key is down for 0.1 sec and up for 0.3 sec repeatedly. The carrier is 1 Mc. Write the transform of the voltage at the antenna (ignore amplitude)

$$f(t) = \sin \omega t; \quad \omega = 2\pi 10^6$$

from this,

$$F(s) = \frac{\omega}{s^2 + \omega^2}$$

The intervals of keying are

$$a = 0.1 \text{ sec}$$
$$\tau = a + 3a = 0.4 \text{ sec}$$

Using (7.77), we write

$$G(s) = \frac{\omega(1 - \varepsilon^{-as})}{(s^2 + \omega^2)(1 - \varepsilon^{-\tau s})}$$

or

$$G(s) = \frac{2\pi 10^6(1 - \varepsilon^{-0.1s})}{(s^2 + 4\pi^2 10^{12})(1 - \varepsilon^{-0.4s})}$$

PROBLEMS

(1) A sine wave $\sin \omega t$ is "keyed on" every other half-cycle by using a rectifier. This results in the same pattern shown in Fig. 7.17, i.e. half-wave rectification. Determine that the transform is

$$F(s) = \frac{\omega}{(s^2 + \omega^2)\left(1 - \varepsilon^{-\frac{\pi s}{\omega}}\right)}$$

by using the theorem developed in this article. In other words, use (7.77) or (7.77a).

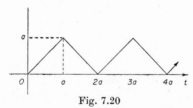

Fig. 7.20

(2) Consider Fig. 7.20. Show that the Laplace transform of the waveform shown in Fig. 7.20 is

$$F(s) = \frac{\tanh{(as/2)}}{s^2}$$

7.11. Transform of a displaced ramp function

Let us determine the transform of the function shown in Fig. 7.21. The function is 0 for values of t less than a, thus, by the direct definition

$$F(s) = \int_a^\infty (t - a)\varepsilon^{-st} dt \tag{7.78}$$

or

$$F(s) = \int_a^\infty t\varepsilon^{-st}\, dt - a \int_a^\infty \varepsilon^{-st}\, dt \tag{7.79}$$

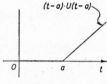

$(t-a)\cdot U(t-a)$

Fig. 7.21

The last term is recognized immediately as the transform of a step function of height a. The first integral is:

$$\int_a^\infty t\varepsilon^{-st}\, dt = \left[\frac{\varepsilon^{-st}}{s^2} (-st - 1) \right]_a^\infty \tag{7.80}$$

$$= \left[\frac{-t\varepsilon^{-st}}{s} \right]_a^\infty - \left[\frac{\varepsilon^{-st}}{s^2} \right]_a^\infty \tag{7.81}$$

The last bracketed term is ε^{-as}/s^2, and the first bracketed term must be evaluated by l'Hospital's rule. The upper limit results in 0, and the lower limit gives ε^{-as}/s. Collecting the parts from (7.81) and (7.79), we have

$$F(s) = \frac{\varepsilon^{-as}}{s} - \frac{\varepsilon^{-as}}{s} + \frac{\varepsilon^{-as}}{s^2} \tag{7.82}$$

or going to the final result, we have

$$F(s) = \frac{\varepsilon^{-as}}{s^2} \tag{7.83}$$

CHAPTER VIII

SPECIALIZED APPLICATIONS OF THE LAPLACE TRANSFORM

8.1. Introduction

IN this last chapter, the writer would like to present several topics which most electronics engineers should find both informative and useful. It has been necessary to postpone some of the more interesting subjects until the reader has progressed through the complete sequence of operations with the Laplace transforms and associated theorems. Now, in accordance with the general intent of this text to enhance the reader's ability to work with modern concepts, we shall discuss several specialized applications of the complex frequency plane and its constellation of poles and zeros.

The Laplace transform has many uses not directly associated with network or waveform analysis. It can generally be used to solve differential equations, including those with an arbitrary number of independent variables, partial differential equations, integrals and finite difference equations. The Laplace transform can also be used to evaluate definite integrals, to sum series and to develop the theory of functions. Extended to distributed parameters, it plays an important role in recent theoretical developments in transmission lines, antenna theory and waveguides.

8.2. Normalization of transfer functions

The reader has now acquired considerable experience with transfer functions and their associated networks. We should at this time discuss two features which apply to all transfer functions, regardless of the ultimate purpose for the corresponding network.

The first feature of interest is the concept of impedance level. When one undertakes the analysis or synthesis of an involved network, it is certainly desirable to simplify the work as much as possible. For example, one way to simplify a network which contains many identical resistances is to label all of the resistances as 1 ohm (Ω). As an illustration, let us consider the transfer function given as form 12, Appendix I(b). If we choose to let R assume the value 1 Ω, we have the circuit shown in Fig. 8.1.

Although the choice of $R = 1\ \Omega$ simplifies some such networks, it will probably be impossible to use such low impedances or impedance levels with practical vacuum tubes or transistors. Therefore,

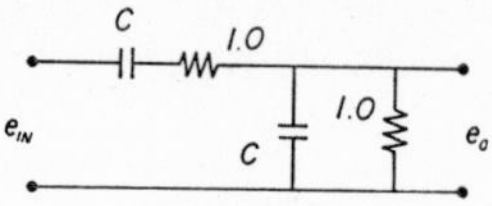

Fig. 8.1

we often have occasion to change the impedance levels of such networks.

The following general rule for changing the impedance level of a network is stated as:

(I) If every individual impedance in a network is multiplied by a constant factor A, the transfer function of the network remains unchanged.

To apply this rule, observe that the three possible impedances in any network are

$$Z_R = R; \qquad Z_C = \frac{1}{sC}; \qquad Z_L = sL \qquad (8.1)$$

If each impedance is increased by the factor A, then

$$Z_R^1 = AR; \qquad Z_C^1 = \frac{A}{sC}; \qquad Z_L^1 = sAL \qquad (8.2)$$

Physically, this means that each resistor in the network is multiplied by A, each inductance is multiplied by A, but that each capacity in the network is divided by A. These operations have no effect on the transfer function.

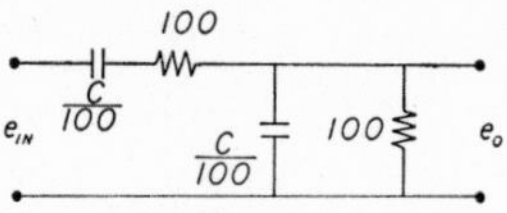

Fig. 8.2

If we should decide to raise the impedance level of Fig. 8.1 by 100 times, the application of the above rule gives the new circuit shown in Fig. 8.2, whose transfer function is the same as that of Fig. 8.1.

The second feature of interest is the concept of normalized frequency. In working with networks, more general results can often be obtained if we choose a critical frequency to be 1 rad/sec, rather than some special frequency which is of interest only in a specific problem. Such a critical frequency might be the upper cutoff frequency of a low-pass filter network, or the frequency of oscillation of the network shown in Fig. 8.2, when used as a Wien-bridge oscillator. To illustrate, we know from earlier work that the frequency of oscillation of a Wien-bridge oscillator, using the network of Fig. 8.2, is

$$f = \frac{1}{2\pi RC} \tag{8.3}$$

Upon examining the network shown in Fig. 8.3, it is seen that we have normalized the impedance level to 1 Ω, and the frequency has

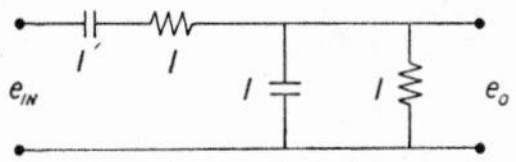

Fig. 8.3

been normalized also to 1 rad/sec. The transfer function for Fig. 8.3 has been simplified to

$$Z_T(s) = \frac{s}{s^2 + 3s + 1} \tag{8.4}$$

Should we be given a network where the frequency has been normalized to unity, we observe from (8.1) that if the frequency should be multiplied by a constant B, the resistors in the network remain as the same impedance. For the inductances in the network, however, we note that if the frequency is multiplied by B, the inductance must be divided by B to maintain the same impedance as before. Finally, all condensers in the network must also be divided by B if their impedances are to remain unchanged at the new frequency.

The general rule for removing a frequency normalization is therefore stated as follows:

(II) To raise the frequency from $\omega = 1$ to $\omega = B$, leave all resistors in the network unchanged, and divide all L's and all C's in the network by B.

EXAMPLE. The low-pass filter shown in Fig. 8.4 has a cut-off frequency of $\omega_C = 1.0$ rad/sec. The output resistance is $1.0 \, \Omega$.

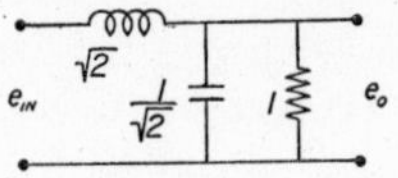

Fig. 8.4

First, let us remove the impedance normalization by using the rule (I). The impedance level is to be increased 10,000 times. From (8.2) we have

$$\left.\begin{aligned} R &= 10,000 \, \Omega \\ C &= \frac{10^{-4}}{\sqrt{2}} \, \text{F} \\ L &= \sqrt{(2)} \cdot 10^4 \, \text{H} \end{aligned}\right\} \tag{8.5}$$

Second, we wish to change the cut-off frequency from the normalized value of 1 rad/sec to a new value, 1,000 rad/sec. Using rule (II), equation (8.5) becomes

$$\left.\begin{aligned} R &= 10,000 \, \Omega \\ C &= 10^{-7}/\sqrt{2} \, \text{F} \\ L &= 10\sqrt{2} \, \text{H} \end{aligned}\right\} \tag{8.6}$$

The concepts of normalized impedance and normalized frequency are of considerable importance in network theory. For example, most data that is presented in handbooks is given for such normalized networks, which makes the data general, and useful for more applications. We shall use both concepts in our discussion of filter theory, which begins in the next article.

One can combine both rules, and remove both normalizations at once. Thus, to raise the impedance level by a factor A, and to raise the frequency by a factor B, one can:

$$\left.\begin{aligned} &\text{multiply each network resistor by } A \\ &\text{multiply each network inductor by } A/B \\ &\text{multiply each network condenser by } 1/AB \end{aligned}\right\} \tag{8.7}$$

This last is useful if a large number of elements are involved in a design, but the writer recommends the reader to work from the two basic concepts instead. The two basic rules may easily be reasoned out if the engineer understands the principles, while special combinations or formulas such as (8.7) are soon forgotten or remembered in error.

8.3. Low-pass filters

One of the most useful low-pass filters that can be devised is the Butterworth filter. This type is based upon the properties of a "maximally flat function", and is named after the man who first used such a function for filter purposes. The primary feature of a Butterworth filter is its amplitude vs. frequency characteristic. The gain, or ratio of e_0/e_{IN} for a Butterworth low-pass filter is

$$A = \frac{e_0}{e_{IN}} = \frac{1}{\sqrt{(1 + \omega^{2n})}} \qquad (8.8)$$

We see by inspection of (8.8) that for values of ω slightly less than 1.0, the gain approximates unity, and the region from 0 to $\omega = 1.0$ is said to be a pass band. For values of ω slightly greater than unity, the gain approximates zero, and therefore little energy is passed at frequency values above $\omega = 1.0$. The approximation to a perfect filter which cuts off abruptly at $\omega = 1.0$ becomes better and better as n is increased. At $\omega = 1.0$, we see that the network gain is 0.707, and by definition this occurs at the upper cut-off frequency which is thus $\omega_0 = 1.0$.

The factor n in the expression is called the "order" of the filter. Thus, for a third-order Butterworth filter, the expression for gain is

$$A = \frac{1}{\sqrt{(1 + \omega^6)}} \qquad (8.9)$$

We can see intuitively that the factor n determines the sharpness of cut-off of the filter at and beyond the point $\omega_0 = 1.0$.

Amplitude curves for the first-, third- and fifth-order Butterworth filters are shown in Fig. 8.5. For the fifth-order Butterworth filter, it is easy to see that the response is perfectly flat over the pass band, up to the point where drop-off begins. This accounts for the term "maximally flat function". If the filter has the true Butterworth shape, there will be no peaks or valleys within the pass band.

The curves of Fig. 8.5 and the function (8.8) have the frequency normalized to 1.0. We can discuss the entire subject of filters on this basis, knowing that when we finally become interested in a specific result, the normalizations can easily be removed by the methods of art. 8.2.

The Butterworth amplitude function (8.8) allows us to determine the order n required for a given cut-off rate. For example, suppose we want to design a filter whose gain is 0.707 at the cut-off frequency

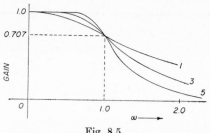

Fig. 8.5

$\omega_0 = 1.0$, and whose gain has dropped to 1.0% at $\omega = 2.0$, i.e. at the second harmonic of the cut-off frequency. For this case

$$\frac{1}{\sqrt{(1 + 2^{2n})}} = \frac{1}{100} \tag{8.10}$$

or

$$1 + 2^{2n} = 10^4 \tag{8.11}$$

and for all practical purposes

$$2^{2n} = 10^4 \tag{8.12}$$

Taking the common logarithm of both sides, we have

$$\log 2^{2n} = 4 \tag{8.13}$$

or

$$2n \log 2 = 4 \tag{8.14}$$

$$n = \frac{2}{\log 2} \tag{8.15}$$

or finally,

$$n = 6.64 \tag{8.16}$$

Apparently we must use the next integral value, which means that we must build a seventh-order Butterworth filter to meet this specification.

It will be found shortly that the value of n is equal to the number of reactive elements in the final version of the filter. Thus, for

$n = 7.0$, to meet the amplitude specification above there must be seven separate reactive elements in the filter network.

8.4. Maximally flat functions

In the design of Butterworth filters, we will be interested in transfer functions which are maximally flat. Such functions of s will have the amplitude characteristic given by (8.8). The value n will correspond to the highest power of s in the transfer function.

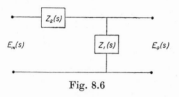

Fig. 8.6

To digress for a moment, suppose we consider Fig. 8.6. It does not require much effort to see that the transfer function of this network is

$$Z_T(s) = \frac{Z_1(s)}{Z_2(s) + Z_1(s)} \tag{8.17}$$

We observe that the entire numerator is contained in the denominator. Now if we can recognize such a correspondence between parts of the numerator and denominator of a given transfer function, it should be possible to draw the network which the function represents, merely by placing the component parameters into the two boxes shown in Fig. 8.6. This type of operation is called network synthesis, and is the opposite of analysis. In analyzing a given network, one proceeds to determine the transfer function. In synthesis, one is given a transfer function from which one must determine a corresponding network.

As an illustration of a very simple type of synthesis, suppose we are given the transfer function

$$Z_T(s) = \frac{1}{s + 1} \tag{8.18}$$

Comparing this with (8.17), we see that the numerator also occurs as part of the denominator. This is to say

$$\left.\begin{array}{l} Z_1(s) = 1.0 \\ Z_2(s) = s \end{array}\right\} \tag{8.19}$$

$Z_2(s)$ evidently corresponds to a 1 H inductance, while $Z_1(s)$ appears to be a 1 Ω resistance. If these values are inserted into the boxes shown in Fig. 8.6, we have synthesized the network which appears in Fig. 8.7. Admittedly, this is a very simple network, but it serves in an elementary way to illustrate the principle.

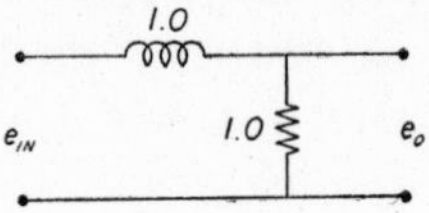

Fig. 8.7

As a further observation about (8.18), note that we can divide both the numerator and the denominator by s without algebraically changing the function, i.e.

$$Z_T(s) = \frac{1/s}{1 + 1/s} \tag{8.20}$$

so that

$$\left. \begin{array}{l} Z_1(s) = \dfrac{1}{s} \\[2mm] Z_2(s) = 1.0 \end{array} \right\} \tag{8.21}$$

In this case $Z_1(s)$ would appear to be a 1 F condenser, while $Z_2(s)$ appears to be a 1 Ω resistor. Using Fig. 8.6 as a guide, the synthesized network is shown in Fig. 8.8. At this point, the reader

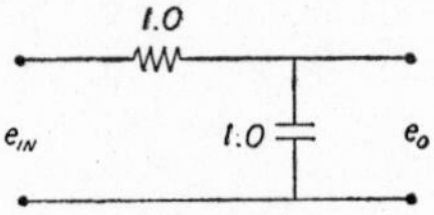

Fig. 8.8

should write the transfer functions for Fig. 8.7 and Fig. 8.8, and show that they are identical. Having digressed to discuss elementary synthesis, let us now examine the following second-order function of s.

$$F(s) = \frac{1}{s^2 + s\sqrt{2} + 1} \tag{8.22}$$

By inserting $j\omega$ for s in (8.22), the reader should ascertain that the magnitude of (8.22) is

$$|F(\omega)| = \frac{1}{\sqrt{(1 + \omega^4)}} \tag{8.23}$$

We observe that the highest power of s in (8.22) is 2.0, and that the amplitude function corresponds to the Butterworth function for $n = 2.0$. We can therefore conclude that (8.22) is the transfer function of a second-order Butterworth low-pass filter.

The numerator of (8.22) is contained in the denominator, but if we try to apply (8.17) immediately, we run into difficulty, as we have no impedance which equals s^2. However, if we first divide both numerator and denominator by s, we have

$$Z_T(s) = \frac{1/s}{s + \sqrt{2} + 1/s} \tag{8.24}$$

If we now let

$$\left. \begin{aligned} Z_1(s) &= \frac{1}{s} \\ Z_2(s) &= \sqrt{2} + s \end{aligned} \right\} \tag{8.25}$$

we can again use Fig. 8.6 as a model, to synthesize the actual circuit which (8.24) represents. This network is shown in Fig. 8.9.

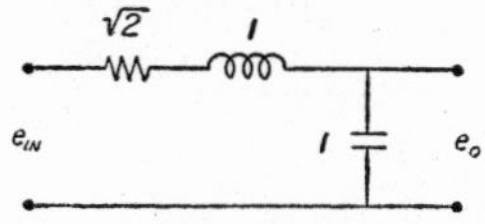

Fig. 8.9

The second-order Butterworth transfer function (8.22) could also be written as

$$Z_T(s) = \frac{1}{s(s + \sqrt{2}) + 1} \tag{8.26}$$

If we now divide both numerator and denominator by the factor $(s + \sqrt{2})$, we have

$$Z_T(s) = \frac{1/(s + \sqrt{2})}{s + 1/(s + \sqrt{2})} \tag{8.27}$$

We can now let

$$Z_1(s) = \frac{1}{s + \sqrt{2}}; \qquad Z_2(s) = s$$

$Z_2(s)$ appears to represent a simple inductance of 1 H, but $Z_1(s)$ seems to be some combination. If we invert $Z_1(s)$ we obtain

$$Y_1(s) = s + \sqrt{2} \tag{8.28}$$

which, in this form, is recognized at once as the parallel combination of the susceptance sC and the conductance $\sqrt{2}$ mho. The parallel combination, with parts labeled as impedances, is shown in Fig. 8.10. Using Fig. 8.6 as a guide, we draw the complete second version of

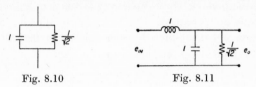

Fig. 8.10   Fig. 8.11

this function as the circuit shown in Fig. 8.11. The reader should write the transfer functions of Fig. 8.11 and Fig. 8.9 separately, to show that they are indeed satisfied by (8.22).

We have demonstrated alternate network solutions for both the very simple first-order and the slightly more involved second-order Butterworth filters. It can be stated as a general rule that a given network can be analyzed and will have only one definite transfer function, but that if a transfer function is given instead, it is possible to synthesize an infinite number of networks which may represent it. Of course the transfer function must actually have a solution.

PROBLEMS

(1) Consider Fig. 8.12, where values are given in ohms (Ω), henrys (H) and farads (F). Show that the transfer function is

$$Z_T(s) = \frac{1}{s^3 + 2s^2 + 2s + 1} \qquad (8.29)$$

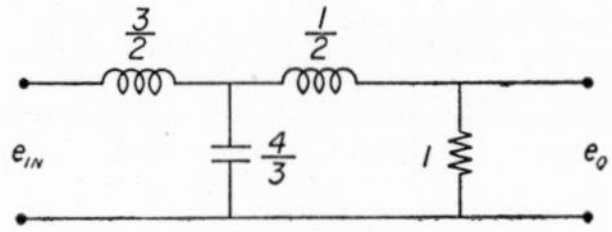

Fig. 8.12

(2) Show that the magnitude, for $s = j\omega$, is the third-order Butterworth filter

$$|Z(\omega)| = \frac{1}{\sqrt{(1 + \omega^6)}} \qquad (8.30)$$

8.5. Pole location for Butterworth functions

The reader has probably begun to suspect that there is more order here than meets the eye thus far; and the orderliness does exist.

This will become evident when we locate the poles of the different order Butterworth functions in the s-plane. We will not go into the theory behind the location of the poles, as this has little interest for the practising electronics engineer. Once we point out the procedure for locating the poles in the s-plane, the formation of the functions will be obvious by inspection.

(a) We state first that an nth order Butterworth function has n poles in the s-plane, i.e. the function involves s to the nth power.

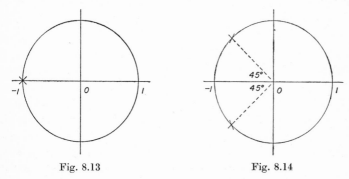

Fig. 8.13   Fig. 8.14

(b) The poles are all located on a circle of unity radius, centered at the origin in the s-plane.

(c) The poles are all located in the left half-plane, and are symmetrical about the point $s = -1$.

Examples of pole locations for the first four orders will make the procedure more clear than trying to explain it by a rule. The first-order Butterworth function has one pole, located on the circle of unity radius at $s = -1$. This is shown in Fig. 8.13. The second-order Butterworth filter, represented by (8.22), has poles at

$$s = -\frac{1}{\sqrt{2}} \pm j \frac{1}{\sqrt{2}} \tag{8.31}$$

and these are also symmetrical on the unit circle, as shown in Fig. 8.14. The third-order Butterworth filter, represented by (8.29), has poles located at

$$\left. \begin{array}{l} s = -1 \\[1.2em] s = \varepsilon^{\frac{j2\pi}{3}} \\[1.2em] s = \varepsilon^{-\frac{j2\pi}{3}} \end{array} \right\} \tag{8.32}$$

and these are shown in Fig. 8.15. The fourth-order Butterworth filter has poles located as in Fig. 8.16. The fifth-order Butterworth filter would have poles at angles of $0°$, $\pm 36°$, $\pm 72°$, measured from the negative real axis. Note that in all cases, the left half-circle is divided into n equal sectors, with one sector between each adjacent pair of poles, and one-half sector located between the top-most pole

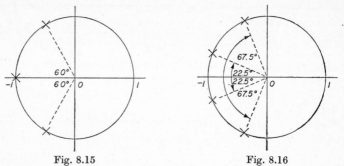

Fig. 8.15   Fig. 8.16

and the upper j-axis, with the remaining half-sector between the bottom-most pole and the $-j$-axis.

To derive the transfer function for a given order filter, it is easiest first to draw the pole diagram. One can then determine each factor in the denominator from the pole diagram.

For example, if there are three poles, one can use Fig. 8.15, and the pole locations given by (8.32) to write

$$Z_T(s) = \frac{1}{(s+1)\left(s - \varepsilon^{\frac{j2\pi}{3}}\right)\left(s - \varepsilon^{-\frac{j2\pi}{3}}\right)} \tag{8.33}$$

which simplifies progressively as

$$Z_T(s) = \frac{1}{(s+1)\left(s^2 - s\varepsilon^{\frac{j2\pi}{3}} - s\varepsilon^{-\frac{j2\pi}{3}} + 1\right)} \tag{8.34}$$

$$Z_T(s) = \frac{1}{(s+1)(s^2 - 2s\cos 2\pi/3 + 1)} \tag{8.35}$$

$$Z_T(s) = \frac{1}{(s+1)(s^2 + s + 1)} \tag{8.36}$$

and finally

$$Z_T(s) = \frac{1}{s^3 + 2s^2 + 2s + 1} \tag{8.37}$$

with the usual property that

$$|Z_T| = \frac{1}{\sqrt{(1 + \omega^6)}} \tag{8.38}$$

If there are an even number of poles, one can take them in pairs. For example, in Fig. 8.16 one can combine both $\pi/8$ and $3\pi/8$ pairs to give

$$Z_T(s) = \frac{1}{(s^2 + 2s \cos \pi/8 + 1)(s^2 + 2s \cos 3\pi/8 + 1)} \tag{8.39}$$

which gives a fourth-order Butterworth function, and if $s = j\omega$, (8.39) becomes

$$|Z_T| = \frac{1}{\sqrt{(1 + \omega^2\sqrt{2} + \omega^4)} \cdot \sqrt{(1 - \omega^2\sqrt{2} + \omega^4)}} \tag{8.40}$$

or

$$|Z_T| = \frac{1}{\sqrt{(1 + \omega^8)}} \tag{8.41}$$

8.6. Synthesis of the third-order maximally flat function

The third-order Butterworth filter has the function

$$Z_T(s) = \frac{1}{s^3 + 2s^2 + 2s + 1} \tag{8.42}$$

As the order of the function increases, the circuit complexity must necessarily increase, and we may expect that the synthesis procedure will become more involved. It was possible to synthesize the first- and second-order functions by inspection, with a little algebraic manipulation of the function in advance. Such a simple procedure fails when we have a third-order function.

There are numerous formal ways of finding the actual circuit which has (8.42) as its transfer function, but the writer would prefer to choose a simplified approach which is certain to be understood by all readers. Let us first make a few observations about (8.42).

(a) We know from observation (or by proof if we should discuss the subject at greater length) that a third-order transfer function such as this will have three reactive elements.

(b) If we choose to have the final element in the filter be a shunt 1 Ω resistance, as in the first two cases, this would make a total of four components, one of which is the 1.0 Ω resistor.

(c) We feel that the input reactance will be a series element, since it would hardly affect the performance of the filter were it to be shunted directly across the input voltage.

(d) Finally, we suspect that in a low-pass filter, the series reactive elements will be inductances, while any shunt reactive elements will be condensers.

The above reasoning, which requires no great imagination, leads us to suspect that the actual circuit arrangement will be as in Fig.

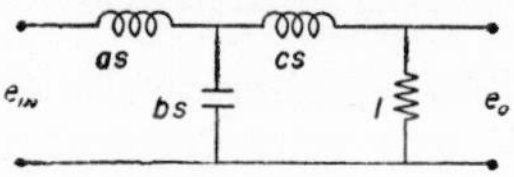

Fig. 8.17

8.17. The values of the three reactances are not yet known, of course, so we merely label them as a, b, c. Now if the reader will analyze this circuit, he will find that the transfer function is

$$Z_T(s) = \frac{1}{abcs^3 + abs^2 + (a + c)s + 1} \tag{8.43}$$

Since we want this to represent (8.42), we can set these two functions equal to each other, i.e.

$$\frac{1}{abcs^3 + abs^2 + (a + c)s + 1} = \frac{1}{s^3 + 2s^2 + 2s + 1} \tag{8.44}$$

The coefficients of like powers of s must be equal to each other, and thus we have

$$abc = 1 \tag{8.45}$$

$$ab = 2 \tag{8.46}$$

$$a + c = 2 \tag{8.47}$$

Inspection of this simple set of equations shows that

$$\left.\begin{aligned} a &= \tfrac{3}{2} \\ b &= \tfrac{4}{3} \\ c &= \tfrac{1}{2} \end{aligned}\right\} \tag{8.48}$$

When these values are inserted in Fig. 8.17, we have completed the problem, and the result appears as in Fig. 8.18. The reader will

gree that this circuit has the transfer function given by (8.42), as
e has already worked the same network as problem 1 in art. 8.4.

In Appendix I(b) he will find a set of networks for the first ten
rders of Butterworth functions. These have all been normalized
) 1.0 Ω impedance level and 1.0 rad/sec frequency.

The reader can thus build up to a tenth-order filter merely by
sing the appropriate network from Appendix I(b), removing
ne normalizations so as to meet his own particular design needs.

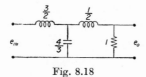

Fig. 8.18

.7. High-pass maximally flat functions

Thus far we have discussed only low-pass filters. All of the
heory thus far applies equally well to the design of high-pass filters.

We recall from Chapter I that startling results can often be
btained by making a change of variables. The low-pass normalized
lters already developed can all be converted to normalized high-pass
lters by making the very simple change of variables

$$S^\star = \frac{1}{s} \tag{8.49}$$

he three possible impedance types in the filters were originally

$$Z_R = R; \qquad Z_C = \frac{1}{sC}; \qquad Z_L = sL \tag{8.50}$$

3y the above transformation (8.49), each impedance becomes

$$Z_R^\star = R; \qquad Z_C^\star = \frac{s^\star}{C}; \qquad Z_L^\star = \frac{L}{s^\star} \tag{8.51}$$

Thus all we have to do to convert the normalized low-pass filter
nto a corresponding normalized high-pass filter is to replace every
:apacity by an inductance of reciprocal numeric value, replace every
nductor by a condenser of inverse numerical value, and leave all

resistors unchanged. As a typical example, the normalized third
order Butterworth filter shown in Fig. 8.18 becomes the high-pass
normalized filter shown in Fig. 8.19.

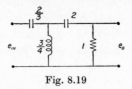

Fig. 8.19

8.8. Maximally flat band-pass filters

The low-pass Butterworth filters which we have discussed in some
detail can also serve as a basis for designing band-pass filters. If we
choose the following definitions for use with the band-pass filters:

$$\left.\begin{array}{l} \omega_H = \text{upper cut-off frequency} \\ \omega_L = \text{lower cut-off frequency} \\ \Delta\omega = \omega_H - \omega_L = \text{bandwidth} \\ \omega_C = \text{center frequency} \end{array}\right\} \qquad (8.52)$$

geometrical symmetry will dictate that

$$\omega_C^2 = \omega_L \omega_H \qquad (8.53)$$

Suppose we take one of the normalized low-pass filters and change
its cut-off frequency to $\Delta\omega$. We can now make a change of variable
whereby

$$s = s^\star + \frac{\omega_C^2}{s^\star} \qquad (8.54)$$

Thus each s in the low-pass filter which has bandwidth $\Delta\omega$ is replaced
by the new value in (8.54).

If we compare the old values with the required new values, we
can arrive at the following simple conclusions:

(a) The normalized low-pass filter of desired order is first changed
to have a cut-off frequency equal to $\Delta\omega$.

(b) Equation (8.54) requires that for every capacity in the network, we add an inductance in parallel whose value is given by

$$L = \frac{1}{\omega_C^2 C} \qquad (8.55)$$

(c) Equation (8.54) requires also that for every inductance in the original network, we add a condenser in series whose value is

$$C = \frac{1}{\omega_C^2 L} \qquad (8.56)$$

(d) All original resistors in the network are left unchanged.

After the above conversion has been made, one can then change the impedance level from $1.0 \, \Omega$ to whatever appropriate level is required. The steps (a), (b) and (c) are so simple that the reader is requested to work out several examples for practice by himself, using any of the low-pass networks already developed.

8.9. Alternate approach to the Laplace integral

As an additional topic, the writer would like to present an alternate development of the Laplace integral, which is based upon the power expansion of a function. A power series is often used to represent some function of time. If the time function is called $f(t)$, then

$$f(t) = a_0 + a_1 t + a_2 t^2 + a_3 t^3 + \cdots a_n t^n \qquad (8.57)$$

We note here that any particular a is a function of n, and therefore,

$$f(t) = \sum_{n=0}^{\infty} a(n) t^n \qquad (8.58)$$

Now since a is a function of n, which will in all probability not have integral values for most practical functions, suppose we allow a to become some general variable which can assume any appropriate value. To do this, let us choose two variables u and v, along with a new function G, and write by comparison with (8.57)

$$G(v) = u_0 + u_1 v + u_2 v^2 + u_3 v^3 + \cdots u_n v^n \qquad (8.59)$$

or

$$G(v) = \sum_{n=0}^{\infty} u(n) v^n \qquad (8.60)$$

If we should factor out a quantity Δn from every term in the series u still remains a function of n, and therefore

$$G(v) = \sum_{n=0}^{\infty} u(n) v^n \Delta n \qquad (8.61)$$

In (8.61), n represents only integral values from 0 to ∞, but to make things more general, suppose we allow n to become another variable w, which can assume any value, then

$$G(v) = \sum_{w=0}^{\infty} u(w)v^w \Delta w \tag{8.62}$$

Now regardless of the value of v, there is always some variable s such that

$$v = \varepsilon^{-s} \tag{8.63}$$

from which we can state that

$$G(v) = F(s) \tag{8.64}$$

Re-writing (8.62), we have

$$F(s) = \int_0^{\infty} u(w)\varepsilon^{-sw}\, dw \tag{8.65}$$

Now if the general variable w should be chosen specifically as time t, then $u(w)$ will be some specific function which we can call $f(t)$, so that (8.65) becomes

$$F(s) = \int_0^{\infty} f(t)\varepsilon^{-st}\, dt \tag{8.66}$$

a result which should appear familiar by this time.

The writer hopes that he will be forgiven by the pure mathematicians (or at least by the engineering reader) for the somewhat unorthodox manipulations which led to (8.66). At any rate, this book is intended for practical electronics engineers who are often accused of similar unconventional approaches to design. The chief reason for this derivation is to permit the reader to relate intuitively the now familiar Laplace transform very closely with operations involving an infinite series.

The reader who pursues the subject of Laplace transforms well beyond the scope of this book will uncover many areas of usefulness not necessarily related to electronics or radio. Since this article has shown the close relation between an infinite series and the Laplace transform integral, we shall now discuss ways of using the Laplace transform to sum an infinite number of terms of a series, to obtain a result in closed form.

8.10. The Laplace integral used to sum infinite series into closed form

Every electronics engineer finds it necessary at times to work with infinite series. There are numerous functions that can only be expressed as some form of infinite series. Many of the large computers will derive values for a function by summing a large number of terms of its corresponding series, this being more practical than to store tabulated values in the computer. We can say that, in general, any detailed engineering analysis is quite likely to encounter an infinite series at some point.

It is unfortunate that most of the series having practical engineering applications converge quite slowly. When evaluating such a series manually this means that considerable work must be expended. When such a series in this form is programmed for evaluation by a digital computer, storage for a large number of terms must be provided. In any event, it is usually desirable, when possible, to express such an infinite series in closed form.

By closed form, one refers to a simple, complete function which represents the infinite series. For example, if

$$f(x) = x - \frac{x^3}{\underline{|3}} + \frac{x^5}{\underline{|5}} - \frac{x^7}{\underline{|7}} + \cdots \qquad (8.67)$$

we say that

$$f(x) = \sin x \qquad (8.68)$$

and therefore the expression $\sin x$ is the closed form of the infinite series given by (8.67).

The reader will recall from his earlier work with series that he can apply various tests to determine whether or not the series converges. Such tests usually involve specific operations with the nth term of the given series.

To be completely known, the nth term of a series must be given, because some series which seem to progress in a fixed manner term by term will suddenly appear to become erratic after a certain number of terms.

If the nth term of a series is known, it would be well to have some procedure available to determine what the closed form of the series would be, if such a closed form exists. The Laplace transform serves as a basis for such a procedure.

Suppose we are given the general, or nth term of some series which we do not recognize. The nth term is then a function of n, or

$$F(n) = n\text{th term} \tag{8.69}$$

(n) is called the dummy index of summation, and would take on successive values from some lower limit to infinity.

Now suppose we associate n, the index of summation, with the complex variable s, and define a function of s as

$$F(s) = \int_0^\infty f(t)\varepsilon^{-st}\,dt \tag{8.70}$$

where (8.70) is the definition of the Laplace transform also, as used throughout the text. If we simulate the nth term of the series as a function of s, it will then be necessary to sum each side of (8.70) in the same way that it was necessary to sum the nth term from the lower limit to infinity. Accordingly, (8.70) can be written as

$$\sum F(s) = \sum \int_0^\infty f(t)\varepsilon^{-st}\,dt \tag{8.71}$$

The summation and integration process can be interchanged for operation on s, because s is not a function of t, and therefore (8.71) can become

$$\sum F(s) = \int_0^\infty f(t)\,dt \sum (\varepsilon^{-t})^s \tag{8.72}$$

Equation (8.72) is now in proper form and ready for use in summing series. First, however, we will list two auxiliary relations with which every electronics engineer is familiar. We write them here merely for reference. These are:

$$\text{(A)} \qquad \sum_{s=0}^\infty a^s = \frac{1}{1-a}, \qquad |s| < 1.0 \tag{8.73}$$

and

$$\text{(B)} \qquad \sum_{s=0}^\infty \frac{a^s}{\underline{|s}} = \varepsilon^a, \qquad |a| \text{ finite} \tag{8.74}$$

Slight variations can be applied if the summation is to begin at some other value such as $s = 1$, $s = 2$, $s = 3$, etc. For example (A) becomes

$$\sum_{s=1}^\infty a^s = \frac{a}{1-a} \tag{8.75}$$

$$\sum_{s=2}^{\infty} a^s = \frac{a^2}{1 - a} \tag{8.76}$$

and

$$\sum_{s=3}^{\infty} a^s = \frac{a^3}{1 - a}, \text{ etc.} \tag{8.77}$$

Having developed (8.72) as the general form for summation, and having listed the obvious relations (8.73) through (8.77), let us apply this technique to evaluate the closed form of several infinite series. It is expected that the reader will see the procedure more clearly by following several examples than by reading a more abstract word description.

EXAMPLE 1. Suppose we choose the series

$$F(n) = \frac{1}{2} + \frac{1}{6} + \frac{1}{12} + \frac{1}{20} + \cdots + \frac{1}{n(n + 1)} \tag{8.78}$$

We now replace n by the Laplace variable s, and write the nth term as

$$F(s) = \frac{1}{s(s + 1)} \tag{8.79}$$

This notation places us upon familiar territory in the s-plane, and we can see from Appendix III that $F(s)$ corresponds to a time function $f(t)$, so that

$$\frac{1}{s(s + 1)} \leftrightarrow (1 - \varepsilon^{-t}) \tag{8.80}$$

In other words

$$\frac{1}{s(s + 1)} = \int_0^{\infty} (1 - \varepsilon^{-t})\varepsilon^{-st} \, dt \tag{8.81}$$

To sum this simulated nth term, say from 1.0 to ∞, we use the general form (8.72) to write

$$\sum_{s=1}^{\infty} \frac{1}{s(s + 1)} = \int_0^{\infty} (1 - \varepsilon^{-t}) \, dt \sum_{s=1}^{\infty} (\varepsilon^{-t})^s \tag{8.82}$$

or, breaking the right-hand side down into two integrals

$$\sum_{s=1}^{\infty} \frac{1}{s(s + 1)} = \int_0^{\infty} \sum_{s=1}^{\infty} (\varepsilon^{-t})^s \, dt - \int_0^{\infty} \varepsilon^{-t} \sum_{s=1}^{\infty} (\varepsilon^{-t})^s \, dt \tag{8.83}$$

For simplification, we can let

$$\left.\begin{aligned}
\varepsilon^{-t} &= a \\
t &= -\ln a \\
dt &= -\frac{da}{a}
\end{aligned}\right\} \tag{8.84}$$

and for the new limits,

$$\left.\begin{aligned}
t &= 0, \quad a = 1 \\
t &= \infty, \ a = 0
\end{aligned}\right\} \tag{8.85}$$

When these substitutions are made, (8.83) becomes

$$\sum_{s=1}^{\infty} \frac{1}{s(s+1)} = -\int_1^0 \sum_{s=1}^{\infty} a^s \frac{da}{a} + \int_1^0 a \sum_{s=1}^{\infty} a^s \frac{da}{a} \tag{8.86}$$

We now observe from (8.75) that

$$\sum_{s=1}^{\infty} a^s = \frac{a}{1-a} \tag{8.87}$$

and by using this information, (8.86) becomes

$$\sum_{s=1}^{\infty} \frac{1}{s(s+1)} = \int_0^1 \frac{da}{1-a} - \int_0^1 \frac{a\,da}{1-a} \tag{8.88}$$

where the signs have been changed merely by interchanging upper and lower limits. This is of minor importance.

The two parts of (8.88) can now be combined into a single integral as follows:

$$\sum_{s=1}^{\infty} \frac{1}{s(s+1)} = \int_0^1 \frac{(1-a)\,da}{(1-a)} \tag{8.89}$$

or

$$\sum_{s=1}^{\infty} \frac{1}{s(s+1)} = \int_0^1 da = 1.0 \tag{8.90}$$

If we now return to the nth term of the series given in (8.78), we can see that the infinite sequence of terms add up to unity and that the closed form is

$$\sum_{n=1}^{\infty} \frac{1}{n(n+1)} = 1.0 \tag{8.91}$$

a result which the writer does not feel is obvious from a casual inspection of (8.78).

EXAMPLE 2. Let us examine the sequence

$$\frac{1}{3} + \frac{1}{8} + \frac{1}{15} + \frac{1}{24} + \cdots + \frac{1}{n^2 - 1} \qquad (8.92)$$

For variation, let us attempt to sum this series from $n = 2$ to $n = \infty$. If we allow n to be replaced by s, so that our work can be done in the familiar s-plane, we observe from the tables of transforms that

$$\frac{1}{s^2 - 1} = \int_0^\infty \sinh t \varepsilon^{-st} \, dt \qquad (8.93)$$

We note in passing that the function of s has two real conjugate poles, symmetrical about zero on the σ axis. The hyperbolic sine of t can be expressed exponentially as

$$\sinh t = \frac{\varepsilon^t}{2} - \frac{\varepsilon^{-t}}{2} \qquad (8.94)$$

from which (8.93) can be written as

$$\frac{1}{s^2 - 1} = \frac{1}{2} \int_0^\infty \varepsilon^t \varepsilon^{-st} \, dt - \frac{1}{2} \int_0^\infty \varepsilon^{-t} \varepsilon^{-st} \, dt \qquad (8.95)$$

Using the general summation form (8.72), this becomes

$$\sum_{s=2}^\infty \frac{1}{s^2 - 1} = \frac{1}{2} \int_0^\infty \varepsilon^t \, dt \sum_{s=2}^\infty (\varepsilon^{-t})^s - \frac{1}{2} \int_0^\infty \varepsilon^{-t} \, dt \sum_{s=2}^\infty (\varepsilon^{-t})^s \qquad (8.96)$$

Let us now make the substitution of variables

$$\left. \begin{array}{l} \varepsilon^{-t} = a \\[4pt] t = -\ln a \\[4pt] dt = -\dfrac{da}{a} \end{array} \right\} \qquad (8.97)$$

and let us also make use of (8.76) to write

$$\sum_{s=2}^\infty a^s = \frac{a^2}{1 - a} \qquad (8.98)$$

Then we note that the new limits will be:

$$t = 0, \quad a = 1 \atop t = \infty, \ a = 0 \Bigg\}$$

(8.99)

Placing these substitutions into (8.96) results in

$$\sum_{s=2}^{\infty} \frac{1}{s^2 - 1} = \frac{1}{2} \int_1^0 \frac{1}{a} \frac{a^2(-da)}{(1-a)a} - \frac{1}{2} \int_1^0 \frac{aa^2(-da)}{(1-a)a}$$

(8.100)

This simplifies to

$$\sum_{s=2}^{\infty} \frac{1}{s^2 - 1} = \frac{1}{2} \int_0^1 \frac{(1-a^2)\,da}{1-a}$$

(8.101)

or

$$\sum_{s=2}^{\infty} \frac{1}{s^2 - 1} = \frac{1}{2} \int_0^1 (1+a)\,da$$

(8.102)

and finally

$$\sum_{s=2}^{\infty} \frac{1}{s^2 - 1} = \frac{1}{2} \left[\frac{(1+a)^2}{2} \right]_0^1$$

(8.103)

Substituting the limits, and replacing s by the original quantity (n), gives the final sum of the series, which is

$$\sum_{n=2}^{\infty} \frac{1}{n^2 - 1} = \frac{3}{4}$$

(8.104)

EXAMPLE 3. As a variation, let us choose a general term whose analog function of s has double order poles. A typical function of this type might be

$$F(n) = \frac{4n}{(n^2 - 1)^2}$$

(8.105)

It is desired to evaluate this series from $n = 2$ to $n = \infty$.

We begin by looking up the analog $F(s)$ in Appendix III. Note that minor sign changes in such functions can usually be handled by inspection. We would use form number 86, replacing α by j, to write

$$\frac{4s}{(s^2 - 1)^2} = 2 \int_0^{\infty} t \sinh t \varepsilon^{-st}\,dt$$

(8.106)

The integral can be written in exponential form as

$$\frac{4s}{(s^2 - 1)^2} = \int_0^\infty t\varepsilon^t \varepsilon^{-st}\, dt - \int_0^\infty t\varepsilon^{-t} \varepsilon^{-st}\, dt \qquad (8.107)$$

At this point we can make the substitutions

$$\left.\begin{aligned} \varepsilon^{-t} &= a \\ t &= -\ln a \\ dt &= -\frac{da}{a} \end{aligned}\right\} \qquad (8.108)$$

from which the new limits are

$$\left.\begin{aligned} t &= 0, \quad a = 1 \\ t &= \infty, \ a = 0 \end{aligned}\right\} \qquad (8.109)$$

With these new quantities inserted, (8.107) becomes

$$\frac{4s}{(s^2 - 1)^2} = \int_1^0 \frac{a^s \ln a\, da}{a^2} - \int_1^0 a^s \ln a\, da \qquad (8.110)$$

The standard summation from (8.72) results in

$$\sum_{s=2}^\infty \frac{4s}{(s^2 - 1)^2} = \int_1^0 \sum_{s=2}^\infty \frac{a^s \ln a\, da}{a^2} - \int_1^0 \sum_{s=2}^\infty a^s \ln a\, da \qquad (8.111)$$

We see from (8.76) that

$$\sum_{s=2}^\infty a^s = \frac{a^2}{1 - a} \qquad (8.112)$$

so that (8.111) will become

$$\sum_{s=2}^\infty \frac{4s}{(s^2 - 1)^2} = \int_1^0 \frac{\ln a\, da}{1 - a} - \int_1^0 \frac{a^2 \ln a\, da}{1 - a} \qquad (8.113)$$

Both integrals are combined to give

$$\sum_{s=2}^\infty \frac{4s}{(s^2 - 1)^2} = \int_1^0 \frac{(1 - a^2) \ln a\, da}{1 - a} \qquad (8.114)$$

$$= \int_1^0 (1 + a) \ln a\, da \qquad (8.115)$$

$$= \int_1^0 \ln a\, da + \int_1^0 a \ln a\, da \qquad (8.116)$$

Both of these are standard forms

$$\sum_{s=2}^{\infty} \frac{4s}{(s^2 - 1)^2} = \left[\left(1 + \frac{a^2}{2}\right) \ln a - a - \frac{a^2}{4} \right]_1^0 \qquad (8.117)$$

When the limits are inserted, and with n replacing s, we have the final result

$$\sum_{n=2}^{\infty} \frac{4n}{(n^2 - 1)^2} = \frac{5}{4} \qquad (8.118)$$

EXAMPLE 4. As another example, let us examine the series

$$F(n) = 1 + \frac{1}{4} + \frac{1}{9} + \frac{1}{16} + \cdots + \frac{1}{n^2} \qquad (8.119)$$

and see if this series can be summed from $n = 1$ to $n = \infty$. As usual we find an analog function of s corresponding to the nth term. From Appendix III, one finds

$$\frac{1}{s^2} = \int_0^{\infty} t\varepsilon^{-st} \, dt \qquad (8.120)$$

Now by the same procedure that went into the derivation of (8.72) we sum both sides as follows:

$$\sum_{s=1}^{\infty} \frac{1}{s^2} = \int_0^{\infty} t \, dt \sum_{s=1}^{\infty} (\varepsilon^{-t})^s \qquad (8.121)$$

If we now make the substitutions

$$\left. \begin{array}{r} \varepsilon^{-t} = a \\[4pt] t = -\ln a \\[4pt] dt = -\dfrac{da}{a} \end{array} \right\} \qquad (8.122)$$

and insert new limits

$$\left. \begin{array}{l} t = 0, \quad a = 1 \\[4pt] t = \infty, \ a = 0 \end{array} \right\} \qquad (8.123)$$

then (8.121) becomes

$$\sum_{s=1}^{\infty} \frac{1}{s^2} = \int_1^0 \frac{\ln a \, da}{1 - a} \qquad (8.124)$$

This is a standard definite integral. We replace s by n, and consult a table of definite integrals to find that

$$\sum_{n=1}^{\infty} \frac{1}{n^2} = \frac{\pi^2}{6} \tag{8.125}$$

EXAMPLE 5. As a final example to illustrate one or two new points, let us find the closed form of the series

$$F(n) = \sum_{n=1}^{\infty} \frac{1}{2^n} \tag{8.126}$$

First, we note that the nth term can be written as

$$\frac{1}{2^n} = \frac{1}{\varepsilon^{an}} \tag{8.127}$$

where

$$\varepsilon^a = 2 \tag{8.128}$$

We now move into the s-plane by the simple process of replacing n by s, and locating a function of s to match, i.e.

$$\frac{1}{\varepsilon^{as}} = \int_0^{\infty} \delta(t - a)\varepsilon^{-st}\, dt \tag{8.129}$$

It appears that the analog of the nth term is a delta function. If the summation is performed as before, we have

$$\sum_{s=1}^{\infty} \frac{1}{\varepsilon^{as}} = \int_0^{\infty} \delta(t - a) \sum_{s=1}^{\infty} (\varepsilon^{-t})^s\, dt \tag{8.130}$$

Observing (8.75), we see that

$$\sum_{s=1}^{\infty} \varepsilon^{-ts} = \frac{\varepsilon^{-t}}{1 - \varepsilon^{-t}} = \frac{1}{\varepsilon^t - 1} \tag{8.131}$$

This is inserted into (8.130) so that

$$\sum_{s=1}^{\infty} \frac{1}{\varepsilon^{as}} = \int_0^{\infty} \frac{\delta(t - a)\, dt}{\varepsilon^t - 1} \tag{8.132}$$

We now recall from art. 7.5 in Chapter VII that the integral of a δ-function and some second function is merely the value of the second function evaluated at the point where it is sampled by the δ-function (see (7.27)). Thus the integral in (8.132) reduces very easily to

$$\sum_{s=1}^{\infty} \frac{1}{\varepsilon^{as}} = \frac{1}{\varepsilon^a - 1} \tag{8.133}$$

and as a last step, if we replace s by n, and make use of (8.128), we have the answer

$$\sum_{n=1}^{\infty} \frac{1}{2^n} = 1 \tag{8.134}$$

The processes illustrated here assume, of course, that the series, as represented by the nth term, is convergent; that we can find a function of s which is the analog of the nth term, and that we can evaluate the integral which results when (8.72) is applied.

APPENDIX I

(a) Driving point transforms

1	$Z = R$	
2	$Z = Ls$	
3	$Z = \dfrac{1}{Cs}$	
4	$Z = R + Ls$	
5	$Z = \dfrac{RCs + 1}{Cs}$	
6	$Z = \dfrac{LCs^2 + 1}{Cs}$	
7	$Z = \dfrac{R}{RCs + 1}$	
8	$Z = \dfrac{RLs}{Ls + R}$	
9	$Z = \dfrac{Ls}{LCs^2 + 1}$	
0	$Z = \dfrac{(R_1 + R_2)Ls + R_1R_2}{Ls + R_2}$	
1	$Z = \dfrac{(R_1 + R_2) + R_1R_2Cs}{R_2Cs + 1}$	

209

12	$Z = \dfrac{RLCs^2 + Ls + R}{LCs^2 + 1}$	
13	$Z = \dfrac{RLs^2 + Ls + R}{s(Ls + R)}$	
14	$Z = \dfrac{R(C_1 + C_2)s + 1}{s(RC_1C_2s + C_1)}$	
15	$Z = \dfrac{L(C_1 + C_2)s^2 + 1}{s(LC_1C_2s^2 + C_1)}$	
16	$Z = \dfrac{LRCs^2 + Ls + R}{RCs + 1}$	
17	$Z = \dfrac{s(L_1L_2s + R[L_1 + L_2])}{L_2s + R}$	
18	$Z = \dfrac{s[L_1L_2Cs^2 + (L_1 + L_2)]}{L_2Cs^2 + 1}$	
19	$Z = \dfrac{Ls + R}{LCs^2 + RCs + 1}$	
20	$Z = \dfrac{s(RLCs + L)}{LCs^2 + RCs + 1}$	
21	$Z = \dfrac{R_1R_2C_1C_2s^2 + (R_1C_1 + R_2C_1 + R_2C_2)s + 1}{s(R_2C_1C_2s + C_1)}$	
22	$Z = \dfrac{R_1R_2C_1C_2s^2 + (R_1C_1 + R_2C_2)s + 1}{s[(R_1 + R_2)C_1C_2s + (C_1 + C_2)]}$	

$$Z_T(s) = \frac{E_0(s)}{E_{\mathrm{IN}}(s)}; \quad T = RC; \quad T_1 = R_1 C_1; \text{ etc.}$$

	Network	$Z_T(s)$
1		$Z_T(s) = \dfrac{1}{RCs + 1}$
2		$Z_T(s) = \dfrac{Ls}{Ls + R}$
3		$Z_T(s) = \dfrac{R}{Ls + R}$
4		$Z_T(s) = \dfrac{RCs}{RCs + 1}$
5		$Z_T(s) = \dfrac{1}{LCs^2 + 1}$
6		$Z_T(s) = \dfrac{LCs^2}{LCs^2 + 1}$

$$Z_T(s) = \frac{E_0(s)}{E_{IN}(s)}; \quad T = RC; \quad T_1 = R_1C_1; \text{ etc.}$$

Network		
7		$Z_T(s) = \dfrac{L^2C^2s^4 + LCs^2}{L^2C^2s^4 + 3LCs^2 + 1}$
8		$Z_T(s) = \dfrac{1}{R^2C^2s^2 + 3RCs + 1}$
9		$Z_T(s) = \dfrac{1}{T^3s^3 + 5T^2s^2 + 6Ts + 1}$
10		$Z_T(s) = \dfrac{1}{T^4s^4 + 7T^3s^3 + 15T^2s^2 + 10Ts + 1}$
11		$Z_T(s) = \dfrac{1}{T^5s^5 + 9T^4s^4 + 28T^3s^3 + 35T^2s^2 + 15Ts + 1}$
12		$Z_T(s) = \dfrac{Ts}{T^2s^2 + 3Ts + 1}$

13		$Z_T(s) = \dfrac{Ts}{T^2s^2 + 3Ts + 1}$ (same transfer function as form #12)
14		$Z_T(s) = \dfrac{4RCs}{4R^2C^2s^2 + 8RCs + 1}$
15	One section isolated (either one) Cathode follower between A and B	$Z_T(s) = \dfrac{1}{(Ts + 1)(T^2s^2 + 3Ts + 1)}$
16		$Z_T(s) = \dfrac{R_1R_2Cs + (R_1 + R_2)}{R_2Cs + 1}$
17		$Z_T(s) = \dfrac{1}{LC}\left(\dfrac{1}{s^2 + \dfrac{s}{RC} + \dfrac{1}{LC}}\right)$
18		$Z_T(s) = \dfrac{1}{L^2C^2s^4 + \dfrac{L^2C^2s^3}{R} + 3LCs^2 + \dfrac{2Ls}{R} + 1}$

$$Z_T(s) = \frac{E_0(s)}{E_{IN}(s)}; \quad T = RC; \quad T_1 = R_1 C_1; \text{ etc.}$$

	Network	$Z_T(s)$
19		$Z_T(s) = \dfrac{1}{T_1 T_2 s^2 + (T_1 + T_2 + R_1 C_2)s + 1}$
20		$Z_T(s) = \dfrac{1}{2Ts + 3}$
21		$Z_T(s) = \dfrac{T_1 T_2 s^2}{T_1 T_2 s^2 + (T_1 + T_2 + R_1 C_2)s + 1}$
22		$Z_T(s) = \dfrac{T^3 s^3}{T^3 s^3 + 6T^2 s^2 + 5Ts + 1}$
23		$Z_T(s) = \dfrac{T^4 s^4}{T^4 s^4 + 10T^3 s^3 + 15T^2 s^2 + 7Ts + 1}$
24		$Z_T(s) = \dfrac{Ts}{T^2 s^2 + 3Ts + 1}$ (same as forms 12 and 13)

No.	Circuit	Impedance
25		$Z_{T(s)} = \dfrac{Ts}{3Ts + 1}$
26		$Z_{T(s)} = \dfrac{Ts + 1}{2Ts + 1}$
27		$Z_{T(s)} = \dfrac{Ts + 1}{2Ts + 1}$ (same as form 26)
28		$Z_{T(s)} = \dfrac{(Ts + 1)^2}{T^2s^2 + 3Ts + 1}$
29		$Z_{T(s)} = \dfrac{Ts + 1}{Ts + 2}$

$$Z_T(s) = \frac{E_0(s)}{E_{IN}(s)}; \quad T = RC; \quad T_1 = R_1C_1; \text{ etc.}$$

Network		
	$Z_T(s) = \dfrac{k(Ts + 1)}{kTs + (1 + k)}$	30
	$Z_T(s) = \dfrac{Ts + 1}{Ts + 2}$ (same as form 29)	31
	$Z_T(s) = \dfrac{Ts + 1}{Ts + 3}$	32
	$Z_T(s) = \dfrac{(Ts + 1)^2}{T^2s^2 + 5Ts + 2}$	33

No.	Circuit	$Z_T(s)$
34		$Z_T(s) = \dfrac{3Ts + 1}{T^2s^2 + 5Ts + 2}$
35		$Z_T(s) = \dfrac{6T^2s^2 + 5Ts + 1}{T^3s^3 + 6T^2s^2 + 5Ts + 1}$
37		$Z_T(s) = \dfrac{T^3s^3 + 5T^2s^2 + 6Ts}{T^3s^3 + 5T^2s^2 + 6Ts + 1}$
38		$Z_T(s) = \dfrac{R_2(T_1s + 1)}{(R_1T_2 + R_2T_1)s + (R_1 + R_2)}$
39		$Z_T(s) = \dfrac{k(Ts + 3)}{2kTs + 3(1 + k)}$

$$Z_T(s) = \frac{E_0(s)}{E_{IN}(s)}; \quad T = RC; \quad T_1 = R_1C_1; \text{ etc.}$$

Network		$Z_T(s)$
	40	$Z_T(s) = \dfrac{2Ts}{T^2s^2 + 4Ts + 1}$
	41	$Z_T(s) = \dfrac{R_2C_1s}{R_1R_2C_1C_2s^2 + (R_1C_1 + R_2C_2 + R_2C_1)s + 1}$
	42	$Z_T(s) = \dfrac{1}{2T^2s^2 + 6Ts + 3}$
	43	$Z_T(s) = \dfrac{1}{R^3C^3s^3 + \dfrac{R^3C^2s^2}{R_1} + 5R^2C^2s^2 + \dfrac{4R^2Cs}{R_1} + 6RCs + \dfrac{3R}{R_1} + 1}$
	44	$Z_T(s) = \dfrac{R_1R_2C^2s^2 + 2R_1Cs + 1}{R_1R_2C^2s^2 + (2R_1 + R_2)Cs + 1}$

45		$Z_T(s) = \dfrac{1}{L^2C^2s^4 + \dfrac{L^2Cs^3}{R} + 3LCs^2 + \dfrac{2Ls}{R} + 1}$
46	(Normalized series)	$Z_T(s) = \dfrac{1}{s + 1}$
47		$Z_T(s) = \dfrac{1}{s^2 + \sqrt{2}s + 1}$
48		$Z_T(s) = \dfrac{1}{s^3 + 2s^2 + 2s + 1}$
49		$Z_T(s) = \dfrac{1}{s^4 + 2.6131s^3 + 3.4142s^2 + 2.6131s + 1}$
50		$Z_T(s) = \dfrac{1}{s^5 + 3.236s^4 + 5.236s^3 + 5.236s^2 + 3.236s + 1}$

$$Z_T(s) = \frac{E_0(s)}{E_{IN}(s)}; \quad T = RC; \quad T_1 = R_1 C_1; \text{ etc.}$$

Network	
51	$Z_T(s) = \dfrac{1}{s^6 + 3.8637s^5 + 7.4641s^4 + 9.1416s^3 + 7.4641s^2 + 3.8637s + 1}$
52	$Z_{T'}(s) = \dfrac{1}{s^7 + 4.4939s^6 + 10.0978s^5 + 14.5918s^4 + 14.5918s^3 + 10.0978s^2 + 4.4939s + 1}$
53	$Z_{T'}(s) = \dfrac{1}{s^8 + 5.126s^7 + 13.14s^6 + 21.85s^5 + 25.69s^4 + 21.85s^3 + 13.14s^2 + 5.126s + 1}$
54	$Z_{T'}(s) = \dfrac{1}{s^9 + 5.759s^8 + 16.58s^7 + 31.16s^6 + 41.99s^5 + 41.99s^4 + 31.16s^3 + 16.58s^2 + 5.759s + 1}$
55	$Z_T(s) = \dfrac{1}{s^{10} + 6.392s^9 + 20.43s^8 + 42.80s^7 + 64.88s^6 + 74.23s^5 + 64.88s^4 + 42.80s^3 + 20.43s^2 + 6.392s + 1}$

Network component values (from the circuit diagrams):

- 51: 1·553, 1·759, 1·653, 1·202, 0·7579, 0·2588
- 52: 1·558, 1·799, 1·659, 1·397, 1·055, 0·656, 2·225
- 53: 1·561, 1·825, 1·729, 1·528, 1·259, 0·5776, 0·937, 0·1951
- 54: 1·563, 1·842, 1·777, 1·620, 1·404, 0·8414, 1·441, 0·1736, 0·5155
- 55: 1·564, 1·855, 1·812, 1·687, 1·510, 1·041, 1·292, 0·4654, 0·7626, 0·1564

(c) Active transfer functions

Amplifiers are shown as either or where e_n is input voltage to the amplifier

1	RC=1	$Z_T(s) = s$
2	RC=1	$Z_T(s) = \dfrac{1}{s}$
3		$Z_T(s) = \dfrac{RCs}{(1-A)R^2C^2s^2 + 3RCs + 1}$
4		$Z_T(s) = \dfrac{RCs}{R^2C^2s^2 + 3RCs + 1 - A}$

5		$$Z_T(s) = \frac{(RCs + 1)^2}{R^2C'^2s^2 + (3 - A)RCs + 1}$$
6		$$Z_T(s) = \frac{1}{R^2C'^2s^2 + (3 - A)RCs + 1}$$
7		$$Z_T(s) = \frac{1}{(RCs + 1)^2}$$
8		$$Z_T(s) = \frac{1}{1 - RCs}$$
9		$$Z_T(s) = \frac{2}{R^2C'^2s^2 + 1}$$

10		$ZY = Z(s)Y(s)$ $Z_T(s) = \dfrac{1}{(1-A)ZY + 1}$
11		$Z_T(s) = \dfrac{1}{(1-B)Z^2Y^2 + (3 - 4B - A)ZY + 1 - 2B}$
12		$Z_T(s) = \dfrac{1}{R^3C^3s^3 + (5-B)R^2C^2s^2 + (6 - 2B - A)RCs + 1}$
13		$Z_T(s) = \dfrac{1}{Z^3Y^3 + (5-B)Z^2Y^2 + (6 - 2B - A)ZY + 1}$
14		$Z_T(s) = \dfrac{1}{Z^4Y^4 + (7-C)Z^3Y^3 + (12 - B)Z^2Y^2 + (10 - 2C - 2B - A)ZY + 1}$

15	$Z_T(s) = -\dfrac{Z_2}{Z_1}$	
16	$Z_T(s) = \dfrac{1}{s^2 + \sqrt{2}s + 1}$	
17	$Z_T(s) = \dfrac{1}{s^3 + 2s^2 + 2s + 1}$	

APPENDIX II

No.	$f(t)$	$F(s)$
1	$af(t)$	$aF(s)$
2	$\varepsilon^{at}f(t)$	$F(s - a)$
3	$-tf(t)$	$\dfrac{dF(s)}{ds}$
4	$f\left(\dfrac{t}{a}\right)$	$aF(as)$
5	$\displaystyle\int_0^t f(t)dt$	$\dfrac{F(s)}{s}$
6	$f^n(t)$	$s^n F(s) - s^{n-1}f(0) - s^{n-2}f'(0) - \cdots - f^{n-1}(0)$
7	$(t - a)U(t - a)$	$\varepsilon^{-as}F(s)$
8	$f(t) = f(t - a)$	$\dfrac{1}{1 - \varepsilon^{-as}} \cdot \displaystyle\int_0^a f(t)\varepsilon^{-st}\,dt$
9	$\displaystyle\lim_{t \to 0} f(t)$	$\displaystyle\lim_{s \to \infty} sF(s)$
10	$\displaystyle\lim_{t \to \infty} f(t)$	$\displaystyle\lim_{s \to 0} sF(s)$
11	$\displaystyle\int_0^t f_1(t - \tau)f_2(\tau)d\tau$	$F_1(s) \cdot F_2(s)$
12	$f'(t)$	$sF(s) - f(0)$

APPENDIX III

TABLE OF LAPLACE TRANSFORM PAIRS

No.	$F(s)$	$f(t)$
1	1	$U_1(t) = \lim_{a \to 0} \dfrac{U(t) - U(t-a)}{a}$, unit impulse
2	s	$U_2(t) = \lim_{a \to 0} \dfrac{U(t) - 2U(t-a) + U(t-2a)}{a^2}$, unit doublet impulse
3	$\dfrac{1}{s}$	$U(t)$, unit step function
4	$\dfrac{1}{s^2}$	t
5	$\dfrac{1}{s^n}(n = 1, 2, 3 \cdots)$	$\dfrac{t^{n-1}}{(n-1)!}$
6	$\dfrac{1}{s^n}(n > 0)$	$\dfrac{t^{n-1}}{\Gamma(n)}$
7	$\dfrac{1}{s^{1/2}}$	$\dfrac{1}{\sqrt{(\pi t)}}$
8	$\dfrac{1}{s^{3/2}}$	$\sqrt{\left(\dfrac{4t}{\pi}\right)}$

9	$\dfrac{1}{s+\alpha}$	$\varepsilon^{-\alpha t}$
10	$\dfrac{1}{(s+\alpha)^n}$	$\dfrac{t^{n-1}\varepsilon^{-\alpha t}}{(n-1)!}$
11	$\dfrac{1}{(s+\alpha)(s+\beta)}$	$\dfrac{\varepsilon^{-\alpha t}-\varepsilon^{-\beta t}}{\beta-\alpha}$
12	$\dfrac{1}{s(s+\alpha)(s+\beta)}$	$\dfrac{1}{\alpha\beta}+\dfrac{\beta\varepsilon^{-\alpha t}-\alpha\varepsilon^{-\beta t}}{\alpha\beta(\alpha-\beta)}$
13	$\dfrac{1}{(s+\alpha)(s+\beta)(s+v)}$	$\dfrac{\varepsilon^{-\alpha t}}{(\beta-\alpha)(v-\alpha)}+\dfrac{\varepsilon^{-\beta t}}{(\alpha-\beta)(v-\beta)}+\dfrac{\varepsilon^{-vt}}{(\alpha-v)(\beta-v)}$
14	$\dfrac{1}{s(s+\alpha)(s+\beta)(s+v)}$	$\dfrac{1}{\alpha\beta v}-\dfrac{\varepsilon^{-vt}}{v(\alpha-v)(\beta-v)}-\dfrac{\varepsilon^{-\beta t}}{\beta(\alpha-\beta)(v-\beta)}-\dfrac{\varepsilon^{-\alpha t}}{\alpha(\beta-\alpha)(v-\alpha)}$
15	$\dfrac{1}{s^2(s+\alpha)}$	$\dfrac{1}{\alpha^2}\left(\varepsilon^{-\alpha t}+\alpha t-1\right)$
16	$\dfrac{1}{s^2(s+\alpha)(s+\beta)}$	$\dfrac{1}{\alpha^2\beta^2}\left[\dfrac{1}{(\alpha-\beta)}\left(\alpha^2\varepsilon^{-\beta t}-\beta^2\varepsilon^{-\alpha t}\right)+\alpha\beta t-\alpha-\beta\right]$
17	$\dfrac{1}{s^2(s+\alpha)(s+\beta)(s+v)}$	$\dfrac{\alpha\beta(vt-1)-\alpha v-\beta v}{(\alpha\beta v)^2}+\dfrac{\varepsilon^{-\alpha t}}{\alpha^2(v-\alpha)(\beta-\alpha)}+\dfrac{\varepsilon^{-\beta t}}{\beta^2(v-\beta)(\alpha-\beta)}+\dfrac{\varepsilon^{-vt}}{v^2(\beta-v)(\alpha-v)}$
18	$\dfrac{1}{s^2+\alpha^2}$	$\dfrac{\sin\alpha t}{\alpha}$
19	$\dfrac{1}{s^2-\alpha^2}$	$\dfrac{\sinh\alpha t}{\alpha}$

No.	$F(s)$	$f(t)$
20	$\dfrac{1}{s(s^2+\alpha^2)}$	$\dfrac{1-\cos\alpha t}{\alpha^2}$
21	$\dfrac{1}{s^2(s^2+\alpha^2)}$	$\dfrac{t}{\alpha^2}-\dfrac{\sin\alpha t}{\alpha^3}$
22	$\dfrac{1}{(s+\alpha)(s^2+\beta^2)}$	$\dfrac{1}{\alpha^2+\beta^2}\left(\varepsilon^{-\alpha t}+\dfrac{\alpha}{\beta}\sin\beta t-\cos\beta t\right)$
23	$\dfrac{1}{s(s+\alpha)(s^2+\beta^2)}$	$\dfrac{1}{\alpha\beta^2}-\dfrac{1}{\alpha^2+\beta^2}\left(\dfrac{\sin\beta t}{\beta}+\dfrac{\alpha\cos\beta t}{\beta^2}+\dfrac{\varepsilon^{-\alpha t}}{\alpha}\right)$
24	$\dfrac{1}{s^2(s+\alpha)(s^2+\beta^2)}$	$\dfrac{t}{\alpha\beta^2}-\dfrac{1}{\alpha^2\beta^2}+\dfrac{\varepsilon^{-\alpha t}}{\alpha^2(\alpha^2+\beta^2)}+\dfrac{\cos(\beta t+\phi)}{\beta^3\sqrt{(\alpha^2+\beta^2)}},\quad \phi=\tan^{-1}\left(\dfrac{\alpha}{\beta}\right)$
25	$\dfrac{1}{(s+\alpha)(s+\beta)(s^2+\nu^2)}$	$\dfrac{\varepsilon^{-\alpha t}}{(\beta-\alpha)(\alpha^2+\nu^2)}+\dfrac{\varepsilon^{-\beta t}}{(\alpha-\beta)(\beta^2+\nu^2)}+\dfrac{\sin(\nu t-\phi)}{\nu\sqrt{\{\nu^2(\alpha+\beta)^2+(\alpha\beta-\nu^2)^2\}}},\quad \phi=\tan^{-1}\left(\dfrac{\nu}{\alpha}\right)+\tan^{-1}\left(\dfrac{\nu}{\beta}\right)$
26	$\dfrac{1}{s(s+\alpha)(s+\beta)(s^2+\nu^2)}$	$\dfrac{1}{\alpha\beta\nu^2}+\dfrac{\varepsilon^{-\alpha t}}{\alpha(\alpha-\beta)(\alpha^2+\nu^2)}+\dfrac{\varepsilon^{-\beta t}}{\beta(\beta-\alpha)(\beta^2+\nu^2)}+\dfrac{\cos(\nu t+\phi)}{\nu^2\sqrt{\{(\alpha\beta-\nu^2)^2+\nu^2(\alpha+\beta)^2\}}},\quad \phi=\tan^{-1}\left(\dfrac{\beta}{\nu}\right)+\tan^{-1}\left(\dfrac{\alpha}{\nu}\right)$
27	$\dfrac{1}{s^2(s+\alpha)(s+\beta)(s^2+\nu^2)}$	$\dfrac{1}{\alpha\beta\nu^2}\left(t-\dfrac{1}{\alpha}-\dfrac{1}{\beta}\right)+\dfrac{\varepsilon^{-\alpha t}}{\alpha^2(\beta-\alpha)(\alpha^2+\nu^2)}+\dfrac{\varepsilon^{-\beta t}}{\beta^2(\alpha-\beta)(\beta^2+\nu^2)}+\dfrac{\cos(\nu t+\phi)}{\nu^3\sqrt{\{(\alpha\beta-\nu^2)^2+(\alpha+\beta)^2\nu^2\}}},\quad \phi=\tan^{-1}\left(\dfrac{\beta}{\nu}\right)-\tan^{-1}\left(\dfrac{\nu}{\alpha}\right)$

	$f(t)$	$F(s)$
28	$\dfrac{1}{\beta^2-\alpha^2}\left(\dfrac{\sin\alpha t}{\alpha}-\dfrac{\sin\beta t}{\beta}\right)$	$\dfrac{1}{(s^2+\alpha^2)(s^2+\beta^2)}$
29	$\dfrac{\varepsilon^{-\alpha t}\sin\beta t}{\beta}$	$\dfrac{1}{(s+\alpha)^2+\beta^2}$
30	$\dfrac{1}{\alpha^2+\beta^2}\left(t-\dfrac{2\alpha}{\alpha^2+\beta^2}\right)+\dfrac{\varepsilon^{-\alpha t}\sin(\beta t+\phi)}{\beta(\alpha^2+\beta^2)},\qquad \phi=2\tan^{-1}\left(\dfrac{\beta}{\alpha}\right)$	$\dfrac{1}{s^2[(s+\alpha)^2+\beta^2]}$
31	$\dfrac{\varepsilon^{-\nu t}}{\beta^2+(\nu-\alpha)^2}+\dfrac{\varepsilon^{-\alpha t}\sin(\beta t-\phi)}{\beta\sqrt{(\nu-\alpha)^2+\beta^2}},\qquad \phi=\tan^{-1}\left(\dfrac{\beta}{\nu-\alpha}\right)$	$\dfrac{1}{(s+\nu)[(s+\alpha)^2+\beta^2]}$
32	$\dfrac{1}{\nu(\alpha^2+\beta^2)}-\dfrac{\varepsilon^{-\nu t}}{\nu[(\nu-\alpha)^2+\beta^2]}+\dfrac{\varepsilon^{-\alpha t}\sin(\beta t+\phi)}{\beta\sqrt{(\alpha^2+\beta^2)[(\alpha-\nu)^2+\beta^2]}},$ $\phi=\tan^{-1}\left(\dfrac{\beta}{\alpha}\right)+\tan^{-1}\left(\dfrac{\beta}{\alpha-\nu}\right)$	$\dfrac{1}{\nu(s+\nu)[(s+\alpha)^2+\beta^2]}$
33	$\dfrac{1}{\nu(\alpha^2+\beta^2)}\left(t-\dfrac{1}{\nu}-\dfrac{2\alpha}{\alpha^2+\beta^2}\right)+\dfrac{\varepsilon^{-\nu t}}{\nu^2[(\nu-\alpha)^2+\beta^2]}+\dfrac{\varepsilon^{-\alpha t}\sin(\beta t+\phi)}{\beta(\alpha^2+\beta^2)\sqrt{(\nu-\alpha)^2+\beta^2}},$ $\phi=2\tan^{-1}\left(\dfrac{\beta}{\alpha}\right)-\tan^{-1}\left(\dfrac{\beta}{\nu-\alpha}\right)$	$\dfrac{1}{s^2(s+\nu)[(s+\alpha)^2+\beta^2]}$
34	$\dfrac{\varepsilon^{-\nu t}}{(\delta-\nu)[(\alpha-\nu)^2+\beta^2]}+\dfrac{\varepsilon^{-\delta t}}{(\nu-\delta)[(\alpha-\delta)^2+\beta^2]}+\dfrac{\varepsilon^{-\alpha t}\cos(\beta t+\phi)}{\beta\sqrt{[(\alpha-\delta)^2+\beta^2][(\alpha-\nu)^2+\beta^2]}},$ $\phi=\tan^{-1}\left(\dfrac{\beta}{\alpha-\delta}\right)-\tan^{-1}\left(\dfrac{\alpha-\nu}{\beta}\right)$	$\dfrac{1}{(s+\nu)(s+\delta)[(s+\alpha)^2+\beta^2]}$
35	$\dfrac{\beta\sin(\nu t+\phi_1)+\nu\varepsilon^{-\alpha t}\sin(\beta t+\phi_2)}{\beta\nu\sqrt{\{4\alpha^2\nu^2+(\alpha^2+\beta^2-\nu^2)^2\}}},\qquad \phi_1=\tan^{-1}\left(\dfrac{2\alpha\nu}{\nu^2-\alpha^2-\beta^2}\right),\qquad \phi_2=\tan^{-1}\left[\dfrac{2\alpha\beta}{(\alpha^2-\beta^2+\nu^2)}\right]$	$\dfrac{1}{(s^2+\nu^2)[(s+\alpha)^2+\beta^2]}$

No.	$F(s)$	$f(t)$
36	$\dfrac{1}{s(s^2+\nu^2)[(s+\alpha)^2+\beta^2]}$	$\dfrac{1}{\nu^2(\alpha^2+\beta^2)} + \dfrac{\sin(\nu t-\phi_1)}{\beta\sqrt{(\alpha^2+\beta^2)[4\alpha^2\nu^2+(\alpha^2+\beta^2-\nu^2)^2]}} - \dfrac{\sin(\nu t+\phi_2)}{\nu^2\sqrt{4\alpha^2\nu^2+(\alpha^2+\beta^2-\nu^2)^2}}$ $\phi_1 = \tan^{-1}\left(\dfrac{\alpha}{\beta}\right) + \tan^{-1}\left(\dfrac{\alpha^2-\beta^2+\nu^2}{2\alpha\beta}\right), \quad \phi_2 = \tan^{-1}\left(\dfrac{\alpha^2+\beta^2-\nu^2}{2\alpha\beta}\right)$
37	$\dfrac{1}{(s+\nu)(s^2+\delta^2)[(s+\alpha)^2+\beta^2]}$	$\dfrac{\varepsilon^{-\nu t}}{(\nu^2+\delta^2)[(\alpha-\nu)^2+\beta^2]} + \dfrac{\varepsilon^{-\alpha t}\sin(\beta t+\phi_1)}{\beta\sqrt{[(\nu-\alpha)^2+\beta^2][4\alpha^2\delta^2+(\alpha^2+\beta^2-\delta^2)^2]}} + \dfrac{\sin(\delta t+\phi_2)}{\delta\sqrt{(\nu^2+\delta^2)[4\alpha^2\delta^2+(\alpha^2+\beta^2-\delta^2)^2]}}$ $\phi_1 = \tan^{-1}\left(\dfrac{\nu-\alpha}{\beta}\right) - \tan^{-1}\left(\dfrac{\alpha^2-\beta^2+\delta^2}{2\alpha\beta}\right), \quad \phi_2 = \tan^{-1}\left(\dfrac{\nu}{\delta}\right) + \tan^{-1}\left(\dfrac{\alpha^2+\beta^2-\delta^2}{2\alpha\delta}\right)$
38	$\dfrac{1}{s(s+\alpha)^2}$	$\dfrac{1-\varepsilon^{-\alpha t}-\alpha t\varepsilon^{-\alpha t}}{\alpha^2}$
39	$\dfrac{1}{s^2(s+\alpha)^2}$	$\dfrac{t}{\alpha^2} - \dfrac{2}{\alpha^3} + \dfrac{t\varepsilon^{-\alpha t}}{\alpha^2} + \dfrac{2\varepsilon^{-\alpha t}}{\alpha^3}$
40	$\dfrac{1}{(s+\alpha)(s+\beta)^2}$	$\dfrac{\varepsilon^{-\alpha t}}{(\alpha-\beta)^2} + \dfrac{[(\alpha-\beta)t-1]\varepsilon^{-\beta t}}{(\alpha-\beta)^2}$
41	$\dfrac{1}{s(s+\alpha)(s+\beta)^2}$	$\dfrac{1}{\alpha\beta^2} - \dfrac{\varepsilon^{-\alpha t}}{\alpha(\alpha-\beta)^2} - \left[\dfrac{t}{\beta(\alpha-\beta)} + \dfrac{\alpha-2\beta}{\beta^2(\alpha-\beta)^2}\right]\varepsilon^{-\beta t}$
42	$\dfrac{1}{s^2(s+\alpha)(s+\beta)^2}$	$\dfrac{\varepsilon^{-\alpha t}}{\alpha^2(\beta-\alpha)^2} + \dfrac{1}{\alpha\beta^2}\left(t - \dfrac{1}{\alpha} - \dfrac{2}{\beta}\right) + \left[\dfrac{t}{\beta^2(\alpha-\beta)} + \dfrac{2(\alpha-\beta)-\beta}{\beta^3(\beta-\alpha)^2}\right]\varepsilon^{-\beta t}$

No.		
43	$\dfrac{1}{(s+\beta)(s+\nu)(s+\alpha)^2}$	$\left[\dfrac{t}{(\alpha-\beta)(\alpha-\nu)} + \dfrac{2\alpha-\beta-\nu}{(\alpha-\beta)^2(\alpha-\nu)^2}\right]\varepsilon^{-\alpha t} + \dfrac{\varepsilon^{-\beta t}}{(\nu-\beta)(\alpha-\beta)^2} + \dfrac{\varepsilon^{-\nu t}}{(\beta-\nu)(\alpha-\nu)^2}$
44	$\dfrac{1}{s(s+\beta)(s+\nu)(s+\alpha)^2}$	$\dfrac{1}{\beta\nu\alpha^2} + \dfrac{\varepsilon^{-\beta t}}{\beta(\beta-\nu)(\alpha-\beta)^2} + \dfrac{\varepsilon^{-\nu t}}{\nu(\nu-\beta)(\alpha-\nu)^2} + \left[\dfrac{t}{\alpha(\alpha-\nu)(\beta-\alpha)} - \dfrac{(\alpha-\nu)(\alpha-\beta)+\alpha(2\alpha-\nu-\beta)}{\alpha^2(\alpha-\nu)^2(\alpha-\beta)^2}\right]\varepsilon^{-\alpha t}$
45	$\dfrac{1}{s^2(s+\beta)(s+\nu)(s+\alpha)^2}$	$\left[\dfrac{t}{\alpha^2(\alpha-\nu)(\alpha-\beta)} + \dfrac{2(\alpha-\nu)(\alpha-\beta)+\alpha(2\alpha-\nu-\beta)}{\alpha^3(\alpha-\nu)^2(\alpha-\beta)^2}\right]\varepsilon^{-\alpha t} + \dfrac{\varepsilon^{-\beta t}}{\beta^2(\nu-\beta)(\alpha-\beta)^2} + \dfrac{1}{\beta\nu\alpha^2}\left(t - \dfrac{2}{\alpha} - \dfrac{1}{\beta} - \dfrac{1}{\nu}\right) + \dfrac{\varepsilon^{-\nu t}}{\nu^2(\beta-\nu)(\alpha-\nu)^2}$
46	$\dfrac{1}{(s^2+\alpha^2)(s+\beta)^2}$	$\dfrac{\sin(\alpha t+\phi)}{\alpha(\alpha^2+\beta^2)} + \left[\dfrac{t}{\alpha^2+\beta^2} + \dfrac{2\beta}{(\alpha^2+\beta^2)^2}\right]\varepsilon^{-\beta t}, \qquad \phi = 2\tan^{-1}\left(\dfrac{\alpha}{\beta}\right)$
47	$\dfrac{1}{s(s^2+\alpha^2)(s+\beta)^2}$	$\dfrac{1}{\alpha^2\beta^2} - \dfrac{\sin(\alpha t+\phi)}{\alpha^2(\alpha^2+\beta^2)} - \left[\dfrac{t}{\beta(\alpha^2+\beta^2)} + \dfrac{3\beta^2+\alpha^2}{\beta^2(\alpha^2+\beta^2)^2}\right]\varepsilon^{-\beta t}, \qquad \phi = \tan^{-1}\left(\dfrac{\beta}{\alpha}\right) - \tan^{-1}\left(\dfrac{\alpha}{\beta}\right)$
48	$\dfrac{1}{s^2(s^2+\alpha^2)(s+\beta)^2}$	$\dfrac{\sin(\alpha t+\phi)}{\alpha^3(\alpha^2+\beta^2)} + \dfrac{t\varepsilon^{-\beta t}}{\beta^2(\alpha^2+\beta^2)} + \dfrac{2(\alpha^2+2\beta^2)\varepsilon^{-\beta t}}{\beta^3(\alpha^2+\beta^2)^2} + \dfrac{t}{\alpha^2\beta^2} - \dfrac{2}{\alpha^2\beta^3}, \qquad \phi = 2\tan^{-1}\left(\dfrac{\beta}{\alpha}\right)$
49	$\dfrac{1}{(s+\nu)(s^2+\alpha^2)(s+\beta)^2}$	$\dfrac{\sin(\alpha t-\phi)}{\alpha(\alpha^2+\beta^2)\sqrt{(\alpha^2+\nu^2)}} + \dfrac{t\varepsilon^{-\beta t}}{(\nu-\beta)(\alpha^2+\beta^2)} + \left[\dfrac{2(\nu-\beta)\beta-(\alpha^2+\beta^2)}{(\nu-\beta)^2(\alpha^2+\beta^2)^2}\right]\varepsilon^{-\beta t} + \dfrac{\varepsilon^{-\nu t}}{(\alpha^2+\nu^2)(\beta-\nu)^2}, \qquad \phi = 2\tan^{-1}\left(\dfrac{\alpha}{\beta}\right) + \tan^{-1}\left(\dfrac{\alpha}{\nu}\right)$
50	$\dfrac{1}{(s+\nu)^2[(s+\beta)^2+\alpha^2]}$	$\dfrac{\varepsilon^{-\beta t}\sin(\alpha t-\phi)}{\alpha[\alpha^2+(\beta-\nu)^2]} + \dfrac{2(\nu-\beta)\varepsilon^{-\nu t}}{[(\beta-\nu)^2+\alpha^2]^2} + \dfrac{t\varepsilon^{-\nu t}}{\alpha^2+(\beta-\nu)^2}, \qquad \phi = 2\tan^{-1}\left(\dfrac{\alpha}{\nu-\beta}\right)$

No.	$F(s)$	$f(t)$
51	$\dfrac{1}{s(s+v)^2[(s+\beta)^2+\alpha^2]}$	$\dfrac{\varepsilon^{-\beta t}\sin(\alpha t+\phi)}{\alpha[\alpha^2+(\beta-v)^2]\sqrt{\alpha^2+\beta^2}}-\left(\dfrac{[\alpha^2+(\beta-v)^2]^2-2v(\beta-v)}{v^2[\alpha^2+(\beta-v)^2]^2}\right)\varepsilon^{-vt}-\dfrac{t\varepsilon^{-vt}}{v[\alpha^2+(\beta-v)^2]}$ $+\dfrac{1}{v^2(\alpha^2+\beta^2)},\qquad \phi=2\tan^{-1}\left(v-\dfrac{\beta}{\alpha}\right)+\tan^{-1}\left(\dfrac{\alpha}{\beta}\right)$
52	$\dfrac{1}{(s+\alpha)^2(s+\beta)^2}$	$\dfrac{t\varepsilon^{-\alpha t}}{(\beta-\alpha)^2}-\dfrac{2\varepsilon^{-\alpha t}}{(\beta-\alpha)^3}+\dfrac{t\varepsilon^{-\beta t}}{(\alpha-\beta)^2}-\dfrac{2\varepsilon^{-\beta t}}{(\alpha-\beta)^3}$
53	$\dfrac{1}{s(s+\alpha)^2(s+\beta)^2}$	$\dfrac{(3\alpha-\beta)\varepsilon^{-\alpha t}}{\alpha^2(\beta-\alpha)^3}-\dfrac{t\varepsilon^{-\alpha t}}{\alpha(\beta-\alpha)^2}+\dfrac{(3\beta-\alpha)\varepsilon^{-\beta t}}{\beta^2(\alpha-\beta)^3}-\dfrac{t\varepsilon^{-\beta t}}{\beta(\alpha-\beta)^2}+\dfrac{1}{\alpha^2\beta^2}$
54	$\dfrac{1}{s^2(s+\alpha)^2(s+\beta)^2}$	$\dfrac{2(\beta-2\alpha)\varepsilon^{-\alpha t}}{\alpha^3(\beta-\alpha)^3}+\dfrac{t\varepsilon^{-\alpha t}}{\alpha^2(\beta-\alpha)^2}+\dfrac{2(\alpha-2\beta)\varepsilon^{-\beta t}}{\beta^3(\alpha-\beta)^3}+\dfrac{t\varepsilon^{-\beta t}}{\beta^2(\alpha-\beta)^2}+\dfrac{t}{\alpha^2\beta^2}-\dfrac{2(\alpha+\beta)}{\alpha^3\beta^3}$
55	$\dfrac{1}{(s+v)(s+\alpha)^2(s+\beta)^2}$	$\dfrac{\varepsilon^{-vt}}{(\alpha-v)^2(\beta-v)^2}+\dfrac{[3\beta-(\alpha+2v)]\varepsilon^{-\beta t}}{(\alpha-\beta)^3(v-\beta)^2}+\dfrac{t\varepsilon^{-\beta t}}{(v-\beta)(\alpha-\beta)^2}+\dfrac{[3\alpha-(\beta-2v)]\varepsilon^{-\alpha t}}{(v-\alpha)^2(\beta-\alpha)^3}$ $+\dfrac{t\varepsilon^{-\alpha t}}{(v-\alpha)(\beta-\alpha)^2}$
56	$\dfrac{1}{(s^2+v^2)(s+\alpha)^2(s+\beta)^2}$	$\dfrac{\sin(vt+\phi)}{v(\alpha^2+v^2)(\beta^2+v^2)}-2\left[\dfrac{(\alpha^2+v^2)-\alpha(\beta-\alpha)}{(\alpha^2+v^2)(\beta-\alpha)^3}\right]\varepsilon^{-\alpha t}+\dfrac{t\varepsilon^{-\alpha t}}{(\alpha^2+v^2)(\beta-\alpha)^2}$ $-2\left[\dfrac{\beta^2+v^2-\beta(\alpha-\beta)}{(\beta^2+v^2)(\alpha-\beta)^3}\right]\varepsilon^{-\beta t}+\dfrac{t\varepsilon^{-\beta t}}{(\beta^2+v^2)(\alpha-\beta)^2},\qquad \phi=2\tan^{-1}\left(\dfrac{\beta}{v}\right)+2\tan^{-1}\left(\dfrac{\alpha}{v}\right)$
57	$\dfrac{1}{[\alpha^2+(s+\beta)^2]^2}$	$\dfrac{\varepsilon^{-\beta t}(\sin\alpha t-\alpha t\cos\alpha t)}{2\alpha^3}$

58	$\dfrac{1}{(s^2+\alpha^2)^2}$	$\dfrac{\sin \alpha t - \alpha t \cos \alpha t}{2\alpha^3}$
59	$\dfrac{1}{s(s^2+\alpha^2)^2}$	$\dfrac{(1-\cos\alpha t)}{\alpha^4} - \dfrac{t\sin\alpha t}{2\alpha^3}$
60	$\dfrac{1}{s^2(s^2+\alpha^2)^2}$	$\dfrac{3\sin\alpha t}{2\alpha^5} + \dfrac{t\cos\alpha t}{2\alpha^4} + \dfrac{t}{\alpha^4}$
61	$\dfrac{1}{(s+\beta)(s^2+\alpha^2)^2}$	$\dfrac{\varepsilon^{-\beta t}}{(\alpha^2+\beta^2)^2} - \dfrac{t\sin(\alpha t+\phi_1)}{2\alpha^2\sqrt{\alpha^2+\beta^2}} - \dfrac{(\sqrt{\beta^2+4\alpha^2})\cos(\alpha t+\phi_2)}{2\alpha^3(\alpha^2+\beta^2)}$ $\phi_1 = \tan^{-1}\left(\dfrac{\beta}{\alpha}\right),\qquad \phi_2 = \tan^{-1}\left[\dfrac{\beta(3\alpha^2+\beta^2)}{2\alpha^3}\right]$
62	$\dfrac{1}{s(s+\beta)(s^2+\alpha^2)^2}$	$\dfrac{t\cos(\alpha t+\phi_1)}{2\alpha^3\sqrt{\alpha^2+\beta^2}} - \dfrac{(\sqrt{9\alpha^2+4\beta^2})\cos(\alpha t+\phi_2)}{2\alpha^4(\alpha^2+\beta^2)} - \dfrac{\varepsilon^{-\beta t}}{\beta(\alpha^2+\beta^2)^2} + \dfrac{1}{\alpha^4\beta}$ $\phi_1 = \tan^{-1}\left(\dfrac{\beta}{\alpha}\right),\qquad \phi_2 = \tan^{-1}\left(\dfrac{3\alpha}{2\beta}\right) + 2\tan^{-1}\left(\dfrac{\alpha}{\beta}\right)$
63	$\dfrac{1}{s^2(s+\beta)(s^2+\alpha^2)^2}$	$\dfrac{t\sin(\alpha t+\phi_1)}{2\alpha^4\sqrt{\alpha^2+\beta^2}} - \dfrac{(16\alpha^2+9\beta^2)^{1/2}\sin(\alpha t+\phi_2)}{4\alpha^5(\alpha^2+\beta^2)} + \dfrac{\varepsilon^{-\beta t}}{\beta^2(\alpha^2+\beta^2)^2} + \dfrac{t}{\alpha^4\beta^2} - \dfrac{1}{\alpha^4\beta^2}$ $\phi_1 = \tan^{-1}\left(\dfrac{\beta}{\alpha}\right),\qquad \phi_2 = \tan^{-1}\left(\dfrac{4\alpha}{3\beta}\right) - 2\tan^{-1}\left(\dfrac{\alpha}{\beta}\right)$
64	$\dfrac{1}{s(s+\alpha)^3}$	$\dfrac{1}{\alpha^3} - \left(\dfrac{t^2}{2\alpha} + \dfrac{t}{\alpha^2} + \dfrac{1}{\alpha^3}\right)\varepsilon^{-\alpha t}$
65	$\dfrac{1}{s^3(s^2+\alpha^2)}$	$\dfrac{t^2}{2\alpha^2} + \dfrac{(\cos\alpha t - 1)}{\alpha^4}$

No.	$F(s)$	$f(t)$
66	$\dfrac{1}{s^2(s^2-\alpha^2)}$	$\dfrac{\sinh\alpha t}{\alpha^3} - \dfrac{t}{\alpha^2}$
67	$\dfrac{1}{s^3(s^2-\alpha^2)}$	$\dfrac{(\cosh\alpha t - 1)}{\alpha^4} - \dfrac{t^2}{2\alpha^2}$
68	$\dfrac{1}{s^4-\alpha^4}$	$\dfrac{\sinh\alpha t - \sin\alpha t}{2\alpha^3}$
69	$\dfrac{1}{s\sqrt{(s+1)}}$	$\operatorname{erf}(\sqrt{t})$
70	$\dfrac{1}{\sqrt{s^2+\alpha^2}\,(s+\sqrt{s^2+\alpha^2})}$	$\dfrac{J_1(\alpha t)}{\alpha}$
71	$\dfrac{1}{\{s+\sqrt{(s^2+\alpha^2)}\}^n}$	$\dfrac{nJ_n(\alpha t)}{\alpha^n t}$
72	$\dfrac{1}{s\{s+\sqrt{(s^2+\alpha^2)}\}^n}$	$\dfrac{n}{\alpha^n}\displaystyle\int_0^t \dfrac{J_n(\alpha t)}{t}\,dt$
73	$\dfrac{1}{\sqrt{s}(s-1)}$	$\varepsilon^t\operatorname{erf}(\sqrt{t})$
74	$\dfrac{1}{1+\sqrt{s}}$	$\dfrac{1}{\sqrt{(\pi t)}} - \varepsilon^t - \varepsilon^t\operatorname{erf}(\sqrt{t})$
75	$\dfrac{1}{\sqrt{(s^2+\alpha^2)}}$	$J_0(\alpha t)$

No.	$f(t)$	Condition	$F(s)$
76	$J_0(j\alpha t)$		$\dfrac{1}{\sqrt{(s^2 - \alpha^2)}}$
77	$\dfrac{J_1(\alpha t)}{\alpha t}$		$\dfrac{1}{s + \sqrt{(s^2 + \alpha^2)}}$
78	$\dfrac{J_n(\alpha t)}{\alpha^n}$		$\dfrac{1}{\sqrt{s^2 + \alpha^2}\,(s + \sqrt{s^2 + \alpha^2})^n}$
79	$J_0(2\sqrt{\alpha t})$		$\dfrac{1}{s\varepsilon^{\alpha/s}}$
80	$\dfrac{\cos 2\sqrt{(\alpha t)}}{\sqrt{(\pi t)}}$		$\dfrac{1}{\sqrt{s}\varepsilon^{\alpha/s}}$
81	$U(t - a)$		$\dfrac{\varepsilon^{-as}}{s}$
82	$\cos \alpha t$		$\dfrac{s}{s^2 + \alpha^2}$
83	$\cosh \alpha t$		$\dfrac{s}{s^2 - \alpha^2}$
84	$\dfrac{\cos \alpha t - \cos \beta t}{\beta^2 - \alpha^2}$,	$\alpha^2 \neq \beta^2$	$\dfrac{s}{(s^2 + \alpha^2)(s^2 + \beta^2)}$
85	$\dfrac{\sin \beta t \cdot \sin \alpha t}{2\alpha\beta}$		$\dfrac{s}{[s^2 + (\alpha + \beta)^2][s^2 + (\alpha - \beta)^2]}$
86	$\dfrac{t \sin \alpha t}{2\alpha}$		$\dfrac{s}{(s^2 + \alpha^2)^2}$

No.	$f(t)$	$F(s)$
87	$\dfrac{\sin \alpha t + \alpha t \cos \alpha t}{2\alpha}$	$\dfrac{s^2}{(s^2 + \alpha^2)^2}$
88	$\varepsilon^{-\alpha t}(1 - \alpha t)$	$\dfrac{s}{(s + \alpha)^2}$
89	$\dfrac{\cosh \alpha t - \cos \alpha t}{2\alpha^2}$	$\dfrac{s}{s^4 - \alpha^4}$
90	$\dfrac{\sinh \alpha t + \sin \alpha t}{2\alpha}$	$\dfrac{s^2}{s^4 - \alpha^4}$
91	$\dfrac{\cosh \alpha t + \cos \alpha t}{2}$	$\dfrac{s^3}{s^4 - \alpha^4}$
92	$\dfrac{\sinh \alpha t \cdot \sin \alpha t}{2\alpha^2}$	$\dfrac{s}{s^4 + 4\alpha^4}$
93	$\dfrac{\alpha \varepsilon^{-\alpha t} - \beta \varepsilon^{-\beta t}}{\alpha - \beta}, \quad \alpha \neq \beta$	$\dfrac{s}{(s - \alpha)(s - \beta)}$
94	$(1 + \alpha^2 t^2) \sin \alpha t - \alpha t \cos \alpha t$	$\dfrac{8\alpha^3 s^2}{(s^2 + \alpha^2)^3}$
95	$\dfrac{\varepsilon^{\alpha t}(1 + 2\alpha t)}{\sqrt{(\pi t)}}$	$\dfrac{s}{(s - \alpha)^{3/2}}$
96	$\dfrac{1}{\sqrt{(\pi t)}} + \alpha \varepsilon^{\alpha^2 t} \operatorname{erf}(\alpha \sqrt{t})$	$\dfrac{\sqrt{s}}{s - \alpha^2}$

97	$\dfrac{s + a_0}{s(s + \alpha)}$	$\dfrac{a_0 - (a_0 - \alpha)\varepsilon^{-\alpha t}}{\alpha}$
98	$\dfrac{s + a_0}{(s + \alpha)(s + \beta)}$	$\dfrac{(a_0 - \alpha)\varepsilon^{-\alpha t} + (\beta - a_0)\varepsilon^{-\beta t}}{\beta - \alpha}$
99	$\dfrac{s + a_0}{s(s + \alpha)(s + \beta)}$	$\dfrac{a_0}{\alpha\beta} + \dfrac{(\alpha - a_0)\varepsilon^{-\alpha t}}{\alpha(\beta - \alpha)} + \dfrac{(\beta - a_0)\varepsilon^{-\beta t}}{\beta(\alpha - \beta)}$
100	$\dfrac{s + a_0}{s^2(s + \alpha)(s + \beta)}$	$\dfrac{(1 + a_0 t)}{\alpha\beta} - \dfrac{(\alpha + \beta)a_0}{\alpha^2\beta^2} + \dfrac{1}{\beta - \alpha}\left[\dfrac{(a_0 - \alpha)\varepsilon^{-\alpha t}}{\alpha^2} - \dfrac{(a_0 - \beta)\varepsilon^{-\beta t}}{\beta^2}\right]$
101	$\dfrac{s + a_0}{(s + \alpha)(s + \beta)(s + v)}$	$\dfrac{(a_0 - \alpha)\varepsilon^{-\alpha t}}{(v - \alpha)(\beta - \alpha)} + \dfrac{(a_0 - \beta)\varepsilon^{-\beta t}}{(\alpha - \beta)(v - \beta)} + \dfrac{(a_0 - v)\varepsilon^{-vt}}{(\alpha - v)(\beta - v)}$
102	$\dfrac{s + a_0}{s(s + \alpha)(s + \beta)(s + v)}$	$\dfrac{a_0}{\alpha\beta v} + \dfrac{(\alpha - a_0)\varepsilon^{-\alpha t}}{\alpha(\beta - \alpha)(v - \alpha)} + \dfrac{(\beta - a_0)\varepsilon^{-\beta t}}{\beta(\alpha - \beta)(v - \beta)} + \dfrac{(a_0 - v)\varepsilon^{-vt}}{v(\alpha - v)(\beta - v)}$
103	$\dfrac{s + a_0}{s^2(s + \alpha)(s + \beta)(s + v)}$	$\dfrac{1 + a_0 t}{\alpha\beta v} - \dfrac{a_0(\alpha\beta + \beta v + \alpha v)}{\alpha^2\beta^2 v^2} + \dfrac{(a_0 - \alpha)\varepsilon^{-\alpha t}}{\alpha^2(\beta - \alpha)(v - \alpha)} + \dfrac{(\beta - a_0)\varepsilon^{-\beta t}}{\beta^2(\alpha - \beta)(v - \beta)} + \dfrac{(a_0 - v)\varepsilon^{-vt}}{v^2(\alpha - v)(\beta - v)}$
104	$\dfrac{s + a_0}{s^2 + \alpha^2}$	$\dfrac{\sqrt{(a_0{}^2 + \alpha^2)} \sin(\alpha t + \phi)}{\alpha}, \qquad \phi = \tan^{-1}\left(\dfrac{\alpha}{a_0}\right)$
105	$\dfrac{s + a_0}{s(s^2 + \alpha^2)}$	$\dfrac{a_0}{\alpha^2} + \sqrt{\left(\dfrac{1}{\alpha^2} + \dfrac{a_0{}^2}{\alpha^4}\right)} \sin(\alpha t - \phi), \qquad \phi = \tan^{-1}\left(\dfrac{a_0}{\alpha}\right)$
106	$\dfrac{s + a_0}{s^2(s^2 + \alpha^2)}$	$\left[\dfrac{1}{\alpha^2} + \dfrac{a_0 t}{\alpha^2}\right] - \sqrt{\left(\dfrac{1}{\alpha^4} + \dfrac{a_0{}^2}{\alpha^6}\right)} \cdot \sin(\alpha t + \phi), \qquad \phi = \tan^{-1}\left(\dfrac{\alpha}{a_0}\right)$
107	$\dfrac{s + a_0}{(s + \alpha)(s^2 + \beta^2)}$	$\dfrac{(a_0 - \alpha)\varepsilon^{-\alpha t}}{\alpha^2 + \beta^2} + \sqrt{\left(\dfrac{a_0{}^2 + \beta^2}{\alpha^2\beta^2 + \beta^4}\right)} \cdot \sin(\beta t + \phi), \qquad \phi = \tan^{-1}\left(\dfrac{\alpha}{\beta}\right) - \tan^{-1}\left(\dfrac{a_0}{\beta}\right)$

No.	$F(s)$	$f(t)$
108	$\dfrac{s + a_0}{s(s + \alpha)(s^2 + \beta^2)}$	$\dfrac{a_0}{\alpha\beta^2} - \dfrac{(a_0 - \alpha)\varepsilon^{-\alpha t}}{\alpha(\alpha^2 + \beta^2)} - \sqrt{\left(\dfrac{a_0^2 + \beta^2}{\alpha^2\beta^4 + \beta^6}\right)} \cdot \cos(\beta t + \phi), \qquad \phi = \tan^{-1}\left(\dfrac{\alpha}{\beta}\right) - \tan^{-1}\left(\dfrac{a_0}{\beta}\right)$
109	$\dfrac{s + a_0}{s^2(s + \alpha)(s^2 + \beta^2)}$	$\dfrac{1}{\alpha\beta^2}\left(\dfrac{1}{\alpha} - t\right) + \dfrac{a_0\alpha\varepsilon^{-\alpha t}}{\alpha^2(\alpha^2 + \beta^2)} + \dfrac{1}{\beta^3}\sqrt{\left(\dfrac{a_0^2 + \beta^2}{\alpha^2 + \beta^2}\right)} \cdot \cos(\beta t + \phi)$ $\phi = \tan^{-1}\left(\dfrac{\alpha}{\beta}\right) + \tan^{-1}\left(\dfrac{\beta}{a_0}\right)$
110	$\dfrac{s + a_0}{(s + \alpha)(s + \beta)(s^2 + v^2)}$	$\dfrac{(a_0 - \alpha)\varepsilon^{-\alpha t}}{(\beta - \alpha)(\alpha^2 + v^2)} + \dfrac{(a_0 - \beta)\varepsilon^{-\beta t}}{(\alpha - \beta)(v^2 + \beta^2)} + \sqrt{\left(\dfrac{a_0^2 + v^2}{v^2(\alpha^2 + v^2)(v^2 + \beta^2)}\right)} \cdot \sin(vt + \phi)$ $\phi = \tan^{-1}\left(\dfrac{\beta}{v}\right) - \tan^{-1}\left(\dfrac{a_0}{v}\right) - \tan^{-1}\left(\dfrac{v}{\alpha}\right)$
111	$\dfrac{s + a_0}{s(s + \alpha)(s + \beta)(s^2 + v^2)}$	$\dfrac{a_0}{\alpha\beta v^2} + \dfrac{(\alpha - a_0)\varepsilon^{-\alpha t}}{\alpha(\beta - \alpha)(\alpha^2 + v^2)} + \dfrac{(\beta - a_0)\varepsilon^{-\beta t}}{\beta(\alpha - \beta)(\alpha^2 + v^2)} + \dfrac{1}{v^2}\sqrt{\left(\dfrac{v^2 + a_0^2}{v^2(\alpha + \beta)^2 + (\alpha\beta - v^2)^2}\right)} \cdot \sin(vt + \phi)$ $\phi = \tan^{-1}\dfrac{v}{\alpha} + \tan^{-1}\dfrac{v}{\beta} + \tan^{-1}\dfrac{a_0}{v}$
112	$\dfrac{s + a_0}{s^2(s + \alpha)(s + \beta)(s^2 + v^2)}$	$\dfrac{1}{\alpha\beta v^2}\left(t - \dfrac{1}{\beta} - \dfrac{1}{\alpha}\right) + \dfrac{a_0}{\alpha\beta v^2} + \dfrac{(a_0 - \alpha)\varepsilon^{-\alpha t}}{\alpha^2(\beta - \alpha)(\alpha^2 + v^2)} + \dfrac{(a_0 - \beta)\varepsilon^{-\beta t}}{\beta^2(\alpha - \beta)(v^2 + \beta^2)} + \dfrac{1}{v^3}\sqrt{\left(\dfrac{a_0^2 + v^2}{v^2(\alpha + \beta)^2 + (\alpha\beta - v^2)^2}\right)} \cdot \cos(vt + \phi), \qquad \phi = \tan^{-1}\dfrac{v}{\alpha} - \tan^{-1}\dfrac{v}{\beta} + \tan^{-1}\dfrac{v}{a_0}$
113	$\dfrac{s + a_0}{(s^2 + \alpha^2)(s^2 + \beta^2)}$	$\dfrac{1}{\alpha^2 - \beta^2}\left[\sqrt{\left(1 + \dfrac{a_0^2}{\beta^2}\right)} \cdot \cos(\beta t - \phi_1) - \sqrt{\left(1 + \dfrac{a_0^2}{\alpha^2}\right)} \cdot \cos(\alpha t - \phi_2)\right]$ $\phi_1 = \tan^{-1}\dfrac{a_0}{\beta}, \qquad \phi_2 = \tan^{-1}\dfrac{a_0}{\alpha}$

114	$\dfrac{s + a_0}{(s+\alpha)^2 + \beta^2}$	$\sqrt{1 + \dfrac{(a_0 - \alpha)^2}{\beta^2}} \cdot \varepsilon^{-\alpha t} \cdot \sin(\beta t + \phi), \qquad \phi = \tan^{-1}\left(\dfrac{\beta}{a_0 - \alpha}\right)$
115	$\dfrac{s + a_0}{s[(s+\alpha)^2 + \beta^2]}$	$\dfrac{a_0}{\alpha^2 + \beta^2} - \sqrt{\dfrac{\beta^2 + (a_0 - \alpha)^2}{\beta^2(\alpha^2+\beta^2)}} \cdot \varepsilon^{-\alpha t} \cdot \sin(\beta t + \phi), \qquad \phi = \tan^{-1}\dfrac{\beta}{\alpha} + \tan^{-1}\dfrac{\beta}{a_0 - \alpha}$
116	$\dfrac{s + a_0}{s^2[(s+\alpha)^2 + \beta^2]}$	$\dfrac{1 + a_0 t}{\alpha^2 + \beta^2} - \dfrac{2\alpha a_0}{(\alpha^2+\beta^2)^2} + \dfrac{\sqrt{\{\beta^2 + (a_0-\alpha)^2\}}}{\beta(\alpha^2+\beta^2)} \cdot \varepsilon^{-\alpha t} \cdot \sin(\beta t + \phi), \qquad \phi = \tan^{-1}\dfrac{\beta}{a_0 - \alpha} + 2\tan^{-1}\dfrac{\beta}{\alpha}$
117	$\dfrac{s + a_0}{(s + v)[(s+\alpha)^2 + \beta^2]}$	$\dfrac{(a_0 - v)\varepsilon^{-vt}}{(v-\alpha)^2 + \beta^2} + \dfrac{1}{\beta}\sqrt{\dfrac{\beta^2 + (a_0 - \alpha)^2}{\beta^2 + (v - \alpha)^2}} \cdot \varepsilon^{-\alpha t} \cdot \sin(\beta t + \phi),$ $\phi = \tan^{-1}\left(\dfrac{\beta}{a_0 - \alpha}\right) - \tan^{-1}\left(\dfrac{\beta}{v - \alpha}\right)$
118	$\dfrac{s + a_0}{s(s+v)[(s+\alpha)^2 + \beta^2]}$	$\dfrac{a_0}{v(\alpha^2 + \beta^2)} + \dfrac{(v - a_0)\varepsilon^{-vt}}{v[\beta^2 + (\alpha - v)^2]} + \dfrac{1}{\beta\sqrt{(\alpha^2+\beta^2)}}\sqrt{\dfrac{\beta^2 + (a_0 - \alpha)^2}{\beta^2 + (\alpha - v)^2}} \cdot \varepsilon^{-\alpha t} \cdot \sin(\beta t + \phi)$ $\phi = \tan^{-1}\dfrac{\beta}{\alpha} + \tan^{-1}\dfrac{\beta}{a_0 - \alpha} + \tan^{-1}\dfrac{\beta}{\alpha - v}$
119	$\dfrac{s + a_0}{s^2(s+v)[(s+\alpha)^2 + \beta^2]}$	$\dfrac{a_0}{v(\alpha^2 + \beta^2)}\left[t + \dfrac{1}{a_0} - \dfrac{1}{v} - \dfrac{2\alpha}{(\alpha^2+\beta^2)}\right] + \dfrac{(a_0 - v)\varepsilon^{-vt}}{v^2[\beta^2 + (v - \alpha)^2]} + \dfrac{\varepsilon^{-\alpha t}}{\beta(\alpha^2+\beta^2)}\sqrt{\dfrac{\beta^2 + (a_0 - \alpha)^2}{\beta^2 + (v - \alpha)^2}} \cdot \sin(\beta t + \phi),$ $\phi = \tan^{-1}\dfrac{\beta}{a_0 - \alpha} - \tan^{-1}\dfrac{\beta}{v - \alpha} + 2\tan^{-1}\dfrac{\beta}{\alpha}$
120	$\dfrac{s + a_0}{(s + \delta)(s + v)[(s+\alpha)^2 + \beta^2]}$	$\dfrac{(v - a_0)\varepsilon^{-vt}}{(v - \delta)[(\alpha - v)^2 + \beta^2]} + \dfrac{(\delta - a_0)\varepsilon^{-\delta t}}{(\delta - v)[(\alpha - \delta)^2 + \beta^2]} + \sqrt{\dfrac{\beta^2 + (a_0 - \alpha)^2}{[\beta^2][(\alpha - v)^2][\beta^2 + (\alpha - \delta)^2]}} \cdot \varepsilon^{-\alpha t} \cdot \cos(\beta t + \phi),$ $\phi = \tan^{-1}\dfrac{\beta}{a_0 - \alpha} - \tan^{-1}\dfrac{\alpha - v}{\beta} + \tan^{-1}\dfrac{\beta}{\alpha - \delta}$

No.	$F(s)$	$f(t)$
121	$\dfrac{s + a_0}{(s + \alpha)^2}$	$[1 + (a_0 - \alpha)t]\varepsilon^{-\alpha t}$
122	$\dfrac{s + a_0}{s(s + \alpha)^2}$	$\dfrac{a_0}{\alpha} + \left[\left(1 - \dfrac{a_0}{\alpha}\right)t - \dfrac{a_0}{\alpha^2}\right]\varepsilon^{-\alpha t}$
123	$\dfrac{s + a_0}{s^2(s + \alpha)^2}$	$\dfrac{1}{\alpha^2}\left(1 + a_0 t - \dfrac{2a_0}{\alpha}\right) - \dfrac{1}{\alpha^2}\left(1 - \dfrac{2a_0}{\alpha} + [\alpha - a_0]t\right)\varepsilon^{-\alpha t}$
125	$\dfrac{s + a_0}{(s + \beta)(s + \alpha)^2}$	$\dfrac{(a_0 - \beta)\varepsilon^{-\beta t}}{(\beta - \alpha)^2} + \left[\dfrac{a_0 - \alpha}{\beta - \alpha} + \dfrac{\beta - a_0}{(\beta - \alpha)^2}\right]\varepsilon^{-\alpha t}$
126	$\dfrac{s + a_0}{s(s + \beta)(s + \alpha)^2}$	$\dfrac{a_0}{\alpha^2\beta} + \dfrac{(\beta - a_0)\varepsilon^{-\beta t}}{\beta(\alpha - \beta)^2} - \left[\dfrac{(a_0 - \alpha)t}{\alpha(\alpha - \beta)} + \dfrac{\alpha^2 - a_0(2\alpha - \beta)}{\alpha^2(\alpha - \beta)^2}\right]\varepsilon^{-\alpha t}$
127	$\dfrac{s + a_0}{s^2(s + \beta)(s + \alpha)^2}$	$\dfrac{a_0}{\alpha^2\beta}\left(\dfrac{1}{a_0} - \dfrac{1}{\beta} - \dfrac{2}{\alpha} + t\right) + \dfrac{(\beta - a_0)\varepsilon^{-\beta t}}{\beta^2(\alpha - \beta)^2} - \left[\dfrac{\alpha - a_0}{\alpha^2(\beta - \alpha)}t + \dfrac{(2a_0 - \alpha)(2\alpha - \beta) - \alpha a_0}{\alpha^3(\alpha - \beta)^2}\right]\varepsilon^{-\alpha t}$
128	$\dfrac{s + a_0}{(s + \beta)(s + v)(s + \alpha)^2}$	$\dfrac{(a_0 - \beta)\varepsilon^{-\beta t}}{(v - \beta)(\alpha - \beta)^2} + \dfrac{(a_0 - v)\varepsilon^{-vt}}{(\beta - v)(\alpha - v)^2} + \left[\dfrac{a_0 - \alpha}{(\alpha - v)(\alpha - \beta)^2}t + \dfrac{a_0(2\alpha - \beta - v) - \alpha^2 + \beta v}{(\alpha - \beta)^2(\alpha - v)^2}\right]\varepsilon^{-\alpha t}$
130	$\dfrac{s + a_0}{s(s + \beta)(s + v)(s + \alpha)^2}$	$\dfrac{a_0}{\alpha^2\beta v} - \dfrac{(a_0 - v)\varepsilon^{-vt}}{v(\beta - v)(\alpha - v)^2} - \dfrac{(a_0 - \beta)\varepsilon^{-\beta t}}{\beta(v - \beta)(\alpha - \beta)^2}$ $+ \left[\dfrac{(\alpha - a_0)t}{\alpha(\alpha - v)(\alpha - \beta)} - \dfrac{a_0(\alpha - v)(\alpha - \beta) + \alpha(a_0 - \alpha)(2\alpha - \beta - v)}{\alpha^2(\alpha - v)^2(\alpha - \beta)^2}\right]\varepsilon^{-\alpha t}$
131	$\dfrac{s + a_0}{(s^2 + \beta^2)(s + \alpha)^2}$	$\left[\dfrac{2a_0\alpha - \alpha^2 + \beta^2}{(\alpha^2 + \beta^2)^2} - \dfrac{(a_0 - \alpha)t}{\alpha^2 + \beta^2}\right]\varepsilon^{-\alpha t} + \dfrac{\sqrt{(\beta^2 + a_0^2)}}{\beta(\alpha^2 + \beta^2)}\cdot\sin(\beta t + \phi),\quad \phi = \tan^{-1}\dfrac{\beta}{a_0} - \tan^{-1}\dfrac{\beta}{\alpha}$

132	$\dfrac{s + a_0}{s(s^2 + \beta^2)(s + \alpha)^2}$	$\dfrac{a_0}{\alpha^2\beta^2} + \left[\dfrac{2\alpha^2(\alpha - a_0) - a_0(\alpha^2 + \beta^2)}{\alpha^2(\alpha^2 + \beta^2)^2} + \dfrac{(\alpha - a_0)t}{\alpha(\alpha^2 + \beta^2)}\right]\varepsilon^{-\alpha t} - \dfrac{\cos(\beta t + \phi)}{\beta^2(\alpha^2 + \beta^2)}\cdot\sqrt{(a_0^2 + \beta^2)},$ $\phi = \tan^{-1}\dfrac{\beta}{a_0} - 2\tan^{-1}\dfrac{\beta}{\alpha}$
133	$\dfrac{s + a_0}{s^2(s^2 + \beta^2)(s + \alpha)^2}$	$\dfrac{1 + a_0 t}{\alpha^2\beta^2} - \dfrac{2a_0}{\alpha^3\beta^2} + \left[\dfrac{(\alpha^2 + \beta^2)(2a_0 - \alpha) + 2\alpha^2(a_0 - \alpha)}{\alpha^3(\alpha^2 + \beta^2)^2} + \dfrac{(a_0 - \alpha)t}{\alpha^2(\alpha^2 + \beta^2)}\right]\varepsilon^{-\alpha t}$ $+ \dfrac{\sqrt{(a_0^2 + \beta^2)}\sin(\beta t + \phi)}{\beta^3(\alpha^2 + \beta^2)}, \quad \phi = \tan^{-1}\dfrac{\beta}{a_0} + 2\tan^{-1}\dfrac{\alpha}{\beta}$
134	$\dfrac{s + a_0}{(s + v)(s^2 + \beta^2)(s + \alpha)^2}$	$\dfrac{(a_0 - v)\varepsilon^{-vt}}{(\beta^2 + v^2)(\alpha - v)^2} + \left[\dfrac{\alpha^2(\alpha - a_0) + \beta^2(v - a_0) + \alpha(v - \alpha)(2a_0 - \alpha)}{(\alpha^2 + \beta^2)^2(v - \alpha)^2} + \dfrac{(a_0 - \alpha)t}{(v - \alpha)(\alpha^2 + \beta^2)}\right]\varepsilon^{-\alpha t}$ $+ \sqrt{\left(\dfrac{a_0^2 + \beta^2}{\beta^2 + v^2}\right)}\cdot\dfrac{\sin(\beta t + \phi)}{\beta(\alpha^2 + \beta^2)}, \quad \phi = \tan^{-1}\dfrac{v}{\beta} - \tan^{-1}\dfrac{a_0}{\beta} - 2\tan^{-1}\dfrac{\beta}{\alpha}$
135	$\dfrac{s + a_0}{(s + v)^2[(s + \alpha)^2 + \beta^2]}$	$\dfrac{(a_0 - v)t}{\beta^2 + (\alpha - v)^2} + \dfrac{[\alpha^2 + \beta^2 + 2a_0(v - \alpha) - v^2]\varepsilon^{-vt}}{[\beta^2 + (\alpha - v)^2]^2} + \dfrac{\sqrt{\beta^2 + (a_0 - \alpha)^2}}{\beta[\beta^2 + (\alpha - v)^2]}\cdot\varepsilon^{-\alpha t}\cdot\sin(\beta t + \phi),$ $\phi = \tan^{-1}\left(\dfrac{\beta}{a_0 - \alpha}\right) - 2\tan^{-1}\left(\dfrac{\beta}{v - \alpha}\right)$
136	$\dfrac{s + a_0}{s(s + v)^2[(s + \alpha)^2 + \beta^2]}$	$\dfrac{a_0}{v^2(\alpha^2 + \beta^2)} + \dfrac{\varepsilon^{-\alpha t}}{\beta[(v - \alpha)^2 + \beta^2]}\sqrt{\left(\dfrac{(\alpha - a_0)^2 + \beta^2}{\alpha^2 + \beta^2}\right)}\sqrt{\dfrac{\beta^2 + (v - \alpha)^2}{\beta^2}}\cdot\sin(\beta t + \phi) + \cdots$ $\cdots + \dfrac{2v(a_0 - v)(\alpha - v) - a_0[(v - \alpha)^2 + \beta^2]}{v^2[(v - \alpha)^2 + \beta^2]^2} + \dfrac{(v - a_0)t}{v[(v - \alpha)^2 + \beta^2]}\varepsilon^{-vt}$ $\phi = \tan^{-1}\dfrac{\beta}{\alpha} - 2\tan^{-1}\dfrac{\beta}{v - \alpha} - \tan^{-1}\dfrac{\beta}{\alpha - a_0}$

No.	$F(s)$	$f(t)$
137	$\dfrac{s+a_0}{s^2(s+v)^2[(s+\alpha)^2+\beta^2]}$	$\dfrac{a_0 t}{v^2(\alpha^2+\beta^2)} + \dfrac{(v-2a_0)(\alpha^2+\beta^2)-2a_0\alpha v}{v^3(\alpha^2+\beta^2)^2} + \dfrac{\sqrt{(\alpha-a_0)^2+\beta^2}\,\varepsilon^{-\alpha t}}{\beta(\alpha^2+\beta^2)[(\alpha-v)^2+\beta^2]}\sin(\beta t+\phi)+\cdots$ $\cdots+\left[\dfrac{(2a_0-v)[(v-\alpha)^2+\beta^2]+2v(a_0-v)(\alpha-v)}{v^3[(v-\alpha)^2+\beta^2]}+\dfrac{(a_0-v)t}{v^2[(v-\alpha)^2+\beta^2]}\right]\varepsilon^{-vt}$ $\phi=\tan^{-1}\dfrac{\beta}{\alpha}-\tan^{-1}\dfrac{\alpha}{\beta}+\tan^{-1}\left(\dfrac{v-\alpha}{\beta}\right)-\tan^{-1}\left(\dfrac{\beta}{v-\alpha}\right)+\tan^{-1}\left(\dfrac{\beta}{a_0-\alpha}\right)$
138	$\dfrac{s+a_0}{(s+\delta)(s+v)[(s+\alpha)^2+\beta^2]}$	$\dfrac{(a_0-\delta)\varepsilon^{-\delta t}}{(\delta-v)^2[(\delta-\alpha)^2+\beta^2]}+\dfrac{\varepsilon^{-\alpha t}\sin(\beta t+\phi)}{\beta[(\alpha-v)^2+\beta^2]}\sqrt{\dfrac{(\alpha-a_0)^2+\beta^2}{(\alpha-\delta)^2+\beta^2}}+\cdots$ $\cdots+\dfrac{[(\delta-a_0)[(v-\alpha)^2+\beta^2]-2(\alpha-v)(\delta-v)(a_0-v)]}{(v-\delta)^2[\beta^2+(v-\alpha)^2]}\varepsilon^{-vt}$ $\phi=\tan^{-1}\left(\dfrac{\beta}{a_0-\alpha}\right)-2\tan^{-1}\left(\dfrac{\beta}{v-\alpha}\right)-\tan^{-1}\left(\dfrac{\beta}{\delta-\alpha}\right)$
139	$\dfrac{s+a_0}{(s+\alpha)^2(s+\beta)^2}$	$\left[\dfrac{(a_0-\beta)t}{(\alpha-\beta)^2}+\dfrac{\alpha+\beta-2a_0}{(\alpha-\beta)^3}\right]\varepsilon^{-\beta t}+\left[\dfrac{(a_0-\alpha)t}{(\beta-\alpha)^2}+\dfrac{\alpha+\beta-2a_0}{(\beta-\alpha)^3}\right]\varepsilon^{-\alpha t}$
140	$\dfrac{s+a_0}{s(s+\alpha)^2(s+\beta)^2}$	$\dfrac{a_0}{\alpha^2\beta^2}+\left[\dfrac{(\beta-a_0)t}{\beta(\alpha-\beta)^2}+\dfrac{3a_0\beta-a_0\alpha-2\beta^2}{\beta^2(\alpha-\beta)^3}\right]\varepsilon^{-\beta t}+\left[\dfrac{(\alpha-a_0)t}{\alpha(\beta-\alpha)^2}+\dfrac{3a_0\alpha-a_0\beta-2\alpha^2}{\alpha^2(\beta-\alpha)^3}\right]\varepsilon^{-\alpha t}$
141	$\dfrac{s+a_0}{s^2(s+\alpha)^2(s+\beta)^2}$	$\left[\dfrac{1}{\alpha^2\beta^2}+\dfrac{a_0 t}{\alpha^2\beta^2}-\dfrac{2a_0(\alpha+\beta)}{\alpha^3\beta^3}\right]+\left[\dfrac{(a_0-\alpha)t}{\alpha^2(\beta-\alpha)^2}+\dfrac{2a_0(\beta-2\alpha)+\alpha(3\alpha-\beta)}{\alpha^3(\beta-\alpha)^3}\right]\varepsilon^{-\alpha t}$ $+\left[\dfrac{(a_0-\beta)t}{\beta^2(\alpha-\beta)^2}+\dfrac{2a_0(\alpha-2\beta)+\beta(3\beta-\alpha)}{\beta^3(\alpha-\beta)^3}\right]\varepsilon^{-\beta t}$

No.	Transform	Function
142	$\dfrac{s + a_0}{(s + \nu)(s + \alpha)^2(s + \beta)^2}$	$-\dfrac{(a_0 - \nu)}{(\nu - \alpha)^2(\nu - \beta)^2}\epsilon^{-\nu t} + \left[\dfrac{(\alpha - 2a_0)(\nu - \alpha) + (\nu\beta - \alpha^2) - a_0(\beta - \alpha)}{(\alpha - \nu)^2(\alpha - \beta)^3} + \dfrac{(a_0 - \alpha)t}{(\nu - \alpha)(\alpha - \beta)^2}\right]\epsilon^{-\alpha t} + \cdots$ $+ \left[\dfrac{(\beta - 2a_0)(\nu - \beta) + (\nu\alpha - \beta^2) - a_0(\alpha - \beta)}{(\beta - \nu)^2(\alpha - \beta)^3} + \dfrac{(a_0 - \beta)t}{(\nu - \beta)(\alpha - \beta)^2}\right]\epsilon^{-\beta t}$
143	$\dfrac{s + a_0}{(s^2 + \nu^2)(s + \alpha)^2(s + \beta)^2}$	$\left[\dfrac{(a_0 - \alpha)t}{(\alpha - \beta)^2(\alpha^2 + \nu^2)} + \dfrac{2\alpha(a_0 - \alpha)}{(\beta - \alpha)^2(\alpha^2 + \nu^2)^2} + \dfrac{\alpha + \beta - 2a_0}{(\beta - \alpha)^3(\alpha^2 + \nu^2)}\right]\epsilon^{-\alpha t} +$ $\cdots + \left[\dfrac{(a_0 - \beta)t}{(\alpha - \beta)^2(\beta^2 + \nu^2)} + \dfrac{2\beta(a_0 - \beta)}{(\alpha - \beta)^3(\beta^2 + \nu^2)} + \dfrac{\sqrt{a_0^2 + \nu^2}\,\sin(\nu t + \phi)}{\nu(\beta^2 + \nu^2)(\alpha^2 + \nu^2)}\right]\epsilon^{-\beta t}$ $\phi = 2\tan^{-1}\dfrac{\alpha}{\nu} + 2\tan^{-1}\dfrac{\beta}{\nu} + \tan^{-1}\dfrac{\nu}{a_0}$
144	$\dfrac{s + a_0}{[(s + \alpha)^2 + \beta^2]^2}$	$[(a_0 - \alpha + \beta^2 t)\sin\beta t + (\alpha - a_0)\beta t\cos\beta t]\dfrac{\epsilon^{-\alpha t}}{2\beta^3}$
145	$\dfrac{s + a_0}{(s^2 + \alpha^2)^2}$	$\dfrac{(a_0 + \alpha^2 t)\sin\alpha t - a_0\alpha t\cos\alpha t}{2\alpha^3}$
146	$\dfrac{s + a_0}{s(s^2 + \alpha^2)^2}$	$\dfrac{a_0}{\alpha^4} + \dfrac{(1 - a_0 t)\sin\alpha t}{2\alpha^3} - \dfrac{(2a_0 + \alpha^2 t)\cos\alpha t}{2\alpha^4}$
147	$\dfrac{s + a_0}{s^2(s^2 + \alpha^2)^2}$	$\dfrac{1 + a_0 t}{\alpha^4} - \dfrac{\sqrt{(4\alpha^2 + 9a_0^2)}\,\sin(\alpha t + \phi_1)}{2\alpha^5} + \dfrac{(\sqrt{a_0^2 + \alpha^4})\,t\cos(\alpha t + \phi_2)}{2\alpha^4}$ $\phi_1 = \tan^{-1}\dfrac{2\alpha}{3a_0}, \qquad \phi_2 = \tan^{-1}\dfrac{\alpha^2}{a_0}$
148	$\dfrac{s + a_0}{(s + \beta)(s^2 + \alpha^2)^2}$	$\dfrac{(a_0 - \beta)\epsilon^{-\beta t}}{(\alpha^2 + \beta^2)^2} - \dfrac{t}{2\alpha^2}\sqrt{\dfrac{a_0^2 + \alpha^2}{\alpha^2 + \beta^2}}\,\sin(\alpha t + \phi_1) + \dfrac{\sqrt{\{(\alpha^2 - \beta a_0)^2 + 4\beta^2 a_0^2\}}}{2\alpha^3(\alpha^2 + \beta^2)}\cos(\alpha t + \phi_2)$ $\phi_1 = \tan^{-1}\dfrac{\alpha}{a_0} + \tan^{-1}\dfrac{\beta}{\alpha}, \qquad \phi_2 = \tan^{-1}\left(\dfrac{\alpha^2 - \beta a_0}{2\alpha a_0}\right) - 2\tan^{-1}\dfrac{\alpha}{\beta}$

No.	$F(s)$	$f(t)$
149	$\dfrac{s+a_0}{s(s+\beta)(s^2+\alpha^2)^2}$	$\dfrac{a_0}{\beta\alpha^4} + \dfrac{(\beta-a_0)\varepsilon^{-\beta t}}{\beta(\alpha^2+\beta^2)^2} + \dfrac{t}{2\alpha^3}\sqrt{\dfrac{\alpha^2+a_0^2}{\alpha^2+\beta^2}}\cos(\alpha t+\phi_1)$ $-\dfrac{\sqrt{\{\alpha^2(3a_0+\beta)\}^2 + 4\{(\beta a_0-\alpha^2)^2\}}}{2\alpha^4(\alpha^2+\beta^2)}\cos(\alpha t+\phi_2)$ $\phi_1 = \tan^{-1}\dfrac{\alpha}{a_0} + \tan^{-1}\dfrac{\beta}{\alpha},\quad \phi_2 = \tan^{-1}\dfrac{\alpha(3a_0+\beta)}{2(\beta a_0-\alpha^2)} - 2\tan^{-1}\dfrac{\alpha}{\beta}$
150	$\dfrac{s+a_0}{s^2(s+\beta)(s^2+\alpha^2)^2}$	$\dfrac{1 - a_0/\beta + a_0 t}{\alpha^4\beta} + \dfrac{(a_0-\beta)\varepsilon^{-\beta t}}{\beta^2(\alpha^2+\beta^2)^2} + \dfrac{t}{2\alpha^4}\sqrt{\dfrac{\alpha^2+a_0^2}{\alpha^2+\beta^2}}\sin(\alpha t+\phi_1)+\cdots$ $\cdots + \dfrac{\sqrt{\{4\alpha^2(2a_0+\beta)+9(a_0\beta-\alpha^2)^2\}}}{4\alpha^5(\alpha^2+\beta^2)}\sin(\alpha t+\phi_2),$ $\phi_1 = \tan^{-1}\dfrac{\alpha}{a_0} + \tan^{-1}\dfrac{\beta}{\alpha},\quad \phi_2 = \tan^{-1}\dfrac{2\alpha(2a_0+\beta)}{3(a_0\beta-\alpha^2)} - 2\tan^{-1}\dfrac{\alpha}{\beta}$
151	$\dfrac{s+a_0}{(s+\alpha)^3}$	$\left[1+\left(\dfrac{a_0-\alpha}{2}\right)t\right]t\,\varepsilon^{-\alpha t}$
152	$\dfrac{s+a_0}{s(s+\alpha)^3}$	$\dfrac{a_0}{\alpha^3} + \left[\dfrac{(\alpha-a_0)t^2}{2} - \dfrac{2a_0}{\alpha^2} - \dfrac{a_0 t}{\alpha}\right]\varepsilon^{-\alpha t}$
153	$\dfrac{s+a_0}{s^2(s+\alpha)^3}$	$\dfrac{1+a_0 t}{\alpha^3} - \dfrac{3a_0}{\alpha^4} + \left[\dfrac{1}{\alpha^3} + \dfrac{(a_0-\alpha)t^2}{2\alpha^2} + \dfrac{(2a_0-\alpha)t}{\alpha^3}\right]\varepsilon^{-\alpha t}$
154	$\dfrac{s+a_0}{(s+\beta)(s+\alpha)^3}$	$\dfrac{(a_0-\beta)\varepsilon^{-\beta t}}{(\alpha-\beta)^3} + \left[\dfrac{a_0-\beta}{(\beta-\alpha)^3} + \dfrac{(\beta-a_0)t}{(\alpha-\beta)^2} + \dfrac{(a_0-\alpha)t^2}{2(\beta-\alpha)}\right]\varepsilon^{-\alpha t}$
155	$\dfrac{s^2+a_1 s+a_0}{s^2(s+\alpha)}$	$\dfrac{a_1\alpha - a_0 + a_0\alpha t}{\alpha^2} + \dfrac{(\alpha^2 - a_1\alpha + a_0)\varepsilon^{-\alpha t}}{\alpha^2}$

156	$\dfrac{s^2 + a_1 s + a_0}{s(s+\alpha)(s+\beta)}$	$\dfrac{a_0}{\alpha\beta} + \dfrac{(a_1\alpha - a_0 - \alpha^2)\varepsilon^{-\alpha t}}{\alpha(\beta-\alpha)} + \dfrac{(\beta^2 - a_1\beta + a_0)\varepsilon^{-\beta t}}{\beta(\beta-\alpha)}$
157	$\dfrac{s^2 + a_1 s + a_0}{s^2(s+\alpha)(s+\beta)}$	$\dfrac{a_1 + a_0 t}{\alpha\beta} - \dfrac{a_0(\alpha+\beta)}{\alpha^2\beta^2} + \dfrac{1}{\beta-\alpha}\left[\left(1 + \dfrac{a_0}{\alpha^2} - \dfrac{a_1}{\alpha}\right)\varepsilon^{-\alpha t} - \left(1 + \dfrac{a_0}{\beta^2} - \dfrac{a_1}{\beta}\right)\varepsilon^{-\beta t}\right]$
158	$\dfrac{s^2 + a_1 s + a_0}{(s+\alpha)(s+\beta)(s+\nu)}$	$\dfrac{(\alpha^2 - a_1\alpha + a_0)\varepsilon^{-\alpha t}}{(\nu-\alpha)(\beta-\alpha)} + \dfrac{(\nu^2 - a_1\nu + a_0)\varepsilon^{-\nu t}}{(\alpha-\nu)(\beta-\nu)} + \dfrac{(\beta^2 - a_1\beta + a_0)\varepsilon^{-\beta t}}{(\alpha-\beta)(\nu-\beta)}$
159	$\dfrac{s^2 + a_1 s + a_0}{s(s+\alpha)(s+\beta)(s+\nu)}$	$\dfrac{a_0}{\alpha\beta\nu} + \dfrac{(\alpha^2 - a_1\alpha + a_0)\varepsilon^{-\alpha t}}{\alpha(\alpha-\beta)(\nu-\alpha)} + \dfrac{(\beta^2 - a_1\beta + a_0)\varepsilon^{-\beta t}}{\beta(\alpha-\beta)(\beta-\nu)} + \dfrac{(\nu^2 - a_1\nu + a_0)\varepsilon^{-\nu t}}{\nu(\alpha-\nu)(\nu-\beta)}$
160	$\dfrac{s^2 + a_1 s + a_0}{s^2(s+\alpha)(s+\beta)(s+\nu)}$	$\dfrac{a_1 + a_0 t}{\alpha\beta\nu} - \dfrac{a_0(\alpha\beta + \beta\nu + \alpha\nu)}{\alpha^2\beta^2\nu^2} + \dfrac{(\alpha^2 - a_1\alpha + a_0)\varepsilon^{-\alpha t}}{\alpha^2(\alpha-\beta)(\nu-\alpha)} + \dfrac{(\beta^2 - a_1\beta + a_0)\varepsilon^{-\beta t}}{\beta^2(\alpha-\beta)(\beta-\nu)} + \dfrac{(\nu^2 - a_1\nu + a_0)\varepsilon^{-\nu t}}{\nu^2(\nu-\alpha)(\nu-\beta)}$
161	$\dfrac{s^2 + a_1 s + a_0}{s(s^2 + \alpha^2)}$	$\dfrac{a_0}{\alpha^2} + \sqrt{\left(\dfrac{a_1}{\alpha}\right)^2 + \left(\dfrac{a_0}{\alpha^2} - 1\right)^2}\cos(\alpha t + \phi), \qquad \phi = -\tan^{-1}\left(\dfrac{a_1\alpha}{\alpha^2 - a_0}\right)$
162	$\dfrac{s^2 + a_1 s + a_0}{s^2(s^2 + \alpha^2)}$	$\dfrac{a_1 + a_0 t}{\alpha^2} - \dfrac{\sin(\alpha t + \phi)}{\alpha^2}\sqrt{a_1^2 + \left(\alpha - \dfrac{a_0}{\alpha}\right)^2}, \qquad \phi = \tan^{-1}\left(\dfrac{a_1\alpha}{a_0 - \alpha^2}\right)$
163	$\dfrac{s^2 + a_1 s + a_0}{(s+\beta)(s^2 + \alpha^2)}$	$\dfrac{(\beta^2 - a_1\beta + a_0)\varepsilon^{-\beta t}}{\alpha^2 + \beta^2} + \dfrac{\sin(\alpha t + \phi)}{\alpha}\sqrt{\dfrac{(\alpha^2 - a_0)^2 + a_1^2\alpha^2}{\alpha^2 + \beta^2}}, \qquad \phi = \tan^{-1}\left(\dfrac{\beta}{\alpha}\right) - \tan^{-1}\left(\dfrac{a_0 - \alpha^2}{a_1\alpha}\right)$
164	$\dfrac{s^2 + a_1 s + a_0}{s(s+\beta)(s^2 + \alpha^2)}$	$\dfrac{a_0}{\alpha^2\beta} - \dfrac{(\beta^2 - a_1\beta + a_0)\varepsilon^{-\beta t}}{\beta(\alpha^2 + \beta^2)} - \dfrac{\cos(\alpha t + \phi)}{\alpha^2}\sqrt{\dfrac{(\alpha^2 - a_0)^2 + a_1^2\alpha^2}{\alpha^2 + \beta^2}},$ $\phi = \tan^{-1}\left(\dfrac{\beta}{\alpha}\right) - \tan^{-1}\left(\dfrac{a_0 - \alpha^2}{a_1\alpha}\right)$

No.	$F(s)$	$f(t)$
165	$\dfrac{s^2 + a_1 s + a_0}{s^2(s+\beta)(s^2+\alpha^2)}$	$\dfrac{1}{\alpha^2\beta}\left[a_1 - \dfrac{a_0}{\beta} + a_0 t\right] + \dfrac{(\beta^2 - a_1\beta + a_0)\varepsilon^{-\beta t}}{\beta^2(\alpha^2+\beta^2)} + \dfrac{\cos(\alpha t + \phi)}{\alpha^3}\sqrt{\dfrac{(\alpha^2-a_0)^2 + a_1^2\alpha^2}{\alpha^2+\beta^2}}$ $\phi = \tan^{-1}\left(\dfrac{\beta}{\alpha}\right) + \tan^{-1}\left(\dfrac{a_1\alpha}{a_0-\alpha^2}\right)$
166	$\dfrac{s^2 + a_1 s + a_0}{(s+\beta)(s+v)(s^2+\alpha^2)}$	$\dfrac{(\beta^2 - a_1\beta + a_0)\varepsilon^{-\beta t}}{(v-\beta)(\alpha^2+\beta^2)} + \dfrac{(v^2 - a_1 v + a_0)\varepsilon^{-vt}}{(\beta-v)(\alpha^2+v^2)} + \dfrac{\sin(\alpha t + \phi)}{\alpha}\sqrt{\dfrac{(\alpha^2-a_0)^2 + a_1^2\alpha^2}{(\alpha^2+\beta^2)(\alpha^2+v^2)}},$ $\phi = \tan^{-1}\left(\dfrac{a_1\alpha}{a_0-\alpha^2}\right) - \tan^{-1}\left(\dfrac{\alpha}{v}\right) - \tan^{-1}\left(\dfrac{\alpha}{\beta}\right)$
167	$\dfrac{s^2 + a_1 s + a_0}{s(s+\beta)(s+v)(s^2+\alpha^2)}$	$\dfrac{a_0}{\alpha^2\beta v} + \dfrac{\left(\beta - a_1 + \dfrac{a_0}{\beta}\right)\varepsilon^{-\beta t}}{(\beta-v)(\alpha^2+\beta^2)} + \dfrac{\left(v - a_1 + \dfrac{a_0}{v}\right)\varepsilon^{-vt}}{(v-\beta)(\alpha^2+v^2)} + \dfrac{\sin(\alpha t - \phi)}{\alpha^2}\sqrt{\dfrac{(\alpha^2-a_0)^2 + a_1^2\alpha^2}{\alpha^2(\beta+v)^2 + (\alpha^2-\beta v)^2}}$ $\phi = \tan^{-1}\left(\dfrac{\alpha}{\beta}\right) + \tan^{-1}\left(\dfrac{\alpha}{v}\right) + \tan^{-1}\left(\dfrac{a_1\alpha}{a_0-\alpha^2}\right)$
168	$\dfrac{s^2 + a_1 s + a_0}{s^2(s+\beta)(s+v)(s^2+\alpha^2)}$	$\dfrac{a_1 + a_0\left(t - \dfrac{1}{\beta} - \dfrac{1}{v}\right)}{\alpha^2\beta v} + \dfrac{(\beta^2 - a_1\beta + a_0)\varepsilon^{-\beta t}}{\beta^2(v-\beta)(\alpha^2+\beta^2)} + \dfrac{(v^2 - a_1 v + a_0)\varepsilon^{-vt}}{v^2(\beta-v)(\alpha^2+v^2)}$ $+ \dfrac{\cos(\alpha t + \phi)}{\alpha^3}\sqrt{\dfrac{(\alpha^2-a_0)^2 + a_1^2\alpha^2}{\alpha^2(\beta+v)^2 + (\alpha^2-\beta v)^2}}$ $\phi = \tan^{-1}\left(\dfrac{v}{\alpha}\right) + \tan^{-1}\left(\dfrac{\alpha}{v}\right) + \tan^{-1}\left(\dfrac{a_1\alpha}{a_0-\alpha^2}\right) - \tan^{-1}\left(\dfrac{\alpha}{\beta}\right)$
169	$\dfrac{s^2 + a_1 s + a_0}{(s^2+\alpha^2)(s^2+\beta^2)}$	$\dfrac{\cos(\alpha t + \phi_1)}{\beta^2-\alpha^2}\sqrt{\left(a_1^2 + \left(\dfrac{a_0-\alpha^2}{\alpha}\right)^2\right)} + \dfrac{\cos(\beta t + \phi_2)}{\alpha^2-\beta^2}\sqrt{\left(a_1^2 + \left(\dfrac{a_0-\beta^2}{\beta}\right)^2\right)}$ $\phi_1 = \tan^{-1}\left(\dfrac{\alpha^2-a_0}{a_1\alpha}\right),\quad \phi_2 = \tan^{-1}\left(\dfrac{\beta^2-a_0}{a_1\beta}\right)$

No.	Transform	Solution
170	$$\frac{s^2 + a_1 s + a_0}{s[(s+\alpha)^2 + \beta^2]}$$	$$\frac{a_0}{\alpha^2 + \beta^2} - \frac{\varepsilon^{-\alpha t}\sin(\beta t + \phi)}{\beta}\sqrt{\left\{\frac{\beta^2(2\alpha - a_1)^2 + (\alpha^2 - \beta^2 + a_0 - a_1\alpha)^2}{\alpha^2 + \beta^2}\right\}},$$ $$\phi = \tan^{-1}\left(\frac{\beta}{\alpha}\right) + \tan^{-1}\left(\frac{\beta(a_1 - 2\alpha)}{\alpha^2 - \beta^2 + a_0 - a_1\alpha}\right),$$
171	$$\frac{s^2 + a_1 s + a_0}{s^2[(s+\alpha)^2 + \beta^2]}$$	$$\frac{a_1 + a_0 t}{\alpha^2 + \beta^2} + \frac{2a_0\alpha}{(\alpha^2 + \beta^2)^2} + \frac{\varepsilon^{-\alpha t}\sin(\beta t + \phi)}{\beta(\alpha^2 + \beta^2)}\sqrt{\{\beta^2(2\alpha - a_1)^2 + (\alpha^2 - \beta^2 + a_0 - a_1\alpha)^2\}},$$ $$\phi = 2\tan^{-1}\left(\frac{\beta}{\alpha}\right) - \tan^{-1}\left(\frac{\beta(2\alpha - a_1)}{\alpha^2 - \beta^2 + a_0 - a_1\alpha}\right)$$
172	$$\frac{s^2 + a_1 s + a_0}{(s+\nu)[(s+\alpha)^2 + \beta^2]}$$	$$\frac{(\nu^2 - a_1\nu + a_0)\varepsilon^{-\nu t}}{(\alpha - \nu)^2 + \beta^2} + \frac{\varepsilon^{-\alpha t}\sin(\beta t + \phi)}{\beta}\sqrt{\left\{\frac{\beta^2(2\alpha - a_1)^2 + (\alpha^2 - \beta^2 + a_0 - a_1\alpha)^2}{(\alpha - \nu)^2 + \beta^2}\right\}},$$ $$\phi = \tan^{-1}\left[\frac{(a_1 - 2\alpha)\beta}{\alpha^2 - \beta^2 + a_0 - a_1\alpha}\right] - \tan^{-1}\left(\frac{\beta}{\nu - \alpha}\right)$$
173	$$\frac{s^2 + a_1 s + a_0}{s(s+\nu)[(s+\alpha)^2 + \beta^2]}$$	$$\frac{a_0}{(\alpha^2 + \beta^2)\nu} + \frac{(a_1\nu - a_0 - \nu^2)\varepsilon^{-\nu t}}{\nu[(\alpha - \nu)^2 + \beta^2]} + \frac{\varepsilon^{-\alpha t}\sin(\beta t + \phi)}{\beta}\sqrt{\left[\frac{\beta^2(2\alpha - a_1)^2 + (\alpha^2 - \beta^2 - a_1\alpha + a_0)^2}{(\alpha^2 + \beta^2)\{(\alpha - \nu)^2 + \beta^2\}}\right]},$$ $$\phi = \tan^{-1}\left(\frac{\beta}{\alpha}\right) + \tan^{-1}\left(\frac{\beta}{\alpha - \nu}\right) - \tan^{-1}\left(\frac{\beta(2\alpha - a_1)}{\alpha^2 - \beta^2 + a_0 - a_1\alpha}\right)$$
174	$$\frac{s^2 + a_1 s + a_0}{s^2(s+\nu)[(s+\alpha)^2 + \beta^2]}$$	$$\frac{a_0\left(t - \frac{1}{\nu} + \frac{a_1}{a_0}\right)}{\nu(\alpha^2 + \beta^2)} - \frac{2\alpha a_0}{\nu(\alpha^2+\beta^2)^2} + \frac{(\nu^2 - a_1\nu + a_0)\varepsilon^{-\nu t}}{\nu^2[(\alpha-\nu)^2 + \beta^2]} + \frac{\varepsilon^{-\alpha t}\sin(\beta t + \phi)}{\beta(\alpha^2 + \beta^2)}\sqrt{\left\{\frac{\beta^2(2\alpha - a_1)^2 + (\alpha^2 - \beta^2 - a_1\alpha + a_0)^2}{(\alpha - \nu)^2 + \beta^2}\right\}},$$ $$\phi = \tan^{-1}\left[\frac{\beta(a_1 - 2\alpha)}{\alpha^2 - \beta^2 - a_1\alpha + a_0}\right] - \tan^{-1}\left(\frac{\beta}{\nu - \alpha}\right) + 2\tan^{-1}\left(\frac{\beta}{\alpha}\right)$$

No.	$F(s)$	$f(t)$
175	$\dfrac{s^2 + a_1 s + a_0}{(s^2 + \nu^2)[(s+\alpha)^2 + \beta^2]}$	$\dfrac{\varepsilon^{-\alpha t}\sin(\beta t + \phi_1)}{\beta}\sqrt{\dfrac{(\alpha^2 - \beta^2 + a_0 - a_1\alpha)^2 + (2\alpha - a_1)^2\beta^2}{(\alpha^2 + \beta^2 - \nu^2)^2 + (2\alpha\nu)^2}}$ $+ \dfrac{\sin(\nu t + \phi_2)}{\nu}\sqrt{\dfrac{(\nu^2 - a_0)^2 + a_1^2\nu^2}{(\alpha^2 + \beta^2 - \nu^2)^2 + (2\alpha\nu)^2}}$, $\phi_1 = \tan^{-1}\left(\dfrac{2\alpha\beta}{\alpha^2 + \nu^2 - \beta^2}\right) + \tan^{-1}\dfrac{\beta(a_1 - 2\alpha)}{\alpha^2 - \beta^2 + a_0 - a_1\alpha}$, $\phi_2 = \tan^{-1}\left(\dfrac{a_1\nu}{a_0 - \nu^2}\right) - \tan^{-1}\left(\dfrac{2\alpha\nu}{\alpha^2 + \beta^2 - \nu^2}\right)$,
176	$\dfrac{s^2 + a_1 s + a_0}{s(s^2 + \nu^2)[(s+\alpha)^2 + \beta^2]}$	$\dfrac{a_0}{\nu^2(\alpha^2 + \beta^2)} - \dfrac{\varepsilon^{-\alpha t}\sin(\beta t + \phi_1)}{\beta}\sqrt{\dfrac{(\alpha^2 - \beta^2 + a_0 - a_1\alpha)^2 + \beta^2(2\alpha - a_1)^2}{(\alpha^2 + \beta^2)[(\alpha^2 + \beta^2 - \nu^2)^2 + (2\alpha\nu)^2]}}$ $- \dfrac{\sin(\nu t + \phi_2)}{\nu^2}\sqrt{\dfrac{(\nu^2 - a_0)^2 + a_1^2\nu^2}{(\alpha^2 + \beta^2 + a_0 - a_1\alpha)^2 + (2\alpha\nu)^2}}$, $\phi_1 = \tan^{-1}\left(\dfrac{\beta}{\alpha}\right) - \tan^{-1}\left(\dfrac{\alpha^2 - \beta^2 + \nu^2}{2\alpha\beta}\right) + \tan^{-1}\left(\dfrac{\beta(2\alpha - a_1)}{\alpha^2 - \beta^2 + a_0 - a_1\alpha}\right)$, $\phi_2 = \tan^{-1}\left(\dfrac{\alpha^2 + \beta^2 - \nu^2}{2\alpha\nu}\right) + \tan^{-1}\left(\dfrac{a_1\nu}{a_0 - \nu^2}\right)$,
177	$\dfrac{s^2 + a_1 s + a_0}{s(s + \alpha)^2}$	$\dfrac{a_0}{\alpha^2} + \left[\dfrac{(a_1\alpha - a_0 - \alpha^2)t}{\alpha} + \dfrac{\alpha^2 - a_0}{\alpha^2}\right]\varepsilon^{-\alpha t}$
178	$\dfrac{s^2 + a_1 s + a_0}{s^2(s + \alpha)^2}$	$\dfrac{a_1 + a_0 t}{\alpha^2} - \dfrac{2a_0}{\alpha^3} + \dfrac{1}{\alpha^2}\left[\dfrac{2a_0}{\alpha} - a_1 + (\alpha^2 + a_0 - a_1\alpha)t\right]\varepsilon^{-\alpha t}$
179	$\dfrac{s^2 + a_1 s + a_0}{(s + \beta)(s + \alpha)^2}$	$\dfrac{(\beta^2 + a_0 - a_1\beta)\varepsilon^{-\beta t}}{(\alpha - \beta)^2} + \left[\dfrac{\alpha^2 - 2\alpha\beta - a_0 + a_1\beta}{(\alpha - \beta)^2} + \dfrac{(\alpha^2 + a_0 - a_1\alpha)t}{\beta - \alpha}\right]\varepsilon^{-\alpha t}$

No.	Transform	Result
180	$\dfrac{s^2 + a_1 s + a_0}{s(s+\beta)(s+\alpha)^2}$	$\dfrac{a_0}{\alpha^2\beta} + \dfrac{(a_1\beta - a_0 - \beta^2)\varepsilon^{-\beta t}}{\beta(\alpha-\beta)^2} + \dfrac{\varepsilon^{-\alpha t}}{\alpha(\alpha-\beta)}\left[(\alpha^2 - a_1\alpha + a_0)t + \dfrac{\alpha^2(\beta - a_1) + a_0(2\alpha - \beta)}{\alpha(\alpha - \beta)}\right]$
181	$\dfrac{s^2 + a_1 s + a_0}{s^2(s+\beta)(s+\alpha)^2}$	$\dfrac{a_0}{\alpha^2\beta}\left[\dfrac{a_1}{a_0} - \dfrac{1}{\beta} - \dfrac{2}{\alpha} + t\right] + \dfrac{\varepsilon^{-\alpha t}}{\alpha^2(\beta-\alpha)}\left[(\alpha^2 - a_1\alpha + a_0)t + \dfrac{2a_0\beta - \alpha(3a_0 + a_1\beta) + \alpha^2(2a_1 - \alpha)}{\alpha(\beta - \alpha)}\right] + \cdots + \dfrac{(\beta^2 - a_1\beta + a_0)\varepsilon^{-\beta t}}{\beta^2(\beta - \alpha)^2}$
182	$\dfrac{s^2 + a_1 s + a_0}{(s+\beta)(s+v)(s+\alpha)^2}$	$\dfrac{(v^2 - a_1 v + a_0)\varepsilon^{-vt}}{(\beta - v)(\beta - \alpha)^2} + \dfrac{(\beta^2 - a_1\beta + a_0)\varepsilon^{-\beta t}}{(v - \beta)(\alpha - \beta)^2} + \dfrac{\varepsilon^{-\alpha t}}{(\alpha - v)(\alpha - \beta)}\left[(\alpha^2 - a_1\alpha + a_0)t + \dfrac{(v - \beta)(\alpha^2 - a_0) + v\beta(a_1 - 2\alpha) - \alpha(a_1\alpha - 2a_0)}{(\alpha - v)(\alpha - \beta)}\right]$
183	$\dfrac{s^2 + a_1 s + a_0}{(s^2+\beta^2)(s+\alpha)^2}$	$\dfrac{\sin(\beta t + \phi)}{\beta(\alpha^2 + \beta^2)}\sqrt{\{(\beta^2 - a_0)^2 + a_1^2\beta^2\}} + \dfrac{\varepsilon^{-\alpha t}}{\alpha^2 + \beta^2}\left[(\alpha^2 - a_1\alpha + a_0)t + \dfrac{2\alpha(\beta^2 - a_0)^2 + a_1(\beta^2 - \alpha^2)}{(\alpha^2 + \beta^2)}\right]$ $\phi = \tan^{-1}\left(\dfrac{a_1\beta}{a_0 - \beta^2}\right) - 2\tan^{-1}\dfrac{\beta}{\alpha}$
184	$\dfrac{s^2 + a_1 s + a_0}{s(s^2+\beta^2)(s+\alpha)^2}$	$\dfrac{a_0}{\alpha^2\beta^2} - \dfrac{\sin(\beta t + \phi)\sqrt{\{\beta^2 a_1^2 + (\beta^2 - a_0)^2\}}}{\beta^2(\alpha^2 + \beta^2)} - \left[\dfrac{\alpha^2[(\alpha^2 - \beta^2) + a_0(\alpha^2 + \beta^2) + 2(a_0 - a_1\alpha)]}{\alpha^2(\alpha^2 + \beta^2)^2} + \dfrac{(\alpha^2 - a_1\alpha + a_0)t}{\alpha(\alpha^2 + \beta^2)}\right]\cdot\varepsilon^{-\alpha t}$ $\phi = \tan^{-1}\left(\dfrac{\alpha}{\beta}\right) - \tan^{-1}\left(\dfrac{\beta}{\alpha}\right) + \tan^{-1}\left(\dfrac{a_1\beta}{a_0 - \beta^2}\right)$

No.	$F(s)$	$f(t)$
185	$\dfrac{s^2 + a_1 s + a_0}{s^2(s^2+\beta^2)(s+\alpha)^2}$	$\dfrac{a_0 t + a_1 - 2a_0/\alpha}{\alpha^2\beta^2} + \left[\dfrac{(\alpha^2+\beta^2)(2a_0-a_1\alpha) + 2\alpha^2(\alpha^2-a_1\alpha+a_0)}{\alpha^3(\alpha^2+\beta^2)^2} + \dfrac{(\alpha^2-a_1\alpha+a_0)t}{\alpha^2(\alpha^2+\beta^2)}\right]\varepsilon^{-\alpha t}$ $+\ \dfrac{\sqrt{(\beta^2-a_0)^2 + a_1^2\beta^2}\,\sin(\beta t + \phi)}{\beta^3(\alpha^2+\beta^2)}$ $\phi = \tan^{-1}\left(\dfrac{a_1\beta}{a_0-\beta^2}\right) + 2\tan^{-1}\left(\dfrac{\alpha}{\beta}\right)$
186	$\dfrac{s^2 + a_1 s + a_0}{(s+\beta)^2[(s+\alpha)^2+\nu^2]}$	$\dfrac{\varepsilon^{-\alpha t}\sin(\nu t + \phi)\sqrt{\{\nu^2(a_1-2\alpha)^2 + (\alpha^2-\nu^2-a_1\alpha+a_0)^2\}}}{\nu[\nu^2+(\alpha-\beta)^2]}$ $+\ \left[\dfrac{(\beta^2-a_1\beta+a_0)t}{(\beta^2-a_1\beta+a_0)t+(\alpha-\beta)^2}\right]$ $\phi = \tan^{-1}\left[\dfrac{\nu(a_1-2\alpha)}{\alpha^2-\nu^2-a_1\alpha+a_0}\right] - 2\tan^{-1}\left[\dfrac{\nu}{\beta-\alpha}\right]$
187	$\dfrac{s^2 + a_1 s + a_0}{(s+\alpha)^2(s+\beta)^2}$	$\left[\dfrac{a_1(\alpha+\beta) - 2(\alpha\beta+a_0)t}{(\beta-\alpha)^3} + \dfrac{(\alpha^2-a_1\alpha+a_0)t}{(\alpha-\beta)^2}\right]\varepsilon^{-\alpha t}$ $+\ \left[\dfrac{(\beta^2-a_1\beta+a_0)t}{(\alpha-\beta)^2} - \dfrac{a_1(\alpha+\beta)-2(\alpha\beta+a_0)}{(\beta-\alpha)^3}\right]\varepsilon^{-\beta t}$
188	$\dfrac{s^2+a_1 s+a_0}{s(s+\alpha)^2(s+\beta)^2}$	$\dfrac{a_0}{\alpha^2\beta^2} + \left[\dfrac{(a_1\alpha - a_0 - \alpha^2)t}{\alpha(\alpha-\beta)^2} + \dfrac{2\alpha(\alpha^2-a_1\alpha+a_0) + (\alpha^2-a_0)(\beta-\alpha)}{\alpha^2(\beta-\alpha)^3}\right]\varepsilon^{-\alpha t}$ $+\ \left[\dfrac{(a_1\beta - a_0 - \beta^2)t}{\beta(\beta-\alpha)^2} + \dfrac{2\beta(\beta^2-a_1\beta+a_0) + (\beta^2-a_0)(\alpha-\beta)}{\beta^2(\alpha-\beta)^3}\right]\varepsilon^{-\beta t}$
189	$\dfrac{s^2+a_1 s+a_0}{s^2(s+\alpha)^2(s+\beta)^2}$	$\dfrac{a_1 + a_0 t}{\alpha^2\beta^2} - \dfrac{2a_0(\alpha+\beta)}{\alpha^3\beta^3} + \left[\dfrac{(\alpha^2-a_1\alpha+a_0)t}{\alpha^2(\alpha-\beta)^2} + \dfrac{2\alpha(a_1\alpha - a_0 - \alpha^2) + (2a_0-a_1\alpha)(\beta-\alpha)}{\alpha^3(\beta-\alpha)^3}\right]\varepsilon^{-\alpha t}$ $+\ \left[\dfrac{(\beta^2-a_1\beta+a_0)t}{\beta^2(\alpha-\beta)^2} + \dfrac{2\beta(a_1\beta - a_0 - \beta^2) + (2a_0-a_1\beta)(\alpha-\beta)}{\beta^3(\alpha-\beta)^3}\right]\varepsilon^{-\beta t}$

No.		
190	$\dfrac{s^2 + a_1 s + a_0}{[(s+\alpha)^2 + \beta^2]^2}$	$\{[(\alpha^2 + \beta^2) + (a_0 - a_1\alpha) + (a_1 - 2\alpha)\beta^2 t]\sin\beta t + [(a_1\alpha - a_0) - (\alpha^2 - \beta^2)]\beta t \cos\beta t\}\dfrac{\varepsilon^{-\alpha t}}{2\beta^3}$
191	$\dfrac{s^2 + a_1 s + a_0}{(s^2 + \alpha^2)^2}$	$\dfrac{1}{2\alpha^3}\{[a_0 + \alpha^2(1 + a_1 t)]\sin\alpha t + (\alpha^2 - a_0)\alpha t \cos\alpha t\}$
192	$\dfrac{s^2 + a_1 s + a_0}{s(s^2 + \alpha^2)^2}$	$\dfrac{a_0}{\alpha^4} - \dfrac{t\sin(\alpha t + \phi_1)\sqrt{\{(\alpha^2 - a_0)^2 + a_1^2\alpha^2\}}}{2\alpha^3} - \dfrac{\cos(\alpha t + \phi_2)\sqrt{(a_1^2\alpha^2 + 4a_0^2)}}{2\alpha^4},$ $\phi_1 = \tan^{-1}\left(\dfrac{a_1\alpha}{a_0 - \alpha^2}\right),\quad \phi_2 = \tan^{-1}\left(\dfrac{a_1\alpha}{2a_0}\right)$
193	$\dfrac{s^2 + a_1 s + a_0}{s^2(s^2 + \alpha^2)^2}$	$\dfrac{a_1 + a_0 t}{\alpha^4} + \dfrac{t\cos(\alpha t + \phi_1)\sqrt{\{(\alpha^2 - a_0)^2 + a_1^2\alpha^2\}}}{2\alpha^4} - \dfrac{\sin(\alpha t + \phi_2)\sqrt{(\alpha^2 - 3a_0)^2 + 4a_1^2\alpha^2}}{2\alpha^5},$ $\phi_1 = \tan^{-1}\left(\dfrac{a_1\alpha}{a_0 - \alpha^2}\right),\quad \phi_2 = \tan^{-1}\left(\dfrac{2a_1\alpha}{3a_0 - \alpha^2}\right)$
194	$\dfrac{s^2 + a_1 s + a_0}{(s+\alpha)^3}$	$\left[2 + (a_1 - 2\alpha)t + \dfrac{(\alpha^2 + a_1\alpha + a_0)t^2}{2}\right]\varepsilon^{-\alpha t}$
195	$\dfrac{s^2 + a_1 s + a_0}{s(s+\alpha)^3}$	$\dfrac{a_0}{\alpha^3} - \dfrac{\varepsilon^{-\alpha t}}{\alpha}\left[\dfrac{2a_0}{\alpha^2} + \dfrac{(a_0 + \alpha^2)t}{\alpha} + \dfrac{(\alpha^2 - a_1\alpha + a_0)t^2}{2}\right]$
196	$\dfrac{s^2 + a_1 s + a_0}{s^2(s+\alpha)^3}$	$\dfrac{a_1\alpha - 3a_0}{\alpha^4} + \dfrac{a_0 t}{\alpha^3} + \left[\dfrac{3a_0 - a_1\alpha}{\alpha^4} + \dfrac{(2a_0 - a_1\alpha)t}{\alpha^3} + \dfrac{(\alpha^2 - a_1\alpha + a_0)t^2}{2\alpha^2}\right]\varepsilon^{-\alpha t}$
197	$\dfrac{s^3 + a_2 s^2 + a_1 s + a_0}{s^2(s+\alpha)(s+\beta)}$	$\dfrac{a_1 + a_0 t}{\alpha\beta} - \dfrac{a_0(\alpha + \beta)}{\alpha^2\beta^2} + \dfrac{1}{\alpha - \beta}\left[\left(\alpha + \dfrac{a_1}{\alpha} - a_2 - \dfrac{a_0}{\alpha^2}\right)\varepsilon^{-\alpha t} - \left(\beta + \dfrac{a_1}{\beta} - a_2 - \dfrac{a_0}{\beta^2}\right)\varepsilon^{-\beta t}\right]$
198	$\dfrac{s^3 + a_2 s^2 + a_1 s + a_0}{s(s+\alpha)(s+\beta)(s+v)}$	$\dfrac{a_0}{\alpha\beta v} + \dfrac{(\alpha^2 - a_2\alpha + a_1 - a_0/\alpha)\varepsilon^{-\alpha t}}{(v-\alpha)(\beta-\alpha)} + \dfrac{(\beta^2 - a_2\beta + a_1 - a_0/\beta)\varepsilon^{-\beta t}}{(v-\beta)(\alpha-\beta)} + \dfrac{(v^2 - a_2 v + a_1 - a_0/v)\varepsilon^{-vt}}{(\beta-v)(\alpha-v)}$

No.	$F(s)$	$f(t)$
199	$\dfrac{s^3 + a_2 s^2 + a_1 s + a_0}{s^2(s^2 + \alpha^2)}$	$\dfrac{a_1 + a_0 t}{\alpha^2} - \dfrac{\sin(\alpha t + \phi)}{\alpha^2}\sqrt{\{(a_2\alpha - a_0/\alpha)^2 + (\alpha^2 - a_1)^2\}}, \qquad \phi = \tan^{-1}\left[\dfrac{\alpha(a_1 - \alpha^2)}{a_0 - a_2\alpha^2}\right]$
200	$\dfrac{s^3 + a_2 s^2 + a_1 s + a_0}{s(s + \beta)(s^2 + \alpha^2)}$	$\dfrac{a_0}{\alpha^2\beta} + \dfrac{(\beta^3 - a_2\beta^2 + a_1\beta - a_0)\varepsilon^{-\beta t}}{\beta(\alpha^2 + \beta^2)} - \dfrac{\cos(\alpha t + \phi)}{\alpha^2}\sqrt{\left\{\dfrac{\alpha^2(\alpha^2 - a_1)^2 + (a_2\alpha^2 - a_0)^2}{(\alpha^2 + \beta^2)}\right\}},$ $\phi = \tan^{-1}\left(\dfrac{a_1 - \alpha^2}{a_0/\alpha - a_2\alpha}\right) - \tan^{-1}\left(\dfrac{\alpha}{\beta}\right)$
201	$\dfrac{s^3 + a_2 s^2 + a_1 s + a_0}{s^2(s + \beta)(s^2 + \alpha^2)}$	$\dfrac{a_1 + a_0 t}{\alpha^2\beta} - \dfrac{a_0}{\alpha^2\beta^2} + \dfrac{(a_0 - a_1\beta - \beta^3 + a_2\beta^2)\varepsilon^{-\beta t}}{\beta^2(\alpha^2 + \beta^2)} + \dfrac{\cos(\alpha t + \phi)}{\alpha^2}\sqrt{\left\{\dfrac{(a_2\alpha - a_0/\alpha)^2 + (\alpha^2 - a_1)^2}{\alpha^2 + \beta^2}\right\}}$ $\phi = \tan^{-1}\left[\dfrac{\alpha(a_1 - \alpha^2)}{a_0 - a_2\alpha^2}\right] + \tan^{-1}\left(\dfrac{\beta}{\alpha}\right)$
202	$\dfrac{s^3 + a_2 s^2 + a_1 s + a_0}{(s + \beta)(s + \nu)(s^2 + \alpha^2)}$	$\dfrac{(\beta^3 - a_2\alpha^2 + a_1\beta - a_0)\varepsilon^{-\beta t}}{(\beta - \nu)(\alpha^2 + \beta^2)} + \dfrac{(\nu^3 - a_2\nu^2 + a_1\nu - a_0)\varepsilon^{-\nu t}}{(\nu - \beta)(\alpha^2 + \nu^2)}$ $+ \dfrac{\sin(\alpha t + \phi)}{\alpha}\sqrt{\left\{\dfrac{\alpha^2(\alpha^2 - a_1)^2 + (a_2\alpha^2 - a_0)^2}{(\alpha^2 + \beta^2)(\alpha^2 + \nu^2)}\right\}},$ $\phi = \tan^{-1}\left[\dfrac{\alpha(a_1 - \alpha^2)}{a_0 - a_2\alpha^2}\right] - \tan^{-1}\left(\dfrac{\alpha}{\nu}\right) - \tan^{-1}\left(\dfrac{\alpha}{\beta}\right)$
203	$\dfrac{s^3 + a_2 s^2 + a_1 s + a_0}{(s^2 + \alpha^2)(s^2 + \beta^2)}$	$\dfrac{\cos(\beta t + \phi_1)}{\alpha^2 - \beta^2}\sqrt{\left\{(\beta^2 - a_1)^2 + \left(\dfrac{a_2\beta^2 - a_0}{\beta}\right)^2\right\}} + \dfrac{\cos(\alpha t + \phi_2)}{\alpha^2 - \beta^2}\sqrt{\left\{(\alpha^2 - a_1)^2 + \left(\dfrac{a_2\alpha^2 - a_0}{\alpha}\right)^2\right\}},$ $\phi_1 = \tan^{-1}\left[\dfrac{a_2\beta^2 - a_0}{\beta(a_1 - \beta^2)}\right], \qquad \phi_2 = \tan^{-1}\left[\dfrac{a_2\alpha^2 - a_0}{\alpha(a_1 - \alpha^2)}\right]$
204	$\dfrac{s^3 + a_2 s^2 + a_1 s + a_0}{s^2(s^2 + \alpha^2)^2}$	$\dfrac{a_1}{\alpha^2} + \dfrac{a_0 t}{\alpha^2} - \dfrac{2a_0}{\alpha^3} - \dfrac{\varepsilon^{-\alpha t}}{\alpha^2}\left[\alpha^2 - a_1 + \dfrac{2a_0}{\alpha}\right] + (a_0 - a_1\alpha + a_2\alpha^2 - \alpha^3)\dfrac{1}{2}t(\ldots)$

205	$\dfrac{s^3 + a_2 s^2 + a_1 s + a_0}{s(s+\beta)(s+\alpha)^2}$	$\dfrac{a_0}{\alpha^2\beta} + \left[\dfrac{(\beta^3 - a_2\beta^2 + a_1\beta - a_0)\epsilon^{-\beta t}}{\beta(\alpha-\beta)^2} + \dfrac{\alpha^4 - 2\beta\alpha^3 + \alpha^2(a_2\beta - a_1) + a_0(2\alpha - \beta)}{\alpha^2(\alpha-\beta)^2} + \dfrac{(\alpha^3 - a_2\alpha^2 + a_1\alpha - a_0)t}{\alpha(\beta - \alpha)}\right]\epsilon^{-\alpha t}$
206	$\dfrac{s^3 + a_2 s^2 + a_1 s + a_0}{s^2(s+\beta)(s+\alpha)^2}$	$\dfrac{a_0}{\alpha^2\beta}\left[\dfrac{a_1}{a_0} - \dfrac{2}{\alpha} - \dfrac{1}{\beta} + t\right] + \dfrac{(a_0 - a_1\beta + a_2\beta^2 - \beta^3)\epsilon^{-\beta t}}{\beta^2(\alpha - \beta)^2} + \left[\dfrac{a_0(\beta - a_2) + a_0(\beta - \alpha) - (a_1\alpha - a_0)(\beta - 2\alpha)}{\alpha^3(\alpha - \beta)^2} + \dfrac{(a_0 - a_1\alpha + a_2\alpha^2 - \alpha^3)t}{\alpha^2(\beta - \alpha)}\right]\epsilon^{-\alpha t}$
207	$\dfrac{s^3 + a_2 s^2 + a_1 s + a_0}{(s^2+\beta^2)(s+\alpha)^2}$	$\dfrac{\sin(\beta t + \phi)\sqrt{\{\beta^2(a_1 - \beta^2)^2 + (a_0 - a_2\beta^2)^2\}}}{\beta(\alpha^2 + \beta^2)} + \dfrac{\epsilon^{-\alpha t}}{\alpha^2 + \beta^2}\left[(a_0 - a_1\alpha + a_2\alpha^2 - \alpha^3)t + \dfrac{(\alpha^4 + 3\beta^2\alpha^2 - a_1\alpha^2 + a_1\beta^2 + 2a_0\alpha - 2a_2\alpha\beta^2)}{(\alpha^2 + \beta^2)}\right]$ $\phi = \tan^{-1}\left[\dfrac{a_2\beta^2 - a_0}{\beta(a_1 - \beta^2)}\right] - \tan^{-1}\left(\dfrac{\beta}{\alpha}\right) + \tan^{-1}\left(\dfrac{\alpha}{\beta}\right)$
208	$\dfrac{s^3 + a_2 s^2 + a_1 s + a_0}{s(s^2+\beta^2)(s+\alpha)^2}$	$\dfrac{a_0}{\alpha^2\beta^2} + \dfrac{\epsilon^{-\alpha t}}{\alpha(\alpha^2 + \beta^2)}\left[(\alpha^3 - a_2\alpha^2 + a_1\alpha - a_0)t + \dfrac{2\alpha^3(a_1 - \beta^2) - \alpha^2(2a_0 + a_2\alpha^2 - a_2\beta^2) - a_0(\alpha^2 + \beta^2)}{\alpha(\alpha^2 + \beta^2)}\right]$ $+ \dfrac{\sin(\beta t + \phi)\sqrt{\{\beta^2(\beta^2 - a_1)^2 + (a_2\beta^2 - a_0)^2\}}}{\beta^2(\alpha^2 + \beta^2)}$ $\phi = \tan^{-1}\left[\dfrac{\beta(\beta^2 - a_1)}{a_2\beta^2 - a_0}\right] - \tan^{-1}\left(\dfrac{\beta}{\alpha}\right) + \tan^{-1}\left(\dfrac{\alpha}{\beta}\right)$
209	$\dfrac{s^3 + a_2 s^2 + a_1 s + a_0}{(s+\alpha)^2(s+\beta)^2}$	$\left[\dfrac{(a_0 - a_1\alpha + a_2\alpha^2 - \alpha^3)t}{(\alpha - \beta)^2} + \dfrac{\alpha^2(3\beta - \alpha) - 2a_2\alpha\beta + a_1(\alpha + \beta) - 2a_0}{(\beta - \alpha)^3}\right]\epsilon^{-\alpha t}$ $+ \left[\dfrac{(a_0 - a_1\beta + a_2\beta^2 - \beta^3)t}{(\alpha - \beta)^2} + \dfrac{\beta^2(3\alpha - \beta) - 2a_2\alpha\beta + a_1(\alpha + \beta) - 2a_0}{(\alpha - \beta)^3}\right]\epsilon^{-\beta t}$

No.	$F(s)$	$f(t)$
210	$\dfrac{s^3 + a_2 s^2 + a_1 s + a_0}{s(s+\alpha)^2(s+\beta)^2}$	$\dfrac{a_0}{\alpha^2\beta^2} + \left[\dfrac{(\alpha^3 - a_2\alpha^2 + a_1\alpha - a_0)t}{\alpha(\beta-\alpha)^2} + \dfrac{\alpha^2[a_2(\alpha+\beta) - 2(a_1+\alpha\beta)] + a_0(3\alpha-\beta)}{\alpha^2(\beta-\alpha)^3}\right]\varepsilon^{-\alpha t}$ $+ \left[\dfrac{(\beta^3 - a_2\beta^2 + a_1\beta - a_0)t}{\beta(\alpha-\beta)^2} + \dfrac{\beta^2[a_2(\alpha+\beta) - 2(a_1+\alpha\beta)] + a_0(3\beta-\alpha)}{\beta^2(\alpha-\beta)^3}\right]\varepsilon^{-\beta t}$
211	$\dfrac{s^3 + a_2 s^2 + a_1 s + a_0}{[(s+\alpha)^2 + \beta^2]^2}$	$\dfrac{\varepsilon^{-\alpha t}\sin\beta t}{2\beta^3}[(a_2 - \alpha)(\alpha^2 + \beta^2) - \alpha(a_1 + 2\beta^2) + (3\alpha^2 - \beta^2 - 2a_2\alpha + a_1)\beta^2 t + a_0]$ $+ \dfrac{\varepsilon^{-\alpha t}\cos\beta t}{2\beta^3}[2\beta^3 - (a_0 - a_1\alpha + a_2\alpha^2 - \beta^3) + \alpha[3\beta^2 - \alpha^2])\beta t]$
212	$\dfrac{s^3 + a_2 s^2 + a_1 s + a_0}{s^2(s+\alpha)^2}$	$\dfrac{a_1 + a_0 t}{\alpha^4} - \dfrac{\sin(\alpha t + \phi_1)}{2\alpha^5}\sqrt{\{4a_1^2\alpha^2 + (\alpha^2 a_2 - 3a_0)^2\}}$ $+ \dfrac{t\cos(\alpha t + \phi_2)}{2\alpha^4}\sqrt{\{\alpha^2(\alpha^2 - a_1)^2 + (\alpha^2 a_2 - a_0)^2\}}$ $\phi_1 = \tan^{-1}\left(\dfrac{2\alpha a_1}{3a_0 - \alpha^2 a_2}\right), \qquad \phi_2 = \tan^{-1}\left(\dfrac{\alpha(a_1 - \alpha^2)}{a_0 - \alpha^2 a_2}\right)$
213	$\dfrac{s^3 + a_2 s^2 + a_1 s + a_0}{s(s+\alpha)^3}$	$\dfrac{a_0}{\alpha^3} + \left[(\alpha^3 - a_2\alpha^2 + a_1\alpha - a_0)\dfrac{t^2}{2\alpha^2} - \dfrac{(a_0 - a_2\alpha^2 + 2\alpha^3)t}{\alpha^2} + \dfrac{2(a_0 - \alpha^3)}{\alpha^3}\right]\varepsilon^{-\alpha t}$
214	$\dfrac{s^3 + a_2 s^2 + a_1 s + a_0}{s^2(s+\alpha)^3}$	$\dfrac{a_1 + a_0 t}{\alpha^3} - \dfrac{3a_0}{\alpha^4} + \left[\dfrac{(6a_0 - 2\alpha a_1)}{\alpha^4} + \dfrac{(2a_0 - a_1\alpha + \alpha^3)t}{\alpha^3} + \dfrac{(a_0 - a_1\alpha + a_2\alpha^2 - \alpha^3)t^2}{2\alpha^2}\right]\varepsilon^{-\alpha t}$
215	$\sqrt{(s-\alpha)} - \sqrt{(s-\beta)}$	$\dfrac{\varepsilon^{\beta t} - \varepsilon^{\alpha t}}{2\sqrt{(\pi t^3)}}$
216	$\dfrac{\omega\left(\varepsilon^{\frac{\pi s}{2\omega}} + \varepsilon^{-\frac{\pi s}{2\omega}}\right)}{2(s^2 + \omega^2)}$	$|\sin\omega t|$

217	$\dfrac{\varepsilon^{-\frac{a}{s}}}{s}$	$J_0(2\sqrt{(at)})$
218	$\dfrac{\varepsilon^{-\frac{a}{s}}}{\sqrt{s}}$	$\dfrac{\cos 2\sqrt{(at)}}{\sqrt{(\pi t)}}$
219	$\dfrac{\varepsilon^{\frac{a}{s}}}{\sqrt{s}}$	$\dfrac{\cosh 2\sqrt{(at)}}{\sqrt{(\pi t)}}$
220	$\ln\left(\dfrac{s+\alpha}{s+\beta}\right)$	$\dfrac{\varepsilon^{-\beta t}-\varepsilon^{-\alpha t}}{t}$
221	$\dfrac{\ln s}{s}$	$-0.5772 - \ln t$
222	$\dfrac{\ln s}{s^2+1}$	$Si(t)\cos t - Ci(t)\sin t$
223	$\dfrac{s\ln s}{s^2+1}$	$-Si(t)\sin t - Ci(t)\cos t$
224	$\ln\left(\dfrac{s^2+a^2}{s^2}\right)$	$\dfrac{2(1-\cos at)}{t}$
225	$\tan^{-1}\left(\dfrac{a}{s}\right)$	$\dfrac{\sin at}{t}$
226	ε^{-as}	$\delta(t-a)$

No.	$f(t)$	$F(s)$
227	$U(t-a)$	$\dfrac{\varepsilon^{-as}}{s}$
228	$(t-a)U(t-a)$	$\dfrac{\varepsilon^{-as}}{s^2}$
229	$\varepsilon^{-\alpha(t-a)}U(t-a)$	$\dfrac{\varepsilon^{-as}}{(s+\alpha)}$
230	$(t-a)\varepsilon^{-\alpha(t-a)}U(t-a)$	$\dfrac{\varepsilon^{-as}}{(s+\alpha)^2}$
231	$\left[\dfrac{\varepsilon^{-\alpha(t-a)}-\varepsilon^{-\beta(t-a)}}{\beta-\alpha}\right]U(t-a)$	$\dfrac{\varepsilon^{-as}}{(s+\alpha)(s+\beta)}$
232	$U(t)-U(t-a)$	$\dfrac{1-\varepsilon^{-as}}{s}$
233	$\left(t+\dfrac{1}{a}-a\right)U(t-a)$	$\dfrac{(s+a)\varepsilon^{-as}}{as^2}$
234	$\left[\dfrac{1}{\alpha\beta}-\dfrac{\varepsilon^{-\alpha(t-a)}}{\alpha(\beta-\alpha)}-\dfrac{\varepsilon^{-\beta(t-a)}}{\beta(\alpha-\beta)}\right]U(t-a)$	$\dfrac{\varepsilon^{-as}}{s(s+\alpha)(s+\beta)}$

INDEX